CAVALCADE OF AMERICA

"The Signing of the Declaration of Independence." Painting by John Trumbull.

CAVALCADE OF AMERICA

The Deeds and Achievements
of the Men and Women
Who Made Our Country Great

EDITED BY CARL CARMER

This book, based on the "Cavalcade of America" radio series, is published by arrangement with E. I. du Pont de Nemours & Co., Inc., sponsors of the program.

NEW YORK

CROWN PUBLISHERS, INC. · LOTHROP, LEE & SHEPARD CO., INC.

ACKNOWLEDGMENTS

Thanks are due to the many people who helped in the preparation, organization and production of *Cavalcade of America*.

All the stories in this book were written especially for it, but are based on the original radio plays produced for and broadcast on the Cavalcade of America radio program sponsored by E. I. du Pont de Nemours Co., Inc. The publishers extend their grateful appreciation to E. I. du Pont de Nemours Co., Inc. and to the writers and authors of the Cavalcade of America radio program.

The publishers are especially grateful to Dr. Louis Walton Sipley, director of the American Museum of Photography, for his advice and cooperation in connection with the color illustrations; to Robert Cousins for tying many loose ends together; to George Hornby and Gladys Ebert for picture collection and design; and to George Kelley of the New York Life Insurance Company; to Culver Service and the Bettmann Archive for their courtesy, interest and helpfulness in providing illustration material. Full picture credits are listed in the appendix.

Printed in the U.S.A.

TABLE OF CONTENTS

THE MEN OF ENTERPRISE

PURSUERS OF THE AMERICAN DREAM

THE EDUCATORS

THE HUMANITARIANS

THE ARTISTS

APPENDIX

INTRODUCTION

For twenty years, believing that "History is People" E. I. du Pont de Nemours and Company has presented, first over radio and later over television, a series of dramas about significant "true-to-life" persons on programs entitled *Cavalcade of America* and *du Pont Cavalcade Theater*. Advised as to authenticity of subject matter by prominent professional historians, the producers of these weekly performances obtained the services of able dramatists to write the plays and of distinguished actors to assume the important roles. It would be hard indeed to calculate how many millions of people have listened to these historical plays in the last two decades.

It has been the purpose of the publishers, writers, and the editor of this volume to render some of the most representative of these dramatic presentations into narrative prose that will preserve not merely the exciting quality of the original plays but also their historical significance.

Since a comprehensive collection of tales stemming from the *Cavalcade of America* broadcasts was not practicable the problem of choosing the most rewarding was difficult. Final selections depended on many qualifications. Because one purpose was to give the reader as wide a knowledge as possible of our country's continuous story some subjects were chosen for their chronological fitness. Others, which do not deal with the most widely known figures in certain categories, were chosen because the man they celebrated seemed more representative of his period than more obvious choices. It is to be hoped, therefore, the readers will forgive what may at first seem to be unforgivable omissions. It has been the effort to make a gallery of portraits in which certain attributes are recognizable as held in common by those Americans who have made the American record. All of these prose sketches of widely varying individuals will, it is hoped, provide a composite in which one may recognize America itself.

It becomes increasingly evident in the reading of these stories of Americans who have served their country with distinction that without the freedoms provided them by a government devoted to the interests of all its people their contributions might never have been made. This liberty, asserted again and again not only by the leaders who founded the republic but also by all thoughtful Americans in the procession of the generations, has provided a climate in which the free mind may reach its uttermost achievement. The nation has made the effort ever since its inception to encourage its citizens toward such achievements as their especial gifts may qualify them. Despite the handicaps of poverty, misunderstanding and personal disappointments, the courageous and persistent men and women who are memorialized in this book had the consoling knowledge that no governmental taboos would interfere with their progress. A nation whose basic principles safeguard the dignity of the individual and regard his civil rights as sacred could do no less. The United States has ever looked upon its own principles as the antithesis of statism (the sacrifice of individual rights on the altar of the state).

It is needless to say that this group of narratives is meant to be inspiring to its readers. It is the challenge of our past to our present. It calls upon its readers to appraise themselves in the light of a knowledge of the Americans who have preceded them. It says to them: "We are a diverse country of many bloodstrains. The nations of the world are represented here. We are fellow-citizens in a hybrid state where every citizen, regardless of his national origins, is entitled to equal rights."

An essential prerequisite of success in our democratic process, this book assumes, is a knowledge of our nation's history and an intelligent interpretation of its events. That history has convinced us that the thinking of the many is better than the thinking of the few—the aristocrats, the dictators, the commissars—but only if the many have equipped themselves for the problems they face. Hence a book that offers the highlights of our success in the past, that furnishes its readers with the wisdom that has come through the experiences of citizens who have contributed to that success, may be considered a basic weapon against those philosophies which are antagonistic to our own. We rejoice in the fact that each one of us—through his voice, his writings and through his vote—has his own share in the creation of an over-all concept of his country. We are proud that a composite of our separate opinions is democracy's answer to the demagogue who demands that we accept only his opinions. We have come a long way, and we have trusted, through all that danger-fraught distance, in government of, by and for the people. We are now as never before convinced that this is our way as a nation. But we are also certain that dangers such as we have never faced confront us. In such times a knowledge of the past may become an aid toward developing and using the utmost powers of our individual minds that we may broaden and strengthen the road we have chosen to walk down the years. This book was designed to provide some of that knowledge.

To the reader who voices the oft repeated argument that the men and women of the past had greater opportunities for accomplishment than today offers, it need only be said that if they believe this they have not studied the present world. No doubt the unimaginative people who were the contemporaries of those heroes celebrated in these pages felt the same way. But today is a lofty hill whence one may see new vistas that are breathtaking. No period in the history of man has held more of suspense, more of the feeling of high adventure about to begin. Whichever way we look there is work to be done—not plodding, uncreative dead-end work but original, exciting effort in fields not yet explored.

The people of the United States, spurred by the inspirations and necessities of the last few years, have created for themselves such opportunities as men a decade ago had not even dreamed. Since the days of Luther Burbank the good earth of America has given up more of its secrets and farming has again become as stirring a prospect as when the pioneer first made his clearing in the forest. A plane swoops on a field, leaving behind it a white cloud that brings swift death to enemies of the harvest. The desert blossoms with the promise of good picking because we bring it water from the hills. And where there is no soil we have proved that water itself may be the element in which food-plants may grow and ripen. Growing great harvests and selling them has always been a worthy achievement. To know that they will feed those who need food is an even more satisfying experience.

The road ahead is just as full of promise to men whose talents, like those which once blessed Eli Whitney and Cyrus McCormick, lie in improving and producing plows and threshers. In the factories of America men and women now holding their first jobs, thanks to the examples of Charles Goodyear, E. R. Squibb and Éleuthère Irénée Du Pont, are finding the stuff that dreams are made of. Transportation continuously outstrips our conceptions of it. Handicaps—physical weaknesses and the illnesses which the flesh is heir to—are giving way, thanks to the previous labors of Benjamin Waterhouse, Elizabeth Blackwell, Walter Reed, and Harvey Cushing, before the determined attacks of men and women new to the medical profession who know the close association between good health and happiness and insist that the world of tomorrow be happier than that of yesterday. The frontiers of disease are rolling back before ever advancing medical discoveries.

There are builders other than those of the body and they, inspired by the life of Jane Addams, look ahead to the time when the word "slum" shall become only a term in a history book. New houses—sunlit and clean and protected from heat and cold—are all around us. This is a time for architects and builders.

It is a time for teachers, too. Techniques which stem from the inventions of Thomas A. Edison and Alexander Graham Bell can now bring to teacher and pupil the images and the voices of the greatest thinkers of our day. The spirited teacher, led by the ideals once held by Horace Mann, Booker T. Washington and Mary Lyon may make instruction vital and practical through such visual aids as television and motion pictures.

Finally, as a book should, this volume calls to the attention of the living those creative artists who have given of their genius to the great stream of national culture. Out of the writers, the painters, the composers of the past, men like Walt Whitman, Mark Twain, Stephen Foster and James McNeill Whistler, whose works are now admired by a world-wide posterity, comes the offering of their own achievements as goals toward which the American artists of today may aspire.

Out of *Ecclesiasticus* comes a word well spoken: "Let us now praise famous men." For from memorializing great figures of the past comes contemplation that leads toward inspiration and action.

CARL CARMER

Octagon House

Irvington-on-Hudson, N. Y.

CREATORS OF THE NEW WORLD

America came alive in an excited universe. Suddenly to war-scarred Europe came the awareness of a new continent, a land of flowing waters, green leaves and multicolored blossoms, a treasure house of precious minerals, of wild animals that might be slain for food, of unrecognizable plants whose virtues were yet to be discovered. Scant wonder, then, that Italian, Dutch, Spanish, French, Portuguese and English sought through exploration and colonization to claim this wild, fresh, immeasurable country for their own!

And if a Genoese with the mad idea that a maritime captain could reach the east by sailing west should return from his first expedition with proof of his theories and rare new-world treasures for the Spanish Queen who had employed him, then let the cannon roar and all ambitious nations whiten the Ocean Sea with sail. Let the Spaniards land in Florida and seek the Seven Golden Cities of Cibola; let the black-robed Jesuits, heroic men of God, bring the news of the Saviour to the wild men who had not heard of Him; let William Bradford, on whose scratching pen rested the creative spirit that had inhabited the Elizabethan Age, worship as he pleases so long as he and his companions settle a coast that may be ever part of England.

But a feeling was abroad that would, when grasped by the thoughtful and the courageous men of America, result in the country's never belonging to a nation other than itself. Out of the Magna Charta, out of the philosophy of John Locke, out of the wisdom of religious teachings, these men fashioned the structure of a nation.

THE SEEKERS

"I always consider the settlement of America with reverence and wonder, as the opening of a grand scheme and design in Providence for the illumination and emancipation of the slavish part of mankind all over the earth."

JOHN ADAMS, 1765.

THE DISCOVERER
(CHRISTOPHER COLUMBUS)

In an old book in a library in Seville this is written: "An age shall come, after many years, when the ocean will loose the chain of things and a huge land lie revealed." The quotation is from Seneca, the Roman dramatist and philosopher.

Beneath these lines in the old Spanish book are these words: "My father fulfilled this prophecy on October 12, in the Year of Our Lord 1492."

As we know, though Columbus was the explorer to reveal that huge new land, he himself did not realize the great significance of his discovery. And if he had realized it he would have valued such an achievement less than the feat he thought he had accomplished.

To explain this we must go back more than two hundred years before Columbus

"The Debarkation of Columbus." Painting by Edward Moran.

to another Italian adventurer. Marco Polo was a Venetian merchant who had journeyed to India and to China, then called Cathay. When he returned to Italy his tales of the fabulous riches of those Far Eastern lands fired the imagination of all Europe.

Following Polo's trail, European traders began what grew to be a rich commerce with the Orient. They brought back gold and silver, ivory and gems, spices and ointments, silks and rugs. They were engaging, nevertheless, in a risky and exhausting trade, carried on mainly by camel and elephant caravans across deserts, through jungles and over the world's highest mountain ranges.

Then, after 1453, even this long and dangerous route became almost impossible, because of the capture of Constantinople by the Turks. Constantinople was the gateway to the Far Eastern trade, and the Moslem Turks were far from friendly to the Christian merchants who sought to enter it. They gave preference to rival Arab merchants, who shared their own religion.

This made it urgent for Europeans to redouble the efforts they had been making to find a sea route to the Indies and Cathay. Columbus was only one, though the greatest, of many navigators to traverse the oceans in search of such a route.

Yet, from the beginnings of his explorations to this day, a curious doom of ironic frustration hangs over Columbus. By the time he had persuaded Queen Isabella of Spain to finance his major project he had become a weary, moody man, almost worn out by his wanderings from country to country seeking ships for his enterprise. His red hair had turned prematurely gray and his oddly freckled face had become deeply lined.

When Columbus described his project people laughed in his face. The notion that the world was round had been dismissed as sheer nonsense in the days of the ancients. That you could reach the Far East by sailing west seemed the most ridiculous part of a wholly lunatic idea!

And so, with scornful laughter ringing in his ears, Columbus had become a lonely, silent man, speaking only when he felt it was necessary. Later, when he was successful and admired, when he went about in costly robes and was entitled to be addressed by such magnificent titles as "Admiral of the Ocean Sea" and "Viceroy of the Indies," he remembered the fools and paid them back with public contempt. This attitude could not fail to raise

many enemies against him. And when his fortunes fell and he again knew poverty and disgrace and was imprisoned, there were few to come to his aid. His enemies reviled him as one who had dreamed he had discovered a route to the Indies, but had uncovered only a wilderness!

That he had *not* found the passage to the Indies Columbus could not accept. To his dying day he clung to the idea that he had touched upon lands in the Orient.

The achievement of a sea route to the Indies, an achievement in reality less important than his own discovery, was reserved for the Portuguese navigator, Vasco da Gama.

Sailing south, down the coast of Africa, then *east,* not *west,* across the Indian Ocean, Da Gama reached India, the Spice Islands (as the East Indies were then called) and Cathay. There *was* a westward passage to the Indies across the Atlantic, but its discovery was to be the accomplishment of another Portuguese navigator. He was Magellan, whose ships were the first to sail around the world.

Many have wondered why the new world Columbus discovered was not named after him. That honor, however, fell to still another Italian, Amerigo Vespucci. Amerigo was the first to recognize and publicize the fact that the new land Columbus had touched on was not the Indies, but two broad new continents and their fringing islands. The mapmakers of the time named the new region "America." The one name that originated with Columbus has survived only to perpetuate his error. He called the people of the new lands "Indians," thus posing a problem for anthropologists, who have invented the term "Amerinds" to distinguish the American Indians from the Indians of Asia.

History has added still another irony. Research has proved that Columbus was *not* the first European to reach the new New World. Before him had come the Viking, Leif Ericson, and possibly an earlier Norse navigator, Eric the Red.

Yet after all this has been said, Columbus' voyage remains a remarkable achievement. Discoveries which count are those which lead to further exploration and to settlement. Columbus' discovery of the New World was the first to achieve such results.

When we consider what doubts and prejudices Columbus had to overcome and what obstacles and risks he faced, his achievement is truly staggering. He spent half his lifetime wandering from place to place in search of someone patient enough to listen to him and farsighted enough to venture ships and money for his bold enterprise. After he obtained backing, he had to risk the unknown—or rather the falsely known—an ocean filled with fantastic perils.

Even when Columbus set sail with a queen's and a bishop's blessing, few believed that he would ever return. Relatives of his crew mourned on the piers, as if for the already-dead. Among those who prophesied failure were experienced shipmasters, whose predictions were not based solely on the fabled terrors of the western sea but, instead, on the condition of the vessels which Columbus had been forced to accept. His three ships, the *Santa Maria*, the *Pinta*, and the *Niña*, were considered unfit for a long sea voyage.

The shipmasters' predictions were also based on the character of the crew. Few seamen would sign for this voyage. Among his sailors were prisoners who purchased their freedom by agreeing to serve on the expedition. Few of his men had had any real sailing experience.

But, in the minds of most people, the worst dangers the crew had to face were those that eventually turned out to be mythical. If they sailed far enough west the ships would surely reach the edge of the world and fall off, like logs carried over the edge of a great waterfall. It was thought unlikely, however, that they would live to meet this peril. Before they reached the western edge, it was said, they would be devoured by dragons, leviathans or other monsters so gigantic they could swallow entire navies. Or they would be sucked to the bottom by boiling whirlpools, or be shipwrecked by mountainous waves, cyclones or jagged reefs that surpassed any in the known waters of the world.

And Columbus' crew shared the common fear of these fanciful dangers. His hardest task was to keep up their courage lest, carried away by sudden panic, they mutiny, seize the vessels and turn back to Spain. Better mariners than these men had lost heart after weeks on sea wastes, and sailed back.

The last known lands Columbus passed were the Canary Islands. After that there were thirty-four days of endless ocean before another landfall. Columbus spent many an anxious hour talking his men back to sanity. Many a time he barely succeeded in keeping them sailing forward. His experience is movingly expressed in the lines of a well-known poem:

Behind him lay the gray Azores,
    Behind the Gates of Hercules;
Before him not the ghost of shores,
    Before him only shoreless seas.
The good mate said: "Now must we pray,
    For lo! the very stars are gone.
Brave Admiral, speak; what shall I say?"
    "Why, say: 'Sail on! sail on! and on!'"

On the thirty-third day Columbus made this entry in his log: "Today we saw a bird."

Where there were birds, land *must* be near. Every man kept peering ahead. Early the next morning Columbus said to his mate, "I think I see a light."

The mate's gaze followed Columbus' pointing finger. "I think I see it, too."

"It rises and falls," said Columbus.

"Perhaps it is a light carried in a boat."

Then the light disappeared. Columbus'

Columbus before Queen Isabella.

heart sank, but he did not dare show his disappointment. A few hours later came the cry, "Land ho! Land ho!"

The ship's cannon boomed; there were cheers and songs. The world's greatest voyage was over. It had begun as a passage to India, but as Whitman, in the great poem to which he gave that title, wrote, it was a

Passage to more than India!
O secret of the earth and sky!
Of you O waters of the sea! O winding
   creeks and rivers!

Of you O woods and fields! Of you, O
   strong mountains.

Of you O pampas! Of you gray rocks!
O morning red! O clouds! O rain, and
   snows!
O day and night, passage to you!
O sun and moon, and all you stars!
Passage to you!

Columbus died without knowing what land he had found or how much there was of it. It took another five hundred years to find out that he had discovered a new world far richer than fabled Cathay.

"Signing of the Compact." Painting by Percy Moran.

THEY PLANTED THE SEED

(THE *MAYFLOWER* COMPACT)

One day in the summer of 1620, John Alden, a cooper by trade, was working as usual in his dockside shop in Southampton. Suddenly, an old man came into the shop, stood directly in front of Alden, peered into his face and asked him urgently, "Young man, dost love the Lord thy God?"

"'Tis a strange question to pop out so bare among my barrels, old man," said Alden. "I've ne'er given the matter great thought."

"And so—you are not one of us," said the old man with disappointment. "But you do love justice, don't you, young cooper?"

18

"If you seek justice, master, I'd know not where to send you for it, not in all England," said Alden as he turned back to his work.

"I seek refuge from the injustice of the King," said the old man, swiftly now and in a whisper. "The King's bailiff and his men are hard on my heels. Hide me, lad! Hide me quickly and turn them away!"

"And lose my ears? Perchance my life?" said Alden. "What awful thing have you done that they are pursuing you?"

"I have printed the truth," said the old man. "Look into my eyes, lad. Do you see evil? Do you see villainy?"

John Alden saw only gentleness and light in the old man's eyes. He took him quickly by the hand and helped him slip down out of sight in a large hogshead in the rear of the shop. A few moments later, when the bailiff stepped into the shop, Alden lied boldly.

"Yes, I did see such an old man," he said. "In great haste he was, as he went up into the town."

As the bailiff and his men marched up the street, the old man clambered out of the hogshead.

"Thank you, my lad," he said. "But I take it my first words did mystify your ears?"

"Aye," said Alden. " 'Dost love the Lord thy God?' Who can answer that?"

"Some of us can," said the old man. "We have many secret partisans on this coast.

"Landing of the Pilgrims." Painting by Peter Frederick Rothermel.

'Twas a manner of password, a countersign. Lad, I am William Brewster, lately a printer by trade."

"And I am John Alden."

They shook hands and Brewster went on with his story.

"Back in 1608," he said, "a few of us people in Nottinghamshire decided that religion should be free of royal power, and each man should be permitted to worship God after his own manner. This, however, sounded so unpleasant in the King's ear that we were driven to form a secret congregation of free worshipers. We were betrayed by informers, and we would all have been arrested and put to torture if we had not run off to Holland.

"In Amsterdam and Leyden, poverty was our lot and hard labor at unfamiliar tasks, even for the smallest children. It was under the lash of necessity that our thoughts turned, little by little over the years, toward the New World. It is our plan to sail from Southampton this very day, and the ship's papers state that we are to be put ashore on the northern coast of Virginia. We have great hope and inward zeal that we may lay some foundation in those remote parts of the world; yea, though we shall be but stepping-stones unto others for the performing of so great a work."

"And why are you here in England again?" asked Alden.

"Certain tracts that I published," replied Brewster, "offended the Dutch authorities —and it was thought best that I return to England and remain in hiding until our vessel was ready to sail."

"And would you have need of a well-skilled carpenter and cooper?" asked Alden.

"But what about your parents, lad?" asked Brewster.

"I have none," said Alden. "I have these two hands, and tools to fit them. I can read and write, for my uncle taught me. And I have a mind to see this new land."

The ship *Mayflower,* under the command of Captain Christopher Jones, lay in wait out in the harbor. That night the people in the boat that rowers brought alongside the *Mayflower* included John Alden, William Brewster, Priscilla Mullins and her father William. John and Priscilla, at first glance, were taken with each other, and it was not lost on their elders that the first romance of this New World community had begun on the very eve of departure.

Of the one hundred and four passengers on the *Mayflower,* Brewster's congregation numbered only forty-one. The sixty-three others—the "outsiders," or "strangers," as Brewster's people called them—had been lured into the adventure by the promises of the London investors who had furnished the ship for the voyage. Most of these "outsiders" were respectable folk, though less than churchly. A few, however, were little better than vagabonds, the scourings of London gutters. The churchmen insisted on ruling the entire company, but they did permit the others to have one spokesman at the company's conferences.

September 6, 1620—in just a few hours the lights on the English shore dropped below the horizon and the *Mayflower* sailed westward against the great Ocean Sea. It was to be a terrible crossing. Violent storms drove the *Mayflower* off its course, and the first bitter cold of winter brought sickness and death to the passengers. Among the dead was a young boy, Billy Butten. Then, as if to even accounts, a child, to be named Oceanus Hopkins, was born.

When land was first sighted early in November, cries of complaint and dismay ran through the ship. This was a chilly and barren coastline, clearly not Virginia.

"We've been swindled by these psalm-singing, holy pulpit-pounders that call themselves 'Saint,'" shouted John Billington, the toughest of the recruits from the London streets. "These 'Saints' here figure if they go on down to Virginia they'll come once more under the hand of the King—and then they couldn't lord it over the likes of us any longer. I say, let's seize the ship and sail her to Virginia ourselves!"

"If it's action you want," shouted Myles Standish, the little red-headed soldier with a peppery disposition, "if it's action you want, I'll show it to you. Why, I'll take all you would-be mutineers and string you up on a yardarm!"

"Please, Captain Standish," Elder Brewster said as he moved to the center of the crowd on deck. "We have come to this far edge of the earth to try the way of reason and loving-kindness. We must act as brothers, or surely we shall all perish. As for what you say, John Billington, I have just spoken to Captain Jones. He says we are lying off Cape Cod, far to the north of Virginia, and he assures me that he can proceed no farther to the south, lest his supplies for the return voyage give out. I, for one, am content to cast our lot here upon this coast. And you, Captain Standish?"

"'Tis all one to me, if a harbor can be found, and a hill to perch a fort upon," said the captain.

"And I have been meditating a compact for our governance that we could all agree to before stepping ashore," said Elder Brewster. "Will you please all listen to me? You, too, John Billington, and all your friends."

Elder Brewster then took a roll of parchment from his pocket and read the proposed compact in a loud and joyous voice.

"Having undertaken, for the glory of God, and advancement of the Christian faith and honor of our King and Country, a voyage to plant the first colony in the northern parts of Virginia, we do by these presents, solemnly and mutually in the presence of God and one another, covenant and combine ourselves together into a civil body politic, for our better ordering and preservation; and by virtue hereof to enact, constitute and frame such just and equal laws, ordinances, acts, constitutions and offices, from time to time, as shall be thought most meet and convenient for the general good of the colony; unto which we promise all due submission and obedience.

"In witness whereof we have hereunder subscribed our names at Cape Cod the 11th of November in the Year of Our Lord, sixteen hundred and twenty."

"I'll sign that," said John Carver.

"I, too!" said William Bradford.

And they were followed by Edward Winslow, Isaac Allerton and Myles Standish.

"But this compact is for masters and yeomen alike," said Elder Brewster. "Who among the artisans will come forward now?"

John Alden came forward and signed the compact. And as he turned away, he saw that John Billington, too, was standing in line waiting to place his signature after the others. Elder Brewster had won his long battle. Soon his beloved company of "Saints," together with their worldly friends, would disembark on these challenging shores of the New World—a community of people united in the spirit of freedom and equality.

THE HOLY EXPERIMENT

(WILLIAM PENN)

The admiral had raised his son to be a man of consequence in England. Already the lad had served the Duke of York as a dispatch-rider, carrying personal messages to the King. Would he not, someday, become an ambassador or an adviser at the court of Charles II? His future indeed looked bright.

That is, it looked bright until young William began saying "thee" in place of "you" and refusing to take off his hat before any man. Nay, not even for the Duke or good King Charles himself would he doff his hat. "All of us," young William Penn insisted, "are equals in the sight of God."

"Confound it!" the admiral cried one day in 1667. "What's come over you, William? I know you've been amusing yourself among those Quakers, but—"

"Thee is wrong, my dear father," William said gently. "I have not, as thee says, been amusing myself."

But surely his son couldn't be serious! Why, William loved the good things in life too well. These Quakers, the Society of Friends, as they called themselves—well, what were they? Nothing but a crew of solemn-faced fanatics, spouting about the brotherhood of man, freedom of conscience, and—

"I did find giving up the world a sacrifice," William admitted. "Its grandeur is alluring. And I am most sorry to be a disappointment to thee, Father. But I must obey a greater command, that of my conscience. When I first came into the silent assemblies of God's people I felt a strange power among them. And as I gave way to it, I found the evil weakening in me. And the good raised up."

The admiral groaned. He himself was well known at court and he could count himself a friend of the King, such a good friend, in fact, that the King owed him a considerable sum of money.

For all their talk of God's peace, the Quakers were known as notorious disturbers of the King's peace. Their passive resistance could be just as troublesome as armed rioting. Go on this way, thought Admiral Penn, and the boy would end up in the Tower of London, or in Newgate Jail.

"William," he threatened, "if you persist in this folly, I'll disinherit you!"

"If that is what thee wants," William replied.

Before he died, the admiral groaned many times. For William *was* serious, publishing his beliefs, speaking them openly, angering Parliament. Nor could the admiral's influence at court keep William out of jail. In and out the lad went like a jack-in-the-box.

When he died, the admiral, despite his threats, left his estate to his son. And part of his inheritance included sixteen thousand pounds sterling. A goodly sum, but there was just one unfavorable consideration. The sixteen thousand pounds was money owed to the admiral by the King. Such a debt would not be easy to collect.

"We have considered your request," the King told William, "in the matter of this sixteen thousand pounds sterling. I must say, though I was most fond of your father, I am reluctant to grant it to you."

"But," William said, "thee would not be so reluctant if thee knew what a great purpose I have in mind for it."

"I am afraid I do know," King Charles replied. "With so much money, you would be able to turn the realm upside down with your Quaker pamphlets. You and your Society of Friends are the biggest nuisance I have to contend with. I'd like to be rid of you all."

"Perhaps I can show thee a way," William suggested.

"Penn's Treaty with the Indians." Painting by Benjamin West.

"Eh?" said the King.

"A way to get rid of us," William smiled. "Thee need not pay me in money. I will take it in land."

"Land," the King echoed. "What land?"

"In America," William said. "It is the land in America lying between the colonies of Maryland and New York, lying westward from Jersey far beyond the distant mountains."

So the royal debt was paid by wilderness acres in the New World, and the King considered this arrangement a bargain. Not only had he cleared a debt, he had rid himself of hundreds of troublesome Quakers.

To Penn, his new lands were to make possible a "Holy Experiment." He would establish a settlement in the New World dedicated to the principles of equality and the brotherhood of man. Thousands of Quakers would leave England to settle there. Penn Sylvania, the land would be called—Sylvania meaning "The Forest," and "Penn" for the late admiral, his father. How was the King to know that someday Pennsylvania would be recognized as one of the richest areas in the world?

Penn promptly drew up a constitution for the new colony. Meanwhile he sent his cousin William Markham to America. Within the boundaries of the land granted Penn by the King, a few Swedes, Dutch and English had already settled. "Be impartially just and courteous to these people," Penn charged William. "And I would have thee especially careful in the treatment of the Indians. We must live in peace with them."

"But no other colony has been able to do that," some of the Quakers protested.

"We shall try," Penn said, "as no other colony has yet tried."

In April, 1682, Penn's constitution was approved. It contained several provisions similar to those of our own constitution. In general it protected the civil rights of the people. Then, in August, William Penn himself sailed for America. On the ship

with him were one hundred passengers, mostly artisans and craftsmen much needed in the wild new land. When the ship docked at Chester, where Penn met his cousin Markham, they boarded a barge and rowed up the Delaware River to a place called Dock Creek. Here, a town was already springing up.

"We'll name the streets for the trees that grow there," Penn said. "And make fine open parks and commons. Let every house be placed in the middle of its plot, so that there may be ground on each side for gardens, orchards or fields and that it may be a green country town which can never be burnt and will always be wholesome. And may it always be a city of brotherly love," he added.

His "green country town" is now called Philadelphia.

"But the Indians are only wild savages," some of the Quakers said. "How can we love them and make a league with them?"

"If we do not deal with them as brothers and with justice," Penn said, "then our cause is doomed."

"But they claim the land as their own. They say we have no right to it. There will be war."

No, Penn said, there would be no war.

Tradition says he called a meeting in the fall of 1682, at Shackamaxon Creek. Here gathered the Quakers, led by Penn, and the Indians—the Delawares and the Susquehannas—led by their chief, Tammany. And here, Penn made nineteen separate treaties with the tribal chiefs for the purchase of land.

"We shall live as brothers," Penn promised.

Tammany agreed. "As long as sun and moon shine in the sky. We have broad path to walk. If Indian asleep and Yengeesman come, he pass and do no harm to Indian. If Yengeesman sleep in path, Indian pass and do him no harm. Indian say, 'He is Yengees, he loves sleep!'"

Yengees. This was as close as the Indians

could get to pronouncing "English," or, as we now say, "Yankees."

And for nearly a century, from the founding of Penn's colony to the time of the Revolutionary War, the Pennsylvania Yengeesman and the Indians lived in peace. The colony flourished, a "Holy Experiment" dedicated to brotherly love and peace.

WILLIAM PENN.

OLD PEG-LEG

(PETER STUYVESANT)

In the 1640's, the reports reaching Holland from the New Netherlands were alarming. According to some of the irate sea captains employed by the Dutch West India Company, its colony on Manhattan Island—"New Amsterdam"—was going to rack and ruin. The captains pointed to their cargoes, mostly furs. A paltry yield, they said, from what could be a booming trade with the Indians.

And no wonder. Those settlers and traders at New Amsterdam were just about the laziest, the most shiftless lot imaginable. Disorderly, and given to drink, they seemed to have not a shred of self-respect, not to mention a proper respect for the West India Company. If *something* weren't done—they shook their heads gravely—there might even be war with the Indians, which the diffident New Amsterdamers, badly organized as they were, were sure to lose. The English colonies in New England were casting greedy eyes on the New Netherlands. And the way things stood, they could blow the New Amsterdam defenses to bits and seize Manhattan Island for themselves.

It is not surprising, then, that the officials of the West India Company in Holland were disturbed. The governor they had appointed, Willem Kieft, seemed powerless to make the needed changes. A capable new governor must be found who could whip these lazy settlers into shape. In 1646 they found him.

It was another year before Peter Stuyvesant sailed into what we now call New York Bay and came ashore on Manhattan Island. The news of his appointment as Director-General had preceded him, and the easygoing settlers were not looking forward to a stricter regime. This Stuyvesant, as a soldier and the governor of

Curaçao, had gained a reputation as a martinet. In a recent encounter against the Portuguese, he had lost a leg. This, it was said, had made his temper even fiercer.

Peter Stuyvesant fulfilled the New Amsterdamers' worst expectations. He was formally greeted by a roll of drums, firing of cannon and a welcoming committee of the foremost burghers as his ship arrived.

"I am Willem Kieft, Your Excellency, the former governor. We are here to welcome you—"

"Yes, yes," Stuyvesant said impatiently. "Why is that cannon being fired?"

"In your honor, Excellency."

"A waste of good gunpowder. Save it for our enemies." He looked around him and his stern eyes lighted on a slouching soldier. "You! Stand straight, man! Are you a soldier or a peddler!"

So he was to act every day. As he stomped about on his wooden leg through this straggling village on the lower tip of Manhattan Island, his quick temper often flared. He did not miss any of the trappers in their mangy fur caps, Indians smelling of woodsmoke, English adventurers, soldiers in sloppy uniforms and the island's shabby fort—so badly in need of repair that it looked ready to collapse.

"Disorder! Everything in ruins," he said grimly. "Every man walking about as if he were a master! We shall see about this. I shall govern as a father governs his children."

He issued his orders: No more selling whiskey to the Indians. The taverns must close on time, not one minute later than the law allowed. He established a curfew, and woe to the citizen found abroad after the bell tolled.

He had the crumbling fort rebuilt. In his treatment of the Indians, he was fair—

Peter Stuyvesant harangues the citizens
of New Amsterdam.

quick to reward and quick to punish. As time went by, the colonists had to admit it: old Peg-leg got things done. In getting them done, however, he ignored the people's rights and ruled by fear.

At the age of sixty-three, despite rheumatism and his wooden leg, Peter Stuyvesant led an expedition against the Swedish colony on the Delaware River. Everyone at New Amsterdam breathed easier with Stuyvesant away. Many even wished old Peg-leg would stay away.

They were not to utter that wish for long, however. One day, a colonist came

rushing wildly into town and the alarms were sounded. Indians—hundreds, maybe thousands even—were attacking. "They've killed Van Dyck—Werckendam's farm burned down—all his family killed—"

The soldiers left in the garrison on Manhattan Island were in a panic. "God help us all, if the Indians get past the north wall, if they breach the palisades! With ships, we might escape, but we have no ships!"

A message was dispatched to the Dutch soldiers in the hope that it would reach Stuyvesant in time. And, fortunately, word reached Stuyvesant before the main In-

27

dian attack occurred. By forced marches he brought his troops back into town. He had won a victory over the Swedes, but, God in heaven, what did he return to find? Utter disorder.

"Those two Indians in the stocks," he commanded, "release them. Send them to their chiefs as messengers. Tell them I'll meet them outside the palisades tomorrow at dawn. Let them tell their chiefs that Wooden Leg wants peace. And if I don't get it at once, I'll hang every savage to the highest tree in New Netherlands!"

He did get peace. Afterward, however, he roused in the colony more ill-will for himself than ever, by tightening his iron rule.

"We must build new, larger fortifications," he said.

"But, Your Excellency," the burgomaster protested. "The *money* for this work!"

"Money! Money! That's all I hear. The English have started an insurrection among the Indians on Long Island, and you cackle like hens sitting on the roost, waiting for the English fox to gobble you up—"

"But the money," the members of the town council protested, "must come from taxes. And the taxes must come from the people. We must have their consent. After all, Your Excellency, the people *have* a voice—"

"Rule by the people!" Stuyvesant scoffed. "Rule by the fools and the talkers —the clowns and bear-skinners! *I'm* the law here—not the town council—not the tavern loafers!"

Once again, Stuyvesant had his way. But the price he paid proved too high. The colonists began to grumble among themselves, "What difference does it make if the King of England takes New Amsterdam? One tyrant is no worse than another. Old Peg-leg's West India Company, what does it do for us? They send us no powder, no soldiers. Nothing."

Thus, when four English ships sailed into the Bay, Peter Stuyvesant learned that loyalty cannot be forced from discontented people. The citizens of New Amsterdam refused to man the forts. "Traitors!" Peter stormed at them. But in vain. Many looked upon English rule as a deliverance from his tyranny.

"Not a man among us," they said, "will stand with you." What was more, they threatened to burn the fort, rather than allow Stuyvesant to bring on them a possible British bombardment.

Even to so fierce a fighter as Stuyvesant, it was plain the end had come. There lay the four English ships, crowded to the gunwales with trained soldiers.

"Let be, then!" Stuyvesant said to the burgomaster. "Go! Tell your Englishmen we will treat for surrender. And choose among you the greatest coward to haul down our colors!"

It was the end of Peg-leg's one-man rule. The colony of New Amsterdam became New York and flourished under the English flag. Stubborn old Peter Stuyvesant retired to his farm, on the east side of Manhattan, where he raised fruit trees. You can imagine he made them stand straight in their rows; no nonsense about them!

One day when he was well along in years, the English governor of New York province came to see him. "Between one old soldier and another," Nicholls confided, "I'm having trouble. The people are refusing to quarter soldiers in their homes. The town council seems to be at the bottom of it. All this talk about the rights of the people!"

"So," Stuyvesant said. "It's come to you English, too! It's in the air, my friend. The New World—new ideas, new words. Freedom, the rights of the people. I had to bow, too. Those notions of freedom—democracy —people's rights—they are like a tide coming in. No man can stop it. I tried to fight it, but I failed. And you English will fail too." He stumped off to look at his pear trees, the finest in all of New *York*.

A PASSAGE TO GEORGIA

(JAMES EDWARD OGLETHORPE)

James Edward Oglethorpe's visit in 1729 to the London debtors' prison in Fleet Street was the turning-point of his life. In his early thirties, Oglethorpe was a typical English gentleman—Captain of the Foot Guards, Member of Parliament, frequenter of the fashionable coffeehouses, and something of a wit. His visit to the prison came about in this way:

One of Oglethorpe's close friends was Robert Castell, a promising architect. Castell fell into debt and his creditors had him seized and thrown into a debtors' prison.

After pleading unsuccessfully with his creditors for leniency, Robert Castell's wife Anne decided to seek help from Oglethorpe.

"I'm not sure whether he's alive or dead," Anne told him. "The curious irony of the situation is that even in debtors' prison you need money—for favors from the warden! Please, James—you're a Member of Parliament—can't you help me get into the prison to see Bob, to take him a little money?"

Just before James Oglethorpe and Anne Castell appeared for admission to Fleet Street Prison, Warden Bambridge had been instructing a guard in the technique of putting the screws on a debtor. The victim was a man named Isaac Delaney, in jail on the charge that he had concealed assets to the sum of thirty-five pounds, ten shillings and six pence.

"Either you'll pay your creditors, or you'll pay me," said the warden as he gave the screw another turn.

Isaac Delaney was being dragged off in chains when Oglethorpe and Anne were announced.

"You say she's Robert Castell's wife?" said the warden to Oglethorpe. "Well, she can't see him. And neither can you."

"Perhaps, Warden, you aren't aware that I am a Member of Parliament," said Oglethorpe. "I demand an interview with your prisoner."

"Well, now, Mr. Oglethorpe, if you put it that way—" said the warden. Then he added slyly, "Although I'd advise you not to see him. I'd really advise you *not* to see him!"

The warden held a lantern for Oglethorpe and Anne as they walked down into the depths of the prison. Finally, there was Robert Castell before them, lying on the ground, chained to another prisoner.

"Don't touch me, Anne!" he cried, and as he looked up, even in the low light of the lantern, his wife could see that he had contracted smallpox.

"Why haven't you taken this man out of this hole and to a physician?" asked Oglethorpe.

"But that takes money," exclaimed the warden sharply.

"Even if I had the money I wouldn't give Warden Bambridge a farthing!" said Robert Castell.

"You see," said the warden, "your friend Mr. Castell is one of the difficult ones."

"I'll do what I can, Bob, to get you out," said Oglethorpe, "and by heaven, Warden Bambridge, I'll see that you are brought to justice—I'll see that this whole business somehow gets the light of day in Parliament."

Oglethorpe had spoken in Parliament only once before. His seven years of public service had been spent on obscure committees concerned with the improvement of roads, and with regulations governing the work of fishermen, shoemakers and the dock-workers on the Thames. His mother, Lady Oglethorpe, had often twitted him about his concern for the welfare of these common people.

The speech that Oglethorpe made in Parliament concerning the Fleet Street Debtors' Prison vibrated with grief and indignation. His friend Robert Castell had died there before his release could be effected.

As Oglethorpe laid before Parliament an unsparing description of the life of a debtor in an English jail, the scattered remarks of criticism and objection died away.

"I have a solution," concluded Oglethorpe, "for I think it better to support the industrious poor than the idle poor. Nor am I concerned with unworthy debtors, but with those worthy ones like Robert Castell, debtors who became so through no fault of their own, but who were undone by guardians, or lawsuits or accidents of commerce. Surely, there is for them some place better than the loathsome debtors' gaols where they suffer under the whips of such corrupt men as Warden Bambridge. With due care in selecting the prisoners for their character, Mr. Speaker, I would suggest a colony in America."

Three years later, on the 21st of April, 1732, the following proclamation was issued from Whitehall: "Be it known to all those present that we, George II, by the grace of God, of Great Britain and Ireland, King, Defender of the Faith, do hereby grant this charter to the trustees for establishing the colony of Georgia in America."

Warden Bambridge had escaped any prosecution whatsoever and Robert Castell was dead, but Oglethorpe had achieved his ultimate goal. His friends now expected him to turn to other things, but he amazed them by saying, "If it please His Majesty, I have long had a secret wish to accompany these poor subjects to our provinces in America. I should like very much to lead this passage to our colony in Georgia."

It was not long before Oglethorpe's administration of the colony of Georgia was causing much discussion in England. The former prisoners, now free and independent men, were able to send substantial payments to their creditors in England, peace had been achieved with the Indians and a flourishing trade was developing with other American colonies as well as with the mother country. For these achievements Oglethorpe was promoted to a major-generalship and called back to the service of England.

Along with the other colonies, Georgia fought for independence. One of the English liberals who supported the colonists' cause was Oglethorpe. Indeed, he was one of the first Englishmen to call upon John Adams, the first minister of the new American nation to the court of His Majesty, George III.

"I have come to welcome you, Mr. Adams," he said in the Adams' Grosvenor Square drawing-room in June, 1785. "I have retained a great esteem for America, my own colony of Georgia in particular. There was a time when some English statesmen misunderstood America and thought to tax you without your consent, as if they felt you would grow from docile calves to oxen accustomed to the yoke. They would not have thought so, had they

Oglethorpe and the Indians.

ever lived, as I did, in the colonies. I knew from my experience in Georgia that the colonists had tasted freedom and would resist oppression and injustice. Yes, Mr. Adams, I shall die far from home. I think I left my heart in Georgia."

Within the year Oglethorpe's long life came to an end at eighty-eight. During his last years he spoke often of Georgia, where he had observed the transformation of sick, demoralized debtor-prisoners to strong, confident pioneers.

31

COLONIZER OF CALIFORNIA

(JUNIPERO SERRA)

Until 1848 California belonged to Mexico, was part of the Spanish Empire, ruled by a Spanish viceroy. The greatest name in Spanish California history is Fray Junipero Serra, a little Franciscan friar. At just about the time the English colonies on the East Coast were claiming, then fighting for, their independence, Serra was waging a fight for a different sort of independence on the West Coast.

Serra and his companion Fray Francisco Palou came to New Spain from Majorca and were stationed at the Sierra Gorda missions, where their earnest, selfless work, patient understanding and geniality won the confidence of the Mexican Indians. The viceroy learned of their success, and when Serra asked that he and Palou be sent to Alta or Upper California, their request was granted. The Franciscans were to go along as part of an elaborate military expedition. But Serra objected. He wanted complete control of his missionary work;

he refused to be subject to the army's rule.

"Where there is military rule, the natives vanish," Serra told the viceroy. "And then where are Spain's subjects? Simply, there are no subjects. Therefore, what is the good of annexation? Conquest, Your Excellency, must be tempered with reason, the reason that comes from bringing civilization to the natives, from lighting the lamp of Christian teaching and ideals in this land."

"These things cannot happen without military conquest," declared the viceroy. "I hope that you will be able to build your missions, but you shall be accompanied by Spanish soldiers to claim the land in the name of His Gracious Majesty, Charles III. Don Pedro Fages will command the soldiers and Gaspar de Portola will supervise the expedition."

"Then I ask you, Your Excellency," pleaded Junipero, "make it clear, before we set out, that Don Fages is to command only his soldiers. The missions that I hope to establish will be strictly under my author-

32

ity. Too often the soldiers have undone all the good work of the Padres!"

"Very well," said the viceroy. And Don Fages agreed to abide by this decision.

In San Diego, Don Fages erected a fort, while Serra and Palou built the first mission in California, dedicating it to San Diego de Alcala. This outpost of New Spain flourished, and within a year Serra and Don Fages decided to push on farther north, leaving Palou to supervise the community of San Diego.

The expedition marched on to the beautiful Monterey Peninsula, where Serra established the San Carlos Mission and Don Fages built another fort. But the brutality of the homesick, discontented soldiers caused an uprising among the Indians, who attacked the garrison. Don Fages hurried to the mission for a consultation with Serra.

"I have always said, Padre," he began, "that someday you would be glad to have Spanish soldiers around to protect your mission. Now, I must admit that it is just the opposite. Today I have come to you for help against the Indians. Some of the Shastas have followed me into the mission courtyard. Tell them they must submit to the white man's rule. They will believe anything from you."

"No sooner had I gained the trust of these natives," said Serra, "than you betrayed it with your harsh laws and your brutal soldiers. Now you ask me for help."

"I ask you for your help, yes," said Don Fages, "but you must also remember that all I am trying to do is enforce the law— Spanish law."

"And only *you* represent the law?" asked Junipero.

"Yes, I am the law," said Don Fages.

"Then, after this Indian trouble is settled, I must go to Mexico City to take up this question with the viceroy," said Serra. "Come, let us go out into the courtyard."

Paska, chief of the Shastas, stood there, waiting to present his case to Junipero Serra.

"Shasta tribe like words of friar," said the Indian chief. "We want you to teach us how to plant seeds, how to grow food in valleys, how to build homes. We want to move near you, here at San Carlos Mission. But if Spanish soldiers come any more to our camps, doing bad and cruel things, we will fight."

"I built the San Carlos Mission only to make you and your people happy," said Serra to Paska. "I promise you that hereafter we shall live peacefully and prosperously together for many generations. Don Fages will see to it that his soldiers will not bother you any longer."

Paska and his tribe proved so eager to co-operate with Junipero Serra that Don Fages admitted, at long last, that the friar's method of conquest was much more successful than his own.

Leaving behind a few Franciscan friars, Junipero Serra, with Francisco Palou and their young Shasta guide, Moo-Tan, trudged southward down the chain of California missions—San Diego, Santa Clara, San Gabriel, San Juan Capistrano, San Buenaventura, Santa Barbara and the Mission Dolores.

Serra's visit with the viceroy in Mexico City was a triumphant one. But he was impatient with celebrations and honors. The aging friar wanted to return to his California missions.

Those missions can still be seen today— a chain of twenty-one of them along California's Camino Real, or Royal Road, from San Diego to Sonoma. A number of them— like the first, San Diego del Alcala, in 1769 —were established by Serra, but his work was carried on by others, long after Serra's death in 1784 at the age of seventy-one. San Francisco Solano de Sonoma, established in 1823, was the last of the California missions. They stand today as a monument to a great teacher who affected the course of American history in many ways by the civilization he planted on our western shores.

MAKERS OF THE REPUBLIC

"Let us raise a standard to which the wise and honest can repair; the rest is in the hands of God."

GEORGE WASHINGTON, Speech to the Constitutional Convention, 1787.

THE FATHER OF HIS COUNTRY

(GEORGE WASHINGTON)

Just suppose that George Washington had never lived. How would the Revolutionists have fared without him? How different would our history be? The greatness of "The Father of His Country" becomes clear when the answers to these questions are considered.

George Washington was uniquely fitted for his role of commander-in-chief in the Revolutionary War, and probably no other man could have kept the colonies and the Continental Army together during the long and bitter struggle. Probably no other man had the precise combination of qualifications required.

He had excellent military training. When he was thirty he was made an adjutant in Virginia. He saw military service and in 1754, as a lieutenant-colonel, fought against the French at Fort Duquesne and Fort Necessity. He liked action, and his ability as an officer was so highly regarded that General Braddock insisted on his being a member of his staff. But Washington, an ardent Virginia patriot, refused Braddock's commission because, as a colonial officer, his rank would be below that of any British officer. Braddock, determined to have this most able man on his staff, found a way to avoid this situation, and Washington accepted a special post offered him by the British general. In the famous battle against the French and the Indians, during which Braddock was killed, George Washington distinguished himself and his fame spread. In a few years he was made commander of all the Virginia forces.

He was a man of broad horizons and wide experience. When he was sixteen he had helped to survey all of the Shenandoah Valley, and later had become the official surveyor of Fairfax County. He had traveled to the West Indies. He had embarked on a project to open the West to settlement, and he had planned a canal to join the Ohio and Potomac Rivers.

He was a man of quality and substance. Farmer, owner of plantations, he directed the work of many men besides the hundreds of slaves on the virtually self-contained estates. He was respected as a leading citizen, not only of Virginia but of the American colonies generally.

He was a man of great character; his integrity was unimpeachable. His discipline was strict and yet sympathetic, and though he was often regarded as cold, he

George Washington at the Battle of Trenton. Painting by John Trumbull.

won the allegiance of all who worked for or served under him. Of courage, he had shown that he had more than a lion's share.

He was a Virginian. That last fact, somehow, was the crucial factor in his appointment, in 1775, as commander-in-chief. The Revolutionary War had started at Lexington and Concord, and it was still a New England war, for the Southern colonies had not yet come in. When the Second Continental Congress met, John Adams succeeded in having Washington, the eminent Virginian, made commander-in-chief of the American Army. Adams knew that the Southern colonies would hesitate to join forces with the New Englanders unless a Southern general were the commander-in-chief.

It was a monumental job that George Washington had to undertake. His army was raw, unconditioned, virtually without uniforms, without supplies, without money, without organization. As commander-in-chief he had to form and train his forces even as he fought his battles. Before vastly superior forces, the Continentals had to retreat again and again. When that happens, it is almost inevitable that demoralization will set in, that soldiers will desert, that the army will evaporate, that the cause will be lost.

Yet Washington kept his army in being in the face of what would have seemed to almost any other man insuperable odds. He built, trained, encouraged and inspired his army and prepared to make the tide turn.

Matters came to a crisis during the bitter winter of 1777, when Washington's army was encamped at Valley Forge in Pennsylvania. The British had captured Philadelphia, the colonists' first capital, and Congress had fled to Baltimore. From there it kept despatching frantic orders to Washington to come to their defense.

In spite of these orders, Congress still would not authorize their general to ap-

point a competent quartermaster to organize a supply system. It took no step to raise money for soldiers' pay and supplies. And it made no effort, itself, to provide food, clothing, arms, firewood, or other necessities for the hungry, shivering men.

Seldom in history has an army been kept together under such difficulties. Unable to stand the privations, many men whose terms of enlistment had expired refused to re-enlist, and left the camp. The death toll from pneumonia, influenza, consumption and diseases of malnutrition and exposure was fearfully high. The hungry men had so few warm clothes that they took turns wearing them when detailed to reconnaissance or sentry duty.

Then came a soul-testing ordeal. Knowing the desperate condition of Washington's troops, General Howe, the British commander, proposed a conference for a possible ending of the war. Washington could not reject it, because it was important for him to know what terms Howe would offer. A faction in Congress, and among Washington's own officers, was quite ready to come to terms with the British.

While Washington and his aides were on their way to the meeting, some of his soldiers raided a British supply dump to procure food for themselves and their starving comrades. A skirmish resulted in some casualties, and Washington had the torment of watching two of his men in their death throes. As they were dying, they called on him to continue the fight. Others among his soldiers made the same plea.

"I am a servant of these men," said Washington to Howe. "This war is not mine to end but theirs. And they command me to continue it until we are offered terms which will leave us an independent nation."

Washington left the conference with the knowledge that the new nation could preserve its independence only by continuing the war. He sent new appeals to Congress for supplies. Congress told him to "live off the country," to take whatever he needed from the surrounding farmers. Despite this authorization Washington refused. It would turn his army into a band of robbers, he explained, and it would cost Congress the support of the people, who were themselves subsisting on bare necessities.

At last things took a turn for the better. From Philadelphia, under the very noses of the British occupation officials, the patriotic banker Robert Morris sent a large sum of money to Washington for the purchase of supplies. On the pledge by Washington and a number of his officers of all their personal property, other sums were also raised.

Finally, Congress passed a resolution giving Washington complete authority in all war operations. His first use of this authority was to appoint a new quartermaster, General Greene, who organized an efficient supply system.

This was followed by the arrival of the artillery captain, Harry Knox, bringing with him the big guns captured from the British at Fort Ticonderoga. He had hauled them in midwinter over blocked roads all the way to Pennsylvania. At last Washington could enter battle with proper artillery support.

And, fully as valuable as the artillery was the appearance at Valley Forge of Baron Friedrich von Steuben. He was Europe's finest drillmaster, and after a few weeks of his expert drilling, Washington's raw troops were formed into a smart and disciplined army.

For Von Steuben's arrival, Washington had Benjamin Franklin to thank. He had spoken to Franklin of his need for an officer to drill his men in military tactics so that they might be familiar in the field with the maneuvers of trained British troops and know how to deal with them.

Hearing that Von Steuben, despite his august titles, had, like the Marquis de Lafayette, a touch of the democrat in him, Franklin requested aid from him and discovered that he was eager to help the new democratic nation.

By skillful secret arrangement, Franklin obtained for Von Steuben transportation on a vessel with disguised registry and false sailing orders. The German officer arrived in time to drill the men at Valley Forge for the forthcoming campaign.

With trained troops, well-provisioned, well-clothed and well-armed, and with adequate artillery support, Washington made his famous winter crossing of the Delaware. He took a Hessian army, quartered at Trenton, by surprise and destroyed it. Washington reported the victory to the Congress of the United States of America: "I have the pleasure of congratulating you upon the success of an enterprise I have formed against the enemy lying at Trenton, which was executed yesterday morning. When they came to the charge, each man seemed to vie with the other in pressing forward, and were I to give a preference to any particular corps, I should do great injustice to the others."

A few days later, Washington won another battle at Princeton, preparing the way for the liberation of Philadelphia.

France now declared open war on England and sent money and supplies to America. Later came the French Army and the French fleet. These made victory certain. It came at Yorktown, with the surrender of Cornwallis' army. There followed peace, and England's recognition of the independence of the United States.

Thus, largely through Washington's courage, wisdom, endurance and personal sacrifice, a new nation came into being. The ordeal of Valley Forge, which would have broken almost any other man, became truly a forge. On it was hardened and shaped a proud nation.

FARMER FROM VIRGINIA AND FIRST PRESIDENT

(GEORGE WASHINGTON)

In 1783, after eight long years of indefatigable leadership, General George Washington put aside his blue-and-buff uniform and returned at last to his beloved Mount Vernon. The American struggle for independence was finally over.

"Now, my dear Martha," he said to his wife, "I can be a farmer again. We will have many happy years together here, you and I."

The next day, Virginia's Governor Randolph arrived. "The Virginia Assembly," he said, "out of their deep gratitude to you for your service during the war, has voted to give you blocks of stock in both the Potomac and James River Companies. I was asked to inform you of it."

"But this savors too much of a pension," exclaimed Washington, "and I cannot accept a pension!"

"We feared you would take this attitude," said Randolph. "But believe me, General, this is no pension—it is merely a way of showing our pride in you, sir."

"But I refused payment from the federal government for my wartime services," pointed out Washington.

"We all know that, General," said Randolph. "But we also know that you contributed most of your fortune to the maintenance of the army. And now you are back in Virginia with no dependable source of income—and no profession."

"I may not be a doctor or a lawyer, Randolph," admitted Washington, "but I do have a profession. I'm a farmer. I intend, Governor, to spend the rest of my life practicing my profession. And I'll wager that I will manage to earn a good living from it and never be in need of a pension from the government! On second thought, however, I'll accept this gift from the Assembly with the understanding that the income from the stocks be used for some public purpose —let us say, education. Yes, use it to support Liberty Hall Academy over in Rockbridge County."

Washington settled down to put his three-thousand-acre plantation on a paying basis. He corresponded with agricultural experts abroad, conducted experimental plantings with seed from all over the world—Siberian wheat, seeds from China, Irish potatoes. And he even invented a plow to be used when deep furrows were required.

Like most Virginia planters, Washington's overseer, John Alton, though radical enough in his politics, was conservative in his farming. He could hardly believe his ears when Washington ordered several hundred acres planted in grasslands.

"For the good of the cattle," explained Washington. "They need better pastureland. And besides, it will make the soil richer." But Alton thought cattle fared well enough on weeds.

His employer's next action shocked Alton even more. Realizing that the single-crop system was depleting the soil and rendering it useless for future generations, Washington ordered another crop planted in the lands where he had been growing tobacco.

"But tobacco is the chief money crop for the whole of Virginia!" cried Alton. "And besides, what if the land you have planted in tobacco *is* worn out in fifty years? There will still be plenty of your acreage left. In the meantime you will be making money from the tobacco while you're still alive!"

Nevertheless, Washington planted practically all of his tobacco land in buckwheat and worked out a rotation program for his other crops as well. At the same time, he experimented with fertilizers.

"The Washington Family." Painting by Edward Savage.

Thus Washington spent the first two years of peace—farming his land. They were two years of contentment and prosperity, and he looked forward to finishing out his life as a farmer. But the new nation had other plans for him. When it came to naming the man who should preside over the Philadelphia constitutional convention in 1785, the choice fell on Washington, who bowed once more to his country's will. He hoped that the time required to cover the business of the convention would be brief, but the writing of a democratic constitution proved a long and difficult task. The final document took two years to complete.

Once more, in 1787, as in 1783, he hurried back to his Mount Vernon farm, determined never to leave his land again. For a year, he lived the farmer's life he had come to love. And then, in the fall of 1788, his friend James Madison visited him.

"You are truly content, then, to remain a private citizen, a farmer?" asked Madison after a tour of the estate.

"Farming is the most satisfying occupation in the world!" exclaimed Washington. "For it I have gladly turned my back on public life. I am proving to my neighbors that the single-crop system is ruinous, that fertilizer is essential to the soil, that young trees must be planted to replace those which have been cut down, that cattle need good pastureland. Victories in cornfields are less spectacular than those on the battlefield, but they are equally important to our nation."

"You make it difficult, sir, for me to tell you why I am here," said Madison. "I scarcely know how to broach the subject now. You see, I bring an invitation—virtually a command—that you leave your farm for a third time!"

"Again, at my time of life?" asked Washington.

"Alexander Hamilton and I have spent these past weeks sounding out public opinion," said Madison. "We find there is only one man whom the American people will accept as their first President. That man, General Washington, is you!"

"You are a friend of mine, Madison. You are a bit prejudiced in my favor, I'm afraid," said Washington.

"I am such a friend of yours," Madison said earnestly, "that I would not mention this matter if there were any doubt in my mind. You are indispensable. Upon your decision rests the future of our country."

"No man in the world could place personal preference above public duty," said Washington slowly. He set his jaw and took a lingering look over the rolling land that he had cultivated.

The vote-count of the electors showed that George Washington had been elected unanimously as the first President of the United States. He was to be inaugurated at Federal Hall in New York City on April 30. He left Mount Vernon for New York in a coach provided by the government.

Four million Americans were gaily preparing for their first national holiday. All along the post road from Mount Vernon, Virginia, to New York, new citizens of a new nation hung garlands on bridges and lampposts and cheered Washington as his coach rolled by.

Alexandria. Georgetown. Hyattsville. "Let down the coach window," said Washington to Colonel Humphreys, sitting opposite him. "There's little enough for them to look at, but if they wish it, by all means, let them see me."

Riverdale. Then Baltimore, where Washington was to rest overnight. At the banquet there, toast after toast honored the wisdom and courage of the worn and aging man journeying to serve his countrymen once again.

The next morning, in a gray spring dawn, the inaugural coach lurched and splashed through the red mud of Maryland, accompanied for a long way by a troop of citizens on horseback.

Aberdeen. Wilmington. And then down a winding, rutted road into Pennsylvania where Benjamin Franklin, now eighty-three, was waiting at Malloy's Tavern to join Washington on the ride into Philadelphia.

"You make me ashamed, Dr. Franklin," said Washington, "to be a grumbling old man at fifty-six when you were cheerfully voyaging to France at the age of seventy to enlist aid for us abroad."

"I was quaint to them—an object of curiosity—a fat old Quaker in a plain brown suit. But I managed to coax enough supplies and ships and money out of 'em."

More toasts and flowers and gun salutes at every stop, as the inaugural coach rolled up through the green hills of Pennsylvania to Colvin's Ferry, with Trenton across the Delaware. Thousands lined the banks cheering the coach as it moved aboard a ferryboat flying the new striped and starred flag of the United States of America.

On up through New Jersey, through Princeton, Kingston and New Brunswick, and finally Elizabethtown. Then out of the coach and onto an inaugural barge bound for the foot of Wall Street, past boatloads of cheering citizens. To his former aide-de-camp, Alexander Hamilton, who came aboard in New York, Washington said, "This city is a miracle indeed, settled by the Belgians, seized by the Dutch, conquered by the English, full of Scots and French—yet today all Americans! But this is only the beginning. Now we must all build on the freedom we have won. We must heal the hatred and learn unity."

On April 30, 1789, at high noon, a procession started from Washington's house on Cherry Street to Federal Hall. There, Washington stepped out upon the balcony and a roar of jubilation rose from the crowd in the square below. The next moment there was silence as Chancellor Livingston stepped out beside Washington and held an open Bible before him.

"Do you solemnly swear," said Livingston, after Washington had placed his hand upon the open book, "that you will faithfully execute the office of President of the United States, and will, to the best of your ability, preserve, protect and defend the Constitution of the United States. . . ."

Washington repeated these words firmly and clearly, and then Chancellor Livingston cried out in a ringing voice, "Long live George Washington, President of the United States!"

A new nation was born. And George Washington, the Virginia farmer, entrusted now with the problems of peace, as he had once shouldered the problems of war, bowed humbly to the cheering people assembled to honor him as their first President.

APOSTLE OF FREEDOM

(THOMAS JEFFERSON)

What a man wishes to be remembered for often provides a key to his character.

Jefferson held many high offices—member of Washington's Cabinet, ambassador to France, governor of Virginia, President of the United States. He was also an inventor, a scientist, a writer and a philosopher.

But it was not with any of these that he wished his name forever linked.

Before he died he composed his own epitaph, which was to be carved on the headstone over his grave at Monticello: "Here lies buried Thomas Jefferson, author of the Declaration of Independence, of the

"Jefferson as President." Painting by Gilbert Stuart.

Statute of Virginia for religious freedom, and father of the University of Virginia."

Each of the three achievements for which Jefferson wished most to be remembered is associated with human freedom. The Declaration of Independence proclaimed our country an independent, democratic nation. The Virginia law made the right of religious freedom secure. And the University of Virginia was to carry out a part of his broad plan for universal, free education. To Jefferson, educational opportunity was a bulwark of freedom, because he felt the liberation of men's minds from ignorance and superstition made men more capable of valuing and guarding their freedom.

The University of Virginia was America's first *state* university. As a member of the House of Burgesses, Jefferson had advocated free education for Virginia. As President, he tried to get Congress to establish a national university. When Congress refused, he sought to achieve his aim in another way: he prevailed on the Virginia Legislature to establish a state university. He became its first rector and made it a model institution for other states to follow.

It is as the author of the Declaration of Independence, however, that Thomas Jefferson, America's great apostle of freedom, is best known. Behind its composition lies a memorable story.

In the first place, Jefferson had to fight to have his native Virginia send a delegation committed to independence to the meeting of the Continental Congress in Philadelphia. Several delegations from other colonies were divided on the issue of independence. When the resolution for independence was first introduced by Jefferson's colleague, Richard Henry Lee, action on it was deferred until a later session.

By their sympathetic and reasonable approach to undecided delegates Jefferson and Benjamin Franklin were successful in winning a number of them over to the side of independence, and by the time of the July session of the Continental Congress, they considered it safe to reintroduce Lee's resolution.

The historic session began as John Hancock, as chairman, said, "The Chair recognizes the delegate from Virginia, Mr. Richard Henry Lee."

In a ringing voice Lee said, "Mr. Chairman, Gentlemen of the Continental Congress, I am instructed by the people of Virginia to introduce the following resolution: 'That these United Colonies are, and of right ought to be, free and independent states and that they are absolved from all allegiance to the British Crown; and that all political connection between them and the state of Great Britain is, and of right ought to be, totally dissolved.'"

The resolution was subsequently passed. Technically, our independence began on that day. The Continental Congress, nevertheless, decided that a public declaration, which would present the case for independence to the whole world and for all time, should be prepared.

A committee of five was appointed to draw up the Declaration. It included Jefferson, John Adams and Benjamin Franklin, all of whom favored the Declaration, and Roger Sherman and R. R. Livingston, who were undecided. These two refused to have anything to do with the text of the Declaration. Adams and Franklin persuaded Jefferson to compose it, and then went over his draft. They made only minor changes. For example, in the paragraph reading "When in the course of human events, it becomes necessary for one people to dissolve the political bands which have connected them with another," the word "one" was substituted for Jefferson's "a." And in the paragraph, "We hold these truths to be self-evident," the word "self-evident" was substituted for "sacred and undeniable" in Jefferson's first draft. Both of these changes were at Franklin's suggestion.

Then, on July 4, 1776, Jefferson's text, endorsed by Adams and Franklin, was presented to the Continental Congress. This moving Declaration, probably the most eloquent political document in human history, was read, paragraph by memorable paragraph:

"When in the course of human events, it becomes necessary for one people to dissolve the political bands which have connected them with another, and to assume among the powers of the earth, the separate and equal station to which the Laws of Nature and of Nature's God entitle them, a decent respect to the opinions of mankind requires that they should declare the causes which impel them to the separation.

"We hold these truths to be self-evident, that all men are created equal, that they are endowed by their Creator with certain unalienable Rights, that among these are Life, Liberty and the pursuit of Happiness. That to secure these rights, Governments are instituted among Men, deriving their just powers from the consent of the governed. That whenever any Form of Government becomes destructive of these ends, it is the Right of the People to alter or to abolish it, and to institute new Government, laying its foundation on such principles and organizing its power in such form, as to them shall seem most likely to effect their Safety and Happiness. Prudence, indeed, will dictate that Governments long established should not be changed for light and transient causes; and accordingly all experience hath shewn, that mankind are more disposed to suffer, while evils are sufferable, than to right themselves by abolishing the forms to which they are accustomed. But when a long train of abuses and usurpations, pursuing invariably the same Object evinces a design to reduce them under absolute Despotism, it is their right, it is their duty, to throw off such Government, and to provide new Guards for their future

security.—Such has been the patient suffrance of these Colonies; and such is now the necessity which constrains them to alter their former Systems of Government. The history of the present King of Great Britain is a history of repeated injuries and usurpations, all having in direct object the establishment of an absolute Tyranny over these States. To prove this, let Facts be submitted to a candid world. . . . [There follows a list of tyrannical and unlawful actions.]

"Nor have We been wanting in attentions to our British brethren. We have warned them from time to time of attempts by their legislature to extend an unwarrantable jurisdiction over us. We have reminded them of the circumstances of our emigration and settlement here. We have appealed to their native justice and magnanimity, and we have conjured them by the ties of our common kindred to disavow these usurpations, which would inevitably interrupt our connections and correspondence. They too have been deaf to the voice of justice and of consanguinity. We must, therefore, acquiesce in the necessity, which denounces our Separation, and hold them, as we hold the rest of Mankind, Enemies in War, in Peace Friends.

"We, therefore, the Representatives of the United States of America, in General Congress, Assembled, appealing to the Supreme Judge of the world for the rectitude of our intentions, do, in the Name, and by authority of the good People of these Colonies, solemnly publish and declare, That these United Colonies are, and of Right ought to be, Free and Independent States; that they are Absolved from all Allegiance to the British Crown, and that all political connection between them and the State of Great Britain, is and ought to be totally dissolved; and that as Free and Independent States, they have full power to levy War, conclude Peace, contract Alliances, establish Commerce, and do all other Acts and Things which Independent

States may of right do. And for the support of this Declaration, with a firm reliance on the protection of divine Providence, we mutually pledge to each other our Lives, our Fortunes and our Sacred Honor."

It would be pleasant to record that the Congress accepted the whole of Jefferson's great Declaration. It did not. It insisted on a number of omissions. Among these was a direct condemnation of slavery. The repudiation of slavery in America had to wait for another great apostle of freedom— Abraham Lincoln.

The battle for freedom did not end with the Declaration of Independence. Perhaps it never ends. After the Revolutionary War had been won, antidemocratic forces became more powerful. Jefferson returned from his embassy in France just in time to add to the Constitution of the United States the Bill of Rights which guarantees many of our civil liberties. He campaigned for the Presidency chiefly in order to frustrate new attempts to restrict freedom in America.

He lived to see a half-century of America's history as a free nation. On July 4, 1826, exactly fifty years after the original proclamation, as bells rang out to celebrate our country's independence, Thomas Jefferson died at eighty-three. To his very last day, Jefferson remained an apostle of freedom.

SCIENTIST, WRITER, INVENTOR

(THOMAS JEFFERSON)

The founders of our country were many-sided men. George Washington was not only a great general versed in statecraft; he was also an able administrator, as well as a practical farmer who helped to improve American agriculture by his experiments at Mount Vernon. Alexander Hamilton was a first-rate political economist and financier as well as a statesman. James Madison was a skillful writer and a political philosopher as well as a wise shaper of government policy. Benjamin Franklin was a renowned diplomat, philosopher, writer, businessman, scientist and inventor. All were ardent patriots.

Probably the most notable of them all for variety of interests and abilities was Thomas Jefferson. He was a great statesman, an educator, a philosopher, an agriculturist, a writer, a scientist, an inventor, an architect and, above all, a devoted patriot. His many contributions which gave the citizens of the young Republic guarantees of freedoms and democratic political practices are well known. But too little is known of his other gifts, which were inspired and shaped by Jefferson's pride in his country.

Among his agricultural experiments and inventions was an improved plow. We also owe to Jefferson one of our finest crops: our famous long-grained rice is a product of Italian seed, secured abroad and tested by Jefferson at home at considerable trouble and expense.

Our modern weather bureaus may be said to be an inheritance from Jefferson. At Monticello he set up an observatory and there recorded daily temperatures and other meteorological data. To accomplish this, he rose regularly at dawn. Among his inventions was a device for recording such observations when the weather was too severe to venture outdoors. Only when ur-

46

Jefferson and the Declaration of Independence.

gent public affairs demanded his presence elsewhere did he interrupt these daily personal observations, which were, on such occasions, carried on by his servants, with whom he always left precise instructions. In whatever place he found himself, he quickly set up a temporary observatory.

To establish a nationwide weather service, Jefferson enlisted the aid of his many friends, associates and admirers in all parts of the country. People North and South, in the seaboard cities and in Appalachian frontier outposts, sent him regular reports, which he correlated into data that have proved of great scientific value.

Along with weather observations, Jefferson collected and exchanged many items of knowledge about natural history—plants, birds, fishes, and land animals. His book *A Description of Virginia* provides a wealth of information about early America—an impressive account of the beauty, fertility, mineral wealth and healthfulness of the American land. It was written with a specific patriotic purpose. It not only set forth the attractions of the New World; it ably refuted the misinformation and slanders about America then current in Europe.

Even the world-famous naturalist Georges Buffon, esteemed as the greatest scientist of his time, believed the most outrageous nonsense about America. For example, according to Buffon and his followers, the American Indians lacked both physical and mental vigor. Proof of their lack of physical vigor was supposed to be the scantiness of hair on the bodies of the males. And for proof of their lack of mental vigor, the Buffonians pointed to the primitive state of their culture.

On such grounds foreign scientists, who propounded solemn theories about America without ever seeing it, concluded that ours was a hopelessly inferior continent. They made particular issue of the supposed fact that American animals were puny as compared with those of other continents.

For this sad condition they placed chief blame on our American climate, which was said to stunt animal growth. And it was predicted that in the enfeebling climate of the New World, European settlers would gradually deteriorate to the degenerate condition of the Indians.

In his book on Virginia (which, incidentally, dealt with a much larger territory than the present state of Virginia), Jefferson showed all this to be fable and nonsense. He pointed to great Indian civilizations of the past and to the fact that even the nomadic hunting and fishing tribes had been developing a form of agriculture, with which all civilizations begin. Moreover, he added, Indians who had received European educations showed a mental capacity equal to that of Europeans.

In answer to the charge that they lacked physical vigor, Jefferson supplied many examples of the strength and stamina of the Indians. As for their hairlessness, he argued, aside from the fact that this was no indication in itself of physical inferiority, many tribes were as hairy as Europeans. Their apparent hairlessness was generally due to their preference for a smooth skin. Indians usually shaved other surfaces of their body as well as their faces, using the sharpened edges of shells as razors.

Nor was it true that animals became stunted in America or that the continent had no large animals now or in the past. By comparative measurements Jefferson demonstrated that domestic animals introduced from Europe throve in the New World, generally increasing in size and weight. American bears were certainly sizable beasts, and the American moose was larger than any European member of the deer family.

In his eagerness to prove that America was originally the home of large animals, Jefferson turned to fossil-hunting. He dug up the bones of a gigantic extinct sloth (which, however, he failed to identify correctly) and he supported and encouraged other diggers. Among the extinct animals thus discovered was the American mammoth, which caused an international sensation.

Through such convincing evidence, Jefferson disposed forever of Buffonian scoffers. Nature, he proved, had not condemned America to an inferior place among the continents. And in the course of furnishing these proofs, he contributed information which advanced the natural sciences. Jefferson's scientific interests were so wide and his contributions so many, that it would take a book to do him justice as a scientist.

Let us turn now to a side of Jefferson that shows him in a typical American aspect—Jefferson as inventor and gadgeteer. One can hardly miss this aspect of his genius when visiting his beautiful Monticello home. It was for his original design of this home that he is now rated as a major American architect. What is generally regarded as Jefferson's most important invention, the moldboard plow, is on display there. This lightened the farmer's labor, cut a deeper and straighter furrow and was more durable than the plows then in use. Characteristically, Jefferson did not patent this or any other of his inventions or try to profit from them in any way. They were free to everyone.

The visitor at Monticello may be startled by devices that look oddly modern in such a colonial setting—a swivel chair, a dumb-waiter, a bed that may be tucked out of sight in a recess in the wall, a folding desk and an instrument that he called a polygraph.

The polygraph was invented to save the labor of making copies of letters and other documents. The number of letters that Jefferson had to write each year and of which copies had to be made, ran into the thousands. Jefferson found this an exhausting task; it was one of the few of his public burdens about which he complained. In those days there was no carbon paper or any other duplicating process. Jefferson solved this problem by an arrangement of pens on a board. These were so connected that every stroke of the pen he held was exactly reproduced by the other pens. He had a number of these useful polygraphs constructed for busy colleagues and friends.

Often in his travels Jefferson found no suitable table for his correspondence and other writing. Since he had to travel about the country a great deal, to counter this inconvenience he invented a sturdy, easily-set-up desk, which could be folded up until it was no larger than a good-sized book. He had a number of these built for traveling friends. It was on such a desk, brought with him from Monticello to Philadelphia, that the Declaration of Independence was written.

Few men in history were as versatile as Thomas Jefferson. In his many-sided genius he provided a bold challenge to the supercilious Europeans who doubted that great men could ever grow in America.

Thomas Jefferson's drawing of the desk on which the Declaration of Independence was written.

THE FIRST AMERICAN

(BENJAMIN FRANKLIN)

In 1722, James Franklin, a Boston printer and newspaper publisher, began printing letters submitted by a mysterious "Mistress Silence Dogood." Soon subscribers to James' paper were wondering who the sharp and witty author might be. Who, for instance, had the audacity to speak of Harvard as a place where "most [of the parents] consulted their own purses instead of their children's capacities?"

It never occurred to James Franklin to suspect his younger brother, apprenticed to him in the shop. When young Ben admitted it was he who had written the Dogood letters, James did what he always did when the boy expressed independence and originality: he gave him a sound thrashing. His brother's tyranny over him left Ben with a lifelong aversion to arbitrary power.

A year passed. When Ben was seventeen he ran away from his brother's shop. He walked most of the distance from Boston to Philadelphia, arriving with exactly one Spanish dollar and one English shilling in his pockets. There he took a job as a printer's assistant. But it was not long before he was publishing his own newspaper and the famous *Poor Richard's Almanac*, filled with his shrewd and pithy maxims. By the time Ben was twenty-six, he was the most widely read and quoted author in the colonies. With his "Busy Body" commentary on current events, he became the first columnist in America.

Ben soon became an active member of an organization of forward-looking young men called the Junto. During one of its meetings, at Franklin's suggestion, the first public library in America came into being. His energy and genius also produced in Philadelphia the first organized volunteer fire department, the first police system, the first move toward paved and lighted city streets, the first city hospital, a school which later became the University of Pennsylvania, and the American Philosophical Society—America's first scientific organization.

At the age of forty-two, Franklin sold out his business, so that he might be able to devote more time to scientific studies and experiments. He would have liked to spend the rest of his life in these pursuits, but his fellow-countrymen valued his other talents too well to allow such leisure. He was elected a member of the Pennsylvania Assembly from Philadelphia in 1751. In 1753, he was also elected Postmaster-General for the colonies.

When he was fifty, friction between England and her colonies had reached such a point that he was selected as a special commissioner to discuss the issues with the royal authorities in London. Ben promised Mrs. Franklin that the trip would last only a few months. But the "few months" lengthened into ten and a half years. Except for one visit home, Franklin remained in England as the principal representative of the American colonies during the trying period before the Revolutionary War. He helped bring about the repeal of the Stamp Act. With untiring effort he tried to find a peaceful solution.

He returned to America in 1775 to find his wife dead and his country on the brink of war. He was at once elected one of Pennsylvania's five delegates to the Continental Congress. By now he was seventy—too old, his daughter protested, to become active in a war for independence.

"Old," he told his daughter, "and probably good for nothing. But, as the storekeepers say of remnants of cloth, I am but the fag-end and you may have me for

Young Ben Franklin in the printing shop. Painting by Dean Cornwell.

what you please. My old friend Colonel Washington has been named commander-in-chief of the Continental Army. I cannot refuse to give my services at his command."

The next year, two months after signing the Declaration of Independence, Ben was sent on one of the most difficult missions of his career. After their victory in the battle of Long Island, the military situation strongly favored the British. They sent General Sullivan, whom they had captured, to Philadelphia with a message from Lord Howe—the British commander suggested a conference to discuss peace terms with the American rebels.

On September 10, 1776, the Continental Congress sent three commissioners to meet with Howe on Staten Island: Rutledge, John Adams and Benjamin Franklin. They rode through the British lines to Lord Howe's headquarters, knowing that should the American Army be beaten, there would be a price on their heads. They picked Franklin as their spokesman because he had become a personal friend of Howe's in London.

The British general received them cordially, but as private gentlemen, not as representatives of the Revolutionary Confederation. Howe explained to Franklin that he had stayed on for two months in London in order to obtain authority from the King to negotiate peace, but that during that time, the American Congress had declared its independence.

The Americans insisted that Britain would obtain an advantage from alliance with the new independent states. As co-equal partners, they might spread peace and civilization to every corner of the globe. As unruly subjects, the Americans had cost the British money and blood and would continue to do so.

Howe refused to recognize the colonists' argument. After three hours of debate, Franklin rose from the conference table, saying, "Well, then I fear we three have traveled a long weary road to no purpose. The step of independence was the inevitable result of many earlier steps. We were forced down every inch of that path. Now, sir, our American independence and our American honor are *one*."

Howe appealed to the friendship that had developed abroad between them. But for Franklin this was no personal matter. "I wanted peace, my lord," he told the British commander, "but could I betray my country? We are the victims of history and heartless time. . . . My dear good friend, henceforth you are my enemy. And I am yours. May God bless you, and destroy your armies."

Benjamin Franklin, the man who said there never was a good war or a bad peace, found himself in the very midst of the conflict. Immediately after his return from the unsuccessful conference on Staten Island, the Continental Congress unanimously elected him as special commissioner to France.

Facing defeat for lack of funds and supplies, the Americans needed a treaty of alliance with the French. The wise and witty American savant made many friends at the court of Louis XVI. He secured a huge loan and other assistance. He stayed in France for nine years.

On September 14, 1785, when he arrived in America on the London packet, he was hailed by a cheering crowd in Philadelphia as the "First American Citizen." An official on the welcoming committee asked about his sea voyage. "It was dreadful, dreadful," said Franklin. "I was in my cabin most of the time completing a new paper, 'The Cause and Cure of Smoky Chimneys.'"

"Doctor," called out a committeeman, "we are electing you chairman of the Philadelphia Common Council, and you will undoubtedly be chosen later for the highest office in the state."

Wearily, Franklin replied, "Yes, yes, they have eaten my flesh and, it seems, they are resolved to pick my bones. Perhaps you would all like to hear an epitaph which I wrote when I was younger. I seem to have intruded myself into the company of posterity, when I ought to have been abed and asleep."

Then he read out in a lusty, cheerful voice:

"THE BODY OF
BENJAMIN FRANKLIN, PRINTER,
(LIKE THE COVER OF AN OLD BOOK,
ITS CONTENTS TORN OUT
AND STRIPT OF ITS LETTERING AND GILDING),
LIES HERE, FOOD FOR WORMS;
BUT THE WORK SHALL NOT BE LOST,
FOR IT WILL (AS HE BELIEVED) APPEAR ONCE
MORE

IN A NEW
AND MORE ELEGANT EDITION,
REVISED AND CORRECTED BY THE
AUTHOR."

Benjamin Franklin never realized his ambition to retire from active public life. After his return from France, he served Pennsylvania as governor and took an active part in the Constitutional Convention of 1787. Nor did he diminish his scientific labors or his literary output. Nothing could halt him except death, which came on April 17, 1790, at the age of eighty-four.

Born in America, he thought and acted not as a Britisher, a Yankee or a Pennsylvanian, but as a citizen of a new and independent nation. He was, in many ways, the *first* American.

The famous letter Franklin wrote, but never sent, to a British friend.

Philada July 5. 1775

Mr Strahan,

You are a Member of Parliament, and one of that Majority which has doomed my Country to Destruction — You have begun to burn our Towns and murder our People. — Look upon your Hands! — They are stained with the Blood of your Relations! — You and I were long Friends: — You are now my Enemy. — and

I am, Yours, B Franklin

"THE LAZIEST MAN IN THE WORLD"

(BENJAMIN FRANKLIN)

During the last three years of his life, Benjamin Franklin spent most of his time at his home in Philadelphia. He was now over eighty and had already accomplished far more than most men in one lifetime. He had been a jack-of-all-trades and master of them all—diplomat, scientist, statesman, moralist, wit, writer, publisher, social reformer. His old body might need rest, but his nimble mind was ever turning to new time-savers.

He had already invented a library chair that unfolded into a stepladder. But after climbing up and down several times a day to reach a book he wanted on the upper shelves of his library, he decided there must be some better way. Then he smiled, rose out of his armchair and ambled into his workshop. There he cut a long pole and at one end fastened two prongs, which could be worked by a simple spring mechanism. Returning to his library, he touched the prongs to the volume he wanted. Snap! The prongs grabbed it. A handy device. It could also prove valuable to shopkeepers, who might find it useful for reaching boxes on high shelves.

The motive behind so many of his inventions, Franklin reflected, was to save energy. And settling back in his chair, he remembered the first time he had put his wits to work to spare himself labor.

That had been when he was a boy in Boston. He and a friend had gone swimming in the Charles River. When they started home they were exhausted. Ben had brought a heavy kite. If only it could be put to some use! Then an idea had occurred to him. He asked his friend if he would carry his clothes back to Boston. The friend was willing to oblige and Ben undressed, tied the kite-string around his waist and slipped back into the Charles.

The breeze was blowing townward, and as it caught the kite it pulled Ben through the water after it. . . .

Franklin chuckled. Yes, that had been the beginning. Since that summer day he had invented many things for making everyday life more comfortable. The Franklin stove, for example. Or that contrivance for starting up a fire—all you had to do was pull a cord that opened a little trap-door below the log, creating a draught that turned a little windmill in the chimney.

He also remembered a discovery which may not have been as practical as the others, but was certainly more entertaining. In England, while negotiating for the repeal of the Stamp Act, he had stayed with an English family. One evening at dinner his hosts heard a pure musical note which seemed to come out of the air. "Ssh! What was that noise? It sounded as if it were right here in the room! Spirits, do you think?" The hostess peered out the window and began to prod the heavy curtains. Then she opened the sideboard. "My glassware! It's gone. All my best dinner glasses have been stolen."

Franklin raised his hand, smiling. "Please," he said, "let me reassure you." He dipped his finger in the wine and then ran it gently around the rim of his glass. Again the pure musical note. Taking another glass which was almost full, he tried the experiment again. This time the note had a lower pitch.

"But where is my glassware?" asked his hostess.

"Would you step into the next room, my dear? The concert is about to begin," said Franklin.

He had arranged thirty-six glasses in a row, all of them filled with various levels

Franklin's Experiment, June, 1752. From a Currier and Ives print.

of liquid. He lumbered up and down the row, touching different rims in turn to produce the tune of a Scottish air. The family listened in wonder. But the exertion left Franklin panting, and the guests remarked that this might be an amusing parlor game, but hardly a true musical instrument.

Listening to their comments on his device, the answer came to Franklin. Of course! He would have goblets made without stems and mount them on a spindle, to be revolved by a foot-pedal like a spinning wheel. Then the musician could sit in a comfortable chair, operate the pedal and lightly touch his hand to each glass. From this idea came the instrument he called the harmonica. Within a few years, it was being played all over Europe, even at the court of Vienna.

Franklin looked up from the book he had been reading, scarcely thinking as he did so about the spectacles which allowed him not only to read but also to see at a distance. These, too, had been his own invention. His eyesight had never been good. He had had to use two different pairs of glasses—one for close work, another for seeing things far away. This had meant continually having to change from one to the other. Why couldn't the lenses be ground so as to have two different focuses, the lower part for close reading, the upper for seeing things in the distance. With these first "bifocals" Franklin added still another convenience to his own life— and to the lives of many who were to wear bifocal spectacles after him.

But the efforts which had occupied Franklin most and which he knew would turn out to be of far greater use to mankind than any of his inventions were his experiments in electricity. For years he had tinkered with electrical bottles, batteries and wires. He remembered his "electrical Christmas party." His plan had been to roast the turkey by an electrical jack over a fire kindled by an electrical

bottle, then to serve plum pudding with a flaming sauce ignited by electricity.

Franklin had shown his guests the machine with which he meant to light the tinder. He warned them not to touch the positive and negative connections at the same time. This was something with which he had not yet made sufficient experiments, but it might be dangerous.

"Are we ready?" he had asked. "Then watch. The electrical fluid will leap from the positive to the negative across this gap, igniting the tinder. You will see a flash of electrical fire. Now, we take the negative connection and—"

There was a loud, crackling sound and a flash of light, and the astonished spectators saw Franklin topple to the floor, unconscious. When Franklin revived, he began questioning his guests. He had had a shock, but how had it happened? They had heard a loud crackle, and seen a flash? That was odd, because, he said, you know what it had felt like? Like being struck with lightning. He had received a blow in every part of his body.

Franklin stopped short. Lightning, that was it. Why, there was even a faint sulphurous odor in the room like that following a thunderstorm. It supported a notion which had been hounding him for weeks: that electricity and lightning were one and the same thing!

Not long afterward Benjamin Franklin took his twenty-one-year-old son across a windswept meadow to a hill outside Philadelphia. A storm was coming up. The thunder crashed and lightning illuminated the gray sky. The younger man was embarrassed that they were carrying a kite. "I hope none of the neighbors sees us," he said.

"Why not?" asked his father. "That's the basis of the whole experiment."

"Flying a kite at my age! They'll think I'm not right in the head."

Franklin looked at his son severely. "Don't worry so much about what other people think. We may learn a secret of nature today that philosophers all over the world have been trying to discover."

As the rain began, the two men got the kite up into the air. In order to withstand the storm, it had been made of silk with strong cedar crossbars. The kite rose higher and higher. Franklin attached the end of the line to a silk ribbon, to which he had tied a key. "The sparks should stream off the end of the key," he explained to his son. "And if we get sparks, that proves that lightning *is* electricity."

As they stood under a shed, waiting, Franklin reminded his son of the *Providence* which had burned off the Cape the winter before. The survivors had reported that they had seen a globe of fire on the masthead. It had run down a tarred rope to the deck. The sailors thought it was the wrath of God, but Franklin knew it was lightning. The masthead had attracted the electricity in the lightning, and the tarred rope had acted as a conductor.

"As you expect the kite-line to do now?" asked his son.

No, it wasn't the line itself that was a conductor, but water. They had to wait until the line was drenched and then— "Look!" cried Franklin. The strands of hemp were bristling and sparks were beginning to crackle off the key. Their experiment was a success! Electricity was flowing down the line and off the key!

Once Franklin discovered the electrical fluid in lightning, he lost no time putting his discovery to practical use. The *Providence,* as well as innumerable homes, churches and public buildings, had been burned when struck by lightning. Yet those fires would not have occurred if the buildings had been provided with lightning-rods to conduct the electricity into the ground.

Franklin smiled to himself, thinking that he had invented the lightning-rod out of laziness, too. Before that, whenever a home had been struck by lightning, his

Benj. Franklin

volunteer fire department had had to rush to the spot with their leather buckets, to save lives and property. Often they had arrived too late. But now, when a thunder-gust came in the middle of the night, he could remember that the lightning-rod would take care of it, and comfortably go back to sleep.

He admitted to himself, however, that it wasn't just laziness that had prompted his inventions. People were too important to be climbing up and down ladders all day. That kind of thing made a man a slave. And Franklin foresaw that in time man would be free of much of the drudgery that bound him. He would make extra hands that could work for him, and arms that could reach everywhere. The more control man had over his environment, the more easily he could go on to make a better world in which to live.

Patrick Henry addresses the Virginia Assembly.

THE CLARION CALLER

(PATRICK HENRY)

"I know not what course others may take, but as for me, GIVE ME LIBERTY OR GIVE ME DEATH."

Every American knows Patrick Henry's stirring words which acted as a clarion call to action and moved the American Colonies to revolution. There were other notes to that clarion call.

"They tell us, sir, that we are weak— unable to cope with so formidable an adversary. But when shall we be stronger? Will it be the next week, or the next year? Will it be when we are totally disarmed, and when a British guard shall be stationed in every house? Shall we gather strength by irresolution and inaction?

Shall we acquire the means of effectual resistance by lying supinely on our backs, and hugging the delusive phantom of Hope until our enemies shall have bound us hand and foot? Sir, we are not weak, if we make a proper use of those means which the God of nature hath placed in our power."

And also "Besides, sir, we shall not fight our battles alone. There is a just God who presides over the destinies of nations; and who will raise up friends to fight our battles for us. The battle, sir, is not to the

Patrick Henry

strong alone; it is to the vigilant, the active, the brave."

These words were all from the same short speech that Patrick Henry made in March, 1775, in Virginia's House of Burgesses.

In those days there was no radio, no television, no telegraph—hardly any newspapers. News traveled by word of mouth, from man to man. When there was some exciting event like the Boston Tea Party, the story was told and retold, reaching all the Colonies by a kind of human telegraph. That's the kind of stuff people like to tell, like to hear. Some things, like secret plans for meetings or rebellious riots, were passed along in whispers or codes in accordance with arrangements. But as for speeches, just words—why, the words had to be truly special, short and dramatic to be remembered, to be considered worth passing on.

Patrick Henry's words were all of that. They spread like a broadcast all over the Colonies. The great House of Burgesses address and many another fiery speech by the brilliant orator spurred the Colonists, made their blood tingle, hot for action.

The patriots of the Revolution knew what they were fighting for—Patrick Henry had made it plain for them—and they were glad to fight for it.

The eminent Virginian did not still his miraculous voice when the Revolution was over. The war was won, but Patrick Henry believed the real cause—full liberty, freedom for all—had not yet been achieved. Once again his call was heard; his words spread through the new nation, reminding people of their rights, demanding changes in the Constitution. Thus he helped to make the Bill of Rights part of our Constitution.

Patrick Henry's voice is not yet stilled, nor will it ever be. For whenever there is danger to American ideals Patrick Henry's call for "Liberty!" sounds and resounds, reminding Americans of their priceless heritage and alerting them to vigilance.

Patrick Henry addresses the First Continental Congress.

Procession to celebrate the adoption of the Federal Constitution in New York State.

AMERICA'S MOST FAMOUS DUEL

(ALEXANDER HAMILTON)

At "The Grange," Alexander Hamilton's country estate on upper Manhattan Island, the light in his study burned late. The house was quiet, except for the scratching of Hamilton's quill pen. Then, hearing hoofbeats outside, he laid his pen aside. Who could that be?

Hamilton went to the window. In the moonlight, a shadowy rider dismounted, and walked quickly toward the lighted window. . . .

Upstairs, Hamilton's wife, Elizabeth, awoke. Was that the whinny of a horse? Or had the sound been part of a dream? Throwing a shawl about her shoulders, she went to the bedroom window. A shadow seemed to move across the lawn.

Troubled, Elizabeth sat down. The minutes passed. Below in the house—silence. Why should she have this feeling of alarm? Now, of all times, in this year of 1804, such alarm seemed foolish. Alexander had retired from public life, to devote himself to his law practice. There were some who thought that peculiar, since Hamilton was only forty-seven. "Does a man who has tasted power at twenty-five retire at forty-seven?" Certainly his retirement from public life meant a loss to his country.

Alexander Hamilton's judgment, eloquence, knowledge and patriotism had been vitally important in the founding and development of the United States of America. His *Federalist* papers had done much to achieve popular acceptance of the Constitution. He was the first Secretary of the Treasury and established the first government bank. He had great skill in financial matters and laid the groundwork of the country's monetary and banking system. His vision and ability to plan for the country's growth was not fully appreciated until many years later.

At the time, many of Hamilton's ideas about government were not popular. People thought they were too aristocratic; certainly they were not as democratic as Thomas Jefferson's. Perhaps that is why Hamilton felt he should retire, his job done.

A remarkable statesman, Alexander had fought many harsh political battles. Any political figure makes enemies, and Alexander had more than his share: Aaron Burr, for example, whose hopes of becoming President had been thwarted by Hamilton. Only last month, disappointed again in his hope of becoming Governor of New York, Burr had blamed Hamilton; he had called Burr a dangerous man, not to be trusted with power. A man like Burr might do anything, in retaliation. . . .

Foolish to mull over all this, Elizabeth told herself. That's all over and done with now. There is nothing to worry about any more. . . .

Still . . . impulsively, she hurried down to her husband's study and rapped on the door.

"Betsy," asked Alexander in surprise, "what are you doing up?"

"I thought I heard a horse. And then someone walked across the lawn. I—I thought he might have come in here."

"You have been dreaming," Hamilton said gently.

"No, I—" Looking past him, into the study where the candlelight flickered, she found the room empty, save for her husband.

Alexander said cheerfully, "Worrying about me again—and this time in your sleep, eh, Betsy? Now you go on up and—"

Then he stopped, for Elizabeth had raised her head and was listening. And now there could be no doubt. From outside came the sound of hoofbeats, retreating from the house.

"Well, I did my best," Hamilton explained the next day to his friend Judge Pendleton. "I managed to keep the truth from Betsy. I told her it had been an impatient client. But of course, as you now know, my visitor was Van Ness, bringing Burr's challenge to a duel."

"You mustn't give him the honor of accepting! Besides, Burr is a deadly shot. This wouldn't be his first duel, you know."

"But it would be *my* first duel. And first performances have a way of sticking in the public mind."

Judge Pendleton stared at him. What did Hamilton mean by that?

"There is more to this challenge than meets the eye," Hamilton went on. "I'm not a bad shot myself, so it would be a gamble for Burr. Being the kind of man he is, the stakes must be high for him to risk it. If it were only his personal honor that was involved, why didn't he challenge me long ago?"

Judge Pendleton said, "He had set his heart on the governorship."

"Ah, but why did that mean so much to Burr? You know what I think. We've talked about it before."

"Yes," Pendleton nodded. "But the idea is preposterous. I just don't believe it, Hamilton. Burr is something of an adventurer, true, but what you accuse him of, is—"

"Treason," Hamilton supplied. He held up his hand as Judge Pendleton was about to protest. "True, I cannot, as yet, prove it. But perhaps, soon, I will have that proof."

Not many days later, at the headquarters of the Society of St. Tammany, Hamilton was deep in conversation with one of New York's first political bosses, Swarthout.

Alexander Hamilton. Painting by John Trumbull.

"No," Hamilton said, "I have not as yet decided whether I shall accept your friend's challenge."

"I had not thought that you were a —" and Swarthout hesitated.

"A coward?" Hamilton said. "Perhaps it is because I believe this duel to be unnecessary. Perhaps we can come to an understanding, Swarthout." He paused, as if afraid he might have said too much. Then he resumed harshly, "You know perfectly well that without my support, your party cannot elect Colonel Burr or anyone else to the governorship."

"I had wondered," Swarthout said, studying him closely, "if you wanted the job yourself."

"I resigned from public office once," Hamilton said, "because it did not pay."

Swarthout laughed. "Secretary of the Treasury of the United States—and you couldn't make it pay! Ah, well, apparently you wish to let bygones be bygones, eh?"

"I am not here to amuse myself," Hamilton agreed stiffly.

"But I thought you'd retired from politics, Hamilton?"

"So did I," Hamilton said. "But I was mistaken. I find retirement dull. And perhaps I was wrong about something else. To the right man, public office can offer many—how shall I say it?—many rewards, Mr. Swarthout?"

Mr. Swarthout chuckled. "So you think we might come to an agreement, eh?"

As the conversation continued, it turned out that Hamilton had judged Swarthout correctly. The man was corrupt—"and has a loose tongue," Hamilton told Judge Pendleton. "Allow me to quote the swine; his words are burned in my memory: 'Our friends in New England have taken Colonel Burr into their confidence. They plan that New England and New York shall secede from the Union. What is more, I am confident that the French minister has assured Colonel Burr that France will back us up with all her military power!' That is what he said."

"Secession—with the connivance of Napoleon. And Burr, Swarthout and those others will seize power for themselves—"

"Burr, Swarthout *and* Alexander Hamilton," said Hamilton. "Or so I led Swarthout to believe. . . . Until I could bear it no longer and undeceived him."

Judge Pendleton said, "What Swarthout revealed was spoken in confidence, with no witnesses. You still have no proof, Hamilton. The public will not believe you."

"There is enough proof for me," Hamilton said. "Burr and his friends must be stopped, and without delay."

"But how do you propose to do it?"

"I shall accept Burr's challenge to a duel."

"But, if you killed him—you'd only make him a martyr."

"Ah, but if Burr killed me," Hamilton said, "what then?"

"The scandal would wreck Burr's political career, of course. And his scheme would collapse. But—"

These summer days were happy ones for Elizabeth Hamilton. Alexander had never seemed so alive. His very walk, his bearing, showed elation. James, their eldest son, was almost grown to man's estate, yet Alexander himself seemed as young. Now, indeed, her worries seemed foolish. "Alex," she asked, "what is it these past few weeks? This burst of energy—"

"Do I seem different?"

"You seem like your old self." Betsy smiled. "I remember you like this before— at Philadelphia, when you stood up against your elders for a Constitution *you* wanted. You were so outspoken then. And there were so many hot-headed men there, the kind that fight a duel at a word. . . ."

A strange expression passed over her husband's face. Or did she really see it?

"I have told her nothing, of course," Hamilton said later to Judge Pendleton. "And you must pledge our adversaries to keep this matter secret. If these are to be my last days, I want them to be happy ones for my family."

"I've made all the arrangements," said Pendleton. "July 11, at Weehawken Heights across the Hudson. The New Jersey dueling laws are more liberal than those of New York. But, Hamilton, are you quite sure?"

"My life is a little thing," said Hamilton, "compared to the future of the United States."

On July 11, 1804, Burr and Hamilton met at Weehawken Heights. Present also were three other men—Judge Pendleton, Hamilton's second; Van Ness, second for Burr, and a doctor.

"Fire!" Pendleton called.

Only Burr's pistol exploded. Hamilton groaned, sinking to the grass, his pistol going off as he fell.

"The fool!" Van Ness exclaimed, rushing to Hamilton. "Why did he hold his fire like that? He must be mad! That was suicide!"

The doctor rose from beside Hamilton's still form. "The bullet has entered his lung. I am afraid, gentlemen—"

On the following day, Alexander Hamilton died. By holding his fire, had he deliberately taken the risk that Burr's shot would not do him mortal injury? More than once he had been prepared to risk his life for his country.

Whatever we may believe, history records one certain fact: that July day on Weehawken Heights marked the end of Aaron Burr's political career.

The Hamilton-Burr duel.

PATHFINDERS FOR A NATION

"I do believe we shall continue to grow, to multiply, and prosper until we exhibit an association powerful, wise, and happy beyond what has yet been seen by men."

THOMAS JEFFERSON, Letter to John Adams, 1812.

THE RIGHT TO PETITION

(JOHN QUINCY ADAMS)

In 1830, John Quincy Adams, former President of the United States, returned to Washington as a Representative from Massachusetts. Many of his friends had urged him not to accept the nomination. "It will be beneath your dignity as a former President," they said, "to go to Washington as a mere Congressman."

"No service to the nation can be beneath the dignity of any citizen," Adams replied. "I will accept the nomination, but on this condition: I want it to be known that if I am elected I will be responsible to no party, no faction, but only to my conscience and to the nation."

Some Congressmen were not pleased with the election of Adams. They did not approve his stubborn faith in the will of the people. Among them were Congressmen Marshall and Maine. They had set out to curb the constant petitioning by ordinary citizens who urged the passing of one kind of law or another.

"These petitions clutter up the calendar and are a waste of time," declared Congressman Maine. "And most of them ask for the abolition of slavery. I think it's better for Congress and for the future of the Union that they be left unread. The only one who may take a stand against this is Adams, with his old-fashioned democratic ideas."

"If we act firmly I think he'll go along," said Marshall. "Old Adams is so happy just to be back in politics he won't want to cause any trouble."

As Adams approached the House Chamber to attend his first session of Congress, Marshall made a point of talking with him privately. "I think you'll agree with me, Mr. Adams, after you've been here a while, that Congress has just about reached the limit of its patience. Petitions, petitions, petitions—and many of them make no sense at all."

"But the right to petition is one of the cornerstones of our Constitution," said Adams.

"Yes, of course," said Marshall hastily. "But some of these, as I said, make no sense. And most of them call for the abolition of slavery. When they are read in Congress, all they do is exasperate the South and increase the differences between sections. They're becoming a danger to the Union, Mr. Adams."

"I see what you mean," replied Adams, "but I'm not sure that I agree with you."

On this first day John Quincy Adams shocked Maine, Marshall and others. He stood up and read a petition for the abolition of slavery, following it with this comment: "I hate slavery of all kinds, but under the Constitution Congress can do nothing short of invoking war powers to abolish slavery. Nevertheless, I believe that a citizen has the right to present a petition asking for its abolition. A few moments before this session got under way, I was approached by a Quaker from Pennsylvania. He had asked his own Representative to read this petition, but the gentleman from Pennsylvania refused. That is why *I* am reading it to you."

In the days that followed, Adams maintained his stand. He insisted on reading all petitions which were sent to him, whatever the subject, to the assembled Representatives.

One afternoon he was about to read another petition calling for the abolition of slavery when Congressman Maine leaped to the floor.

"Will the gentleman from Massachusetts yield for a minute?" asked Maine.

"I yield," said Adams, "but only for a minute!"

"I move, Mr. Speaker," said Maine, "that hereafter this House reject unread all petitions regarding slavery!"

There was an overwhelming number of seconds to this motion, and it was some time before Adams could regain the floor.

"Gentlemen," he said, "the very first article of our Bill of Rights guarantees the right of the people to petition the government for redress of grievances. Deny that privilege and next a free press will be denied, and then free speech. In the end, we shall lose all our liberties!"

"It has been moved and seconded," said the singsong voice of the Speaker, "that the House reject, without reading, all petitions regarding slavery. Those in favor?"

Adams cast the only negative vote. As the passage of the motion was recorded, Adams shouted, "The resolution just passed is a gag in the mouth of free speech! It is a direct violation of the Constitution!"

Week after week, Adams fought against the gag rule. Weeks lengthened into months, and still he would not give up. Time after time he rose to the floor of the House and attempted to read a petition,

John Quincy Adams. Painting by Thomas Sully.

only to be greeted by a chorus of shouted reminders: "Mr. Adams is out of order!" "Mr. Adams forgets that there is a rule against reading that petition!" "The gentleman from Massachusetts is again obstructing the business of this session."

The next day, undaunted, Adams would rise and say, "Gentlemen, I have a petition against slavery. . . ."

The people of the country, however, were becoming aware of Adams' fight against the gag rule. They began to put pressure on their own Congressmen. Each time, now, that Adams put his motion for repeal before the House, a few more votes were cast in its favor.

One day Adams rose in the House and said, "This document in my hand is a petition from forty-six citizens of Haverhill, Massachusetts, praying for the peaceable dissolution of the Union. I move the reference of this petition to a select committee, which shall then draw up a report instructing these people why this petition should not be granted."

Marshall was on his feet even before Adams had finished. "In merely bringing this petition before us," he shouted at Adams, "you are guilty of high treason and contempt of this House. I move that the Honorable John Quincy Adams deserves expulsion from Congress for giving aid and comfort to the enemies of the Union!"

"You forget, Mr. Marshall," said Adams, as quietly as he could, "that I asked for the rejection of this petition by a committee. It is the gag rule that is violating the Constitution, not my presentation of this petition. It is the right and duty of every man in this room to preserve the liberties of our government. And the liberties of our government will be destroyed if the people lose the power of petition!"

"Mr. Speaker," said Marshall, "if the gentleman from Massachusetts withdraws the petition, I'll withdraw the resolution for his expulsion."

"I will not withdraw a single word," said Adams. "Expel me if you like, but not one word of any petition will I withdraw!"

Adams' answer to this threat of expulsion was to take his fight directly to the people. For the next months he traveled up and down the country, explaining, to whatever groups he could gather together, the con-

stitutional significance of his fight. And he would always end his speech, "Have you a complaint, a request, a suggestion, a criticism, a demand? Send me your petitions. It is your right as Americans!"

When Adams returned to Washington, he was too exhausted and ill from the long fight to attend a session of Congress for several weeks. But he knew that he had won. The people were on his side; he had managed to arouse their concern and their anger. A majority of the Representatives in Congress *must* pay heed to their constituents and vote for repeal of the gag rule. He would open their eyes.

The day Adams walked into the House again after his long absence, all the Congressmen stood up to do him honor. Slowly he walked down the aisle to his seat, thanked the House for its courtesy and then asked if a motion was in order.

"The chair will entertain your motion, Mr. Adams," said the Speaker.

"I move," said Adams, "that House Rule # 25, the gag rule, be stricken out."

There was not one single vote against the repeal. John Quincy Adams' victory was complete.

And it was a victory for the people. Aware of the danger, they had made their voices heard, declaring to their Representatives that the latter were in Congress to represent the people and to protect their right to petition.

OLD HICKORY

(ANDREW JACKSON)

Andrew Jackson—so tough and durable they called him "Old Hickory"—was strengthened in an indomitable spirit by hardships that would have broken an ordinary man.

At two, he lost his father. At fourteen, he lost his mother and his two brothers and was left alone in the world. But he was so tall and strong that people thought him at least eighteen, as did the recruiting sergeant who accepted the lad as a volunteer in the Revolutionary Army. He fought and was captured by the British and endured the rigors of a prisoner of war.

Alone, with no kin to help him, the boy Andrew Jackson managed to learn to read and write and to educate himself for a profession. He became a lawyer, one of the best in the country. He began his law career in Nashville, only a year or two after the settlement of that town. It was then a rough, raw frontier community. Tennessee itself was still mostly wilderness, not yet a state. To the settled coastal population the Tennessee territory was the "Far West."

As in other frontier towns, law was slow to come to Nashville. Consequently, the welcome accorded Jackson was not what might be described as warm. One of the frontiersmen, a man named Sorel, who ran a trading post, was outspokenly unenthusiastic.

It was rumored that Sorel sold firearms and firewater to the Indians. This was against the law, and naturally he didn't care to see any lawmen settling in Nashville. Heading a grim-looking reception committee, Sorel came to pay Jackson a visit the very day he hung up his shingle.

"We tolerate a judge in Nashville,"

Sorel told Jackson, "only because the governor appointed him. But we don't aim to extend that toleration to any more—not to any Eastern fellers with a parcel of lawbooks. We got our own law here. So you better git!"

Jackson did not quake at this command, as Sorel had expected. "I can practice your kind of law, too," said Jackson. "Put up your fists."

A fight was not exactly what Sorel had come for, but he could not back away from this challenge. He put up his fists and got the worst beating of his life. Jackson's arms were like hickory cudgels. In a minute Sorel was stretched out on the ground, unconscious.

Thus Nashville learned to respect Jackson's abilities in frontier law. In his knowledge of lawbooks he was equally proficient, and he was soon known as the best attorney in the region.

Jackson was a success in other fields as well. He made a fortune as a land speculator and another as a cotton planter. He developed his Hermitage plantation into one of the finest estates of America. Its stately mansion and its beautiful grounds rank with Washington's Mount Vernon and Jefferson's Monticello among our national shrines.

The settlers were not allowed to turn Tennessee's wilderness acres into farmland without an armed protest from the Indians. The tribes raided almost continuously. Security could be won only by constant vigilance and prompt reprisal. Andrew Jackson came to be noted for his courage and persistence as an Indian-fighter.

Allied with the Indians were the British and the officials of what was then Spanish Florida. This territory was used by the Indians as a refuge when the Americans counterattacked in force. Still another enemy of the settlers were renegade Tennesseans like Sorel, who smuggled guns and whiskey to the Indians and plotted to put Tennessee under the Spanish flag, because the Spanish authorities permitted his kind of trading.

Jackson tracked Sorel to an Indian camp and brought him back, roped, to Nashville. Sorel was put behind bars, but the townsmen broke into jail and dragged him out to hang him. Practicing "frontier law" again, Jackson recaptured his prisoner.

To the crowd he said, "Nobody knows better than I what a polecat Sorel is. But I went out and caught him and brought him back here to face law justice, not mob justice. He's going to get a fair trial. Any objections?"

There were no objections.

During the War of 1812, British agents stirred up the Indians to raid the American settlements. By that time Tennessee had become a state, and its legislature elected Jackson a major-general to command the state militia against the Indians. He did so well that the federal government authorized him to lead an expedition against the Creeks, the most active and numerous of the raiding tribes.

Historians are still arguing whether Jackson went beyond his instructions. In any case, the Creeks, as they had done before, fled to Spanish Florida. Unlike previous commanders, Jackson did not halt at the border. He rode across the line, defeated and disarmed the Indians. Then he hunted down a pair of British agents who had instigated the Creek raids and hanged them both.

This caused embarrassing international complications for the government, but it also revealed that in Andrew Jackson the United States had an effective general. As a result the government commissioned Andrew Jackson a major-general of the Army and ordered him to defend New Orleans, against which the British had sent a strong expedition.

At New Orleans Jackson won the greatest victory of the war and became its

Andrew Jackson with the Tennessee forces on the Hickory Grounds (Alabama), 1814.

military hero. He outgeneraled one of England's top commanders and sent a crack British army into headlong flight. This battle was actually fought after a peace treaty had been signed but before news of it had reached Jackson. It showed that America had a powerful fighting reserve and kept the British from challenging American might further.

From then on Jackson was the idol of the West. The settlers of the frontier states were emphatic in demanding a "people's government." This "Western democracy," as it was called, became so identified with Jackson, its chosen leader, that it has been known ever since as "Jacksonian democracy."

By 1824, this popular movement had become strong enough to organize a bid for the Presidency, with Jackson, of course, as its candidate. In a bitterly fought campaign, between four contenders, Jackson received the most votes but fell short of the required majority.

In such a case, by the terms of the Constitution, the election would have to be decided by Congress, and usually Congress ratified the popular choice. But in this instance, Henry Clay, who had ranked third in the balloting, withdrew in favor of John Quincy Adams, who had been second. Through Clay's influence, Congress gave the election to Adams. Since Adams later appointed Clay his Secretary of State, there was considerable suspicion that Clay had made a political deal with Adams in order to avoid the possibility that Jackson would become President.

Many politicians predicted that the election of Adams would end Jackson's Presidential aspirations, but Old Hickory knew that he remained the "people's choice." He was determined that neither he nor they should be frustrated a second time. In 1828, the next Presidential election year, in one of the wildest campaigns of American political history, Jackson won a clear-cut victory.

The campaign was marked by smears, name-calling and violence. Jackson's overseer, while returning to the Hermitage in Jackson's coach, was shot to death. The assassin's bullets had been destined for Old Hickory.

Mrs. Jackson had been married previously and divorced, and when Jackson married her, the divorce decree had evidently not been a final one. To settle any legal doubts, the Jacksons went through a second marriage ceremony. During this campaign, however, Jackson's political enemies whipped up a scandal about it. Their slanders are believed to have contributed to Mrs. Jackson's early death. Jackson had the tragic task of burying her just after his election.

Their marriage had been a happy one, and Jackson's love for her is reflected in the epitaph he composed: "Mrs. Rachel Jackson. Died December 22, 1828. Her face was fair, her person pleasing, her temper amiable, her heart kind. To the poor she was a benefactor, to the rich an example, to the wretched a comforter, and to the prosperous an ornament. She was a being so gentle and virtuous that slander might wound but could not dishonor her. Even Death, when he took her from the arms of her husband, could but transport her to the bosom of her God."

As President of the United States, Jackson followed Jefferson's principles in directing the national policy. Jacksonian democracy was proven to be what the people wanted, for in 1832 they elected Old Hickory to a second term as President. Popular tradition kept them from electing him for a third term, but they elected a man known to be close to him. Martin Van Buren had no need for any other campaign slogan than that he was Jackson's choice.

The framework of American democracy is as strong as it is today because Jacksonian democracy became one of its vital elements.

DANIEL WEBSTER, STATESMAN

In the pre-Civil War years, when oratory was one of the principal paths to power and fame, Daniel Webster wore the laurels of America's greatest orator. Many reports left by those who heard him testify to his uncanny power to move a jury, to swing a crucial vote in Congress or to enthrall a crowd.

A man with thick raven hair, piercing black eyes and a dark complexion, he was popularly known as "Black Dan with the silver tongue." A collection of his orations has been a steady best-seller, and Woodrow Wilson recalled how he had used the thick volume for practice in speaking in public. On weekdays he would take it into the church where his father preached on Sunday, stand up in the pulpit and roll out Webster's eloquent phrases into the echoing aisles.

Webster himself practiced oratory in a unique fashion. As a boy he was quite shy, so he decided to master this failing by learning how to speak out in public. Standing on a rock in one of his father's pastures, he would harangue the cows and sheep. People were later to remark that his oratory could bewitch them until they became as docile as sheep under his spell.

Dan Webster, born in the backwoods of New Hampshire, became the favorite son and pride of that state and for many years he was the spokesman of New England. He was immensely popular and the hero of many legends.

His career as a public speaker began in his junior year at Dartmouth College. No one would have dreamed that the poised and confident youth who so distinguished himself in the classroom and at debates, was at ease in any company and always ready with appropriate words on any occasion had ever suffered from shyness. Such

was his repute as an orator even then that, though still an underclassman, he won an honor usually reserved for seniors: he was elected to deliver the college's annual Fourth of July oration.

But it is not because of his "silver tongue" alone that Webster has left such a shining mark in American history. It is for the good uses to which he put his oratorical gifts. Webster's matchless oratory was exerted in the best interests of the nation for more than thirty years of public service as Congressman, Senator and Cabinet member, when sectional differences were pushing the country toward civil war and the integrity of the Constitution was threatened on more than one issue. One of the great classics of oratory was Webster's reply to Hayne, in the great debate of 1830 when Daniel Webster defended the Union and the Constitution against the South Carolina Senator's arguments for states' rights and nullification.

Daniel Webster. Painting by H. Healy.

Webster's orations are full of exhortations to maintain the Union, to preserve the Constitution and to avoid war:

"One country, one Constitution, one destiny."

"Whatever government is not a government of laws is a despotism, let it be called what it may."

"Union is the great fundamental principle."

This singular devotion to national unity and the preservation of the Constitution often brought him into direct conflict with the particular interests of his party and of the North, which regarded him as one of its leaders. These conflicts appear to have cost Webster the Presidency of the United States.

Daniel Webster had no false modesty. He publicly avowed his ambition to become President. Again and again he appeared to be the logical candidate of the

Whigs, but each time a situation would arise in which Webster would once more make the decision to place loyalty to the nation above loyalty to his political party. The enraged Whig leaders would consequently turn to other candidates.

The first of these occasions came during the nullification controversy of 1830. Congress had passed a tariff act to which the South had objected because, it said, it would increase costs for the cotton planters while bringing greater profits to the merchants and manufacturers of the North. In South Carolina, feeling against it ran so high that the legislature nullified the tariff act and threatened secession.

Andrew Jackson, heading a Democratic administration, was then President, and the Whigs were the opposition party. Webster, as one of the leading Whig Senators, was expected to use the Southern dissatisfaction and threat of secession to render Jackson's course more difficult. Instead, Webster spoke out in support of Jackson's efforts to prevent nullification and secession, putting the unity of the states and respect for the Constitution above party interests.

In 1840 Webster again appeared to be a leading candidate. The country had weathered a depression and the voters were clearly eager for a change in Washington. Now, at last, the Whigs had an excellent chance to unseat the Democrats, who had held office for twelve years. But again the Whigs passed Webster by. They nominated William Henry Harrison, the hero of the War of 1812, who, like Jackson, had won victories over the British and their Indian allies. There was a Whig landslide and Harrison was elected. He took Webster into his Cabinet as Secretary of State.

The Whigs had nominated an ex-Democrat from Virginia, John Tyler, as Vice-President. They had done so with the hope of gaining votes in the South. They soon had to ponder whether those gains were

Webster Replying to Hayne. Painting by G. P. A. Healy.

worthwhile. A month after he had been inaugurated, President Harrison was stricken with pneumonia and died. On succeeding him, John Tyler immediately took a position in opposition to the policies of the Whigs. To punish Tyler, the Whig Party chiefs ordered the entire Cabinet to resign.

Once more, Webster put the interest of the country above those of his party. As Secretary of State he had been negotiating a treaty with Great Britain for the settlement of a long-standing dispute concerning the border line between Canada and two states, New Hampshire and Maine. More than once it had threatened to flare up into war.

Ignoring the party's orders, Webster remained in office until the pact known as the Webster-Ashburton Treaty was signed. This adjusted the disputed border on terms favorable to the United States. Only then did Webster join his party's protest and resign his office. The party chiefs resented his delay, and at the next nominating convention he was passed over again.

In 1850, eleven years before the Civil War began, came Webster's last great test of conscience. The war with Mexico had been followed by bitter controversies between North and South over the new states formed out of the western territories. Were these to be slave states or free? Other disagreements involved a stronger Fugitive Slave Law. Should the property right of a Southern planter to reclaim his runaway slave be respected?

To pacify both sides, Henry Clay worked out his famous compromise, the Compromise of 1850. In this plan, concessions were made to the North, among them the admission of California as a free state. Balancing concessions were also made to the South, among them a more rigorous Fugitive Slave Act. This delayed the Civil War for ten years, though, as history has shown, it could not prevent it.

Now the New Hampshire voters, who had sent Webster to the Senate, fully expected him to speak out against this compromise. Instead, in one of the most magnificent orations of his entire career, he defied his party and his constituency and spoke out in its support. The nation was faced, he pointed out, by community suicide. "As men may be protected against murder but cannot be guarded against suicide, so a government may be shielded from the assaults of external foes, but nothing can save it when it chooses to lay violent hands on itself."

The Compromise of 1850 won a passage through Congress largely through Webster's oratory. But on the Senate floor and in many newspaper editorials and sermons and at public meetings throughout the North, he was called a "turncoat" and a "traitor." Again, he had put his concern for the unity of his country above every other loyalty.

Two years later, in 1852, death finally stilled Webster's magnificent voice at the age of seventy. Now his birthplace in Concord, New Hampshire, has become a national shrine, and every year thousands of Americans come to pay their respects to a great American who chose to be a statesman rather than a politician.

THE GREAT COMPROMISER

(HENRY CLAY)

Everybody thought that the career of Henry Clay, the Great Compromiser, had ended. Had he not retired from the Senate to live out his days quietly in his beloved Kentucky? And yet here he was in 1849, a man of seventy-two, on his way back to the Senate in Washington. The swaying carriage rattled over the twisting and rutted roads of the National Pike, down through the Valley of the Cumberland. "Faster, Tom, faster!" cried Henry Clay. "Yassuh, Marse Henry, yassuh," said the driver, as he leaned forward and cracked his whip over the backs of his team.

Henry Clay sat back in the carriage, pinch-faced, hollow-eyed and haggard. He was feeling a touch of fever tonight. Yet he must reach Cumberland in time to make a connection for Washington. He urged his driver onward again.

But the hurtling carriage careened off the road and overturned. Neither Tom nor Henry Clay was injured, but one wheel of the carriage was broken to bits. They stabled the horses at the nearby tavern and Clay went into the taproom to see if there might not be someone to drive him on down to Cumberland.

The taproom was resounding with a loud discussion. As Henry Clay reached the doorway he heard what sounded like an argument. "So you think we fought Mexico so the South can run the country!"

"That's a Yankee slur! I merely suggested we could get along very well without the North."

And with that the two men came to blows.

Martha, the tavern hostess, with the assistance of Clay, pulled the men apart. Clay then said to them, "I came in here hoping someone would help me. My carriage broke down and it's very important that I get to Washington."

"My name is George Johnson," said the man from the South. "I have a coach and you're welcome to ride with me."

"And I'm Frank Peabody," said the man from the North. "If you prefer the company of a Yankee to a Tarheel, I'd be glad to have you ride with me."

"It's very kind of both of you," said Henry Clay. Then he told the men who he was.

"Henry Clay!" exclaimed Peabody. "I've heard of you and your compromising tricks. A Southerner at heart, pretending to Northern principles. I'd advise you to go back to Kentucky!"

"At least I can agree with this Yankee on that," said Johnson. "Go back to Kentucky!" And both men turned away abruptly.

"And this is the state of the nation,"

Henry Clay. Painting by E. D. Marchant.

to be no more common ground at all between anti-slavery men like Daniel Webster in the North and pro-slavery men like John Calhoun in the South. What was to be done about California and all this new territory in the Southwest?

The old atmosphere of the Missouri Compromise seemed gone forever. The North would not allow a stricter Fugitive Slave Law, and of course the South would not consider the abolition of slavery, even in the small area of the District of Columbia. Worst of all, a convention of delegates from the South was gathering in Nashville to consider the possibility of secession.

"Secession." The word rang in Clay's ears like the tolling of a bell of doom, and he realized that the Union to which he had devoted his life was on the brink of war. He had known that there was grave danger and had hurried back to Washington to give the last of his energy and all his legislative experience to the preservation of the Union. But he had not expected to find disaster so close at hand.

Clay had barely exchanged greetings with John Calhoun when the latter declared, "I know you have come back to the Senate, Henry, in the hope that you can find some compromise. Do you think I forgot how you and I worked for the Missouri Compromise? I fought then as hard as you did to save the Union. But now it cannot be saved. We of the South have no patience for further compromise. Daniel Webster will tell you that it is the same with the people of the North. The Union and the rights of the Southern States are no longer compatible. It's secession the South wants, and that's my last word on it, Henry."

"Secession." With the terrible word again pounding in his ears, Henry Clay called on Daniel Webster. It was a difficult thing for him to do. He and Webster had engaged in such bitter legislative struggles that they had become completely estranged and had not spoken to

said Clay as much to himself as to Martha as they watched the two men walk off. "This is what happens when men have only anger in their hearts. It deafens them to any voice that speaks for common sense. This is why I must get to Washington as soon as I can—before all chance for reason is lost, before there is nothing left but violence."

"Don't worry, Mr. Clay," said Martha quietly. "I'll get you to Cumberland in time. I'll have my cousin James come over from the next farm and he'll drive you there."

Upon his arrival in the capital, Clay discovered that things had gone much further than he had imagined. Congress was hopelessly divided, and there seemed

each other for the last nine years.

"It's been a long time, Dan," said Clay as he entered Webster's study.

"Yes, Henry," said Webster. "And I think I know why you returned to the Senate. You want me to compromise once more. But will my constituents in the North accept compromise? Will the South?"

"I admit," said Clay, "that issues will always divide men as they have divided us. In face of this fact, it is my contention that the problem will always be to find an issue that will unite men."

"I agree," said Webster, "that democracy is a give-and-take and that compromise is its essence. It was so in 1787. It is still so in every town meeting throughout the country. But in Congress itself, representing the entire nation, what compromise will work today? Where will we ever find one?"

"The details are less important than the *spirit* of compromise," said Clay. "Give each side some concessions and if there's reason left, they'll take it. Make California free, give the South an open chance at Utah and New Mexico, abolish the slave trade here in the District of Columbia, and give the South the Fugitive Slave Law it wants. It's the spirit that counts."

A blizzard blew up outside in the city as the two men went on talking and Mrs. Webster served them some hot punch. It was much later when the two men stood up to drink a toast.

"To your plan for compromise," said Webster. "May it appeal to all reasonable men, North and South."

"To the Union," said Clay, "which will last as long as people prefer reason to violence."

Throughout the remaining weeks of winter, all during the spring and on into the summer, Henry Clay stood up again and again in the Senate to appeal for a compromise, but the extremists were stubborn. Calhoun would repeat that unless

the differences could be settled on the broad principle of justice to the South, it would be better that North and South separate and part in peace. And then Senator Chase of Ohio would leap up to say that the North was not to be deflected from its determination to abolish slavery in all the territories of the United States. By September Congress had passed a series of bills constituting the Compromise of 1850. Many people regarded this as a genuine, definitive settlement of the difficulties between the North and the South. Henry Clay knew better. He knew that there had not been the true spirit of compromise, that the settlement was only temporary.

Heartsick and weary, Clay made his farewell speech to the Senate. "As the last blessing which Heaven can bestow upon me on this earth, I implore that if the direful and sad event of the dissolution of the Union shall happen, I may not survive to behold it. Gentlemen, you speak of the North or of the South. I owe allegiance to no South, no North, no East, no West. I owe allegiance only to the Union!"

Henry Clay returned to Kentucky, knowing that he had achieved only a superficial healing of the mortal wounds of the nation. Two years later he was dead.

No one knew better than Henry Clay, the Great Compromiser, how thankless and frustrating it is to be the pacificator, the arbitrator-without-authority, between two bitterly opposed groups. And it may seem that all his work in preserving the uneasy peace was wasted. The war did come, but thanks to the compromise that Henry Clay helped to bring about, crucial, invaluable time was gained. The Missouri Compromise was effective in 1820, but there were forty years of peace after it. For the years, or *days*, of peace that were gained by his efforts to avert a Civil War the nation is profoundly indebted to Henry Clay.

Clay urging his "Omnibus" Bill in the Senate, 1850.

HONEST ABE

(ABRAHAM LINCOLN)

He was lean and long—six feet four in his stocking feet. He stooped, as very tall men do, and his gait was awkward and shambling. He had long ago given up any effort to impose grace on his gangling body. Even in the White House his wife could not get him fully "harnessed," as he put it, to formal clothes and elegant manners. He had a craggy face. His enemies called him "Ape" Lincoln and offered bets that an uglier man could not be found in all America. Yet, after people got to know him, they grew to trust him. They admired, they loved him. Many, indeed, came to see beauty in his homely features.

It takes a long time for a populous nation to know even its most celebrated citizens. It took a long time for Americans to get to know the obscure backwoods lawyer. But Abe Lincoln became one of the best-loved of all their heroes.

The course by which he became well known to his countrymen, the road that took him to the White House, began in the small, dim, log cabin, far from any school, where he spent his boyhood. His mother, Nancy Hanks Lincoln, died when he was only ten. His father then married a widow with three children. Years later, William Herndon, one of Lincoln's biographers, visited Sarah Bush Lincoln when he was collecting material for his book. She poured out to him recollections of Abe's affection and consideration. Even when the cares of the Presidency weighed heaviest upon him, he did not forget her birthday. Despite risks and hardships, he never failed to visit her on that midwinter day. "I loved my own son John," his stepmother said, "but not a bit more than Abe. He was a good son to me. I can say what not one mother in a thousand can say—Abe never gave me a cross word."

Honest Abe was a nickname he earned very early. Even as a boy he became known among the neighbors for his conscientiousness. For example, there was the farmer over the way who owned a library of two books—the Bible and Parson Weems' *Life of Washington*. Abe borrowed the *Life of Washington* and read it one early evening until the light failed. Then he put it carefully on a shelf high up on the chinked log wall. During the night a storm rose. It blew in the clay plugs in the chinks and the rain drenched the precious volume, blurring the print and pasting together many of the pages. Abe insisted on working out the value of the book, and put in three hard days of corn-pulling for the farmer.

Twice local merchants took Honest Abe

into partnership, though he hadn't a dollar of capital to invest. Both of the stores failed, some said, because Abe was *too* honest; he would not short-weight or short-change an unwary customer nor "talk up" sleazy goods.

He may not have been a good business-man, but people remembered this honest, friendly, humorous man. They trusted him. In time, as the word about him got around, the people in his county—Sangamon County—elected him to represent them in the Illinois State Legislature.

Before that happened, he had taken up law and had impressed people as both an able and an honest lawyer. Strangely enough, it was by way of a trade made at the second bankrupt store that Abe started on his law schooling.

One of the many farmers trekking West to new lands stopped his covered wagon before the store. The horses were breath-ing hard from their heavy load. To lighten it the farmer decided to jettison a barrel full of attic scourings. He gladly took a half-dollar for it from Abe. Even if the con-tents were junk, Abe thought, he could get close to a half-dollar for the barrel. He began to empty it, dredging out just about what he had expected to find—old andirons, cracked dishes, cups without handles, bent pewter spoons. But at the very bottom were four fat volumes—Blackstone's *Com-mentaries,* the standard law textbooks of the time.

Lincoln had had to give half a week's labor to pay for the ruined *Life of Wash-ington;* the Blackstone volumes were price-less. For a long time Abe had wanted to become a lawyer. His major obstacle, up to now, had been lack of books. Now sud-denly the door of his chosen livelihood was opened to him.

Lincoln became a successful lawyer, and a scrupulous and generous one. Sometime in the summer of 1850 he wrote some notes of advice to young men who wished to take up law:

". . . Discourage litigation. Persuade your neighbors to compromise whenever you can. Point out to them how the nominal winner is often the real loser—in fees, ex-penses and waste of time. As a peacemaker the lawyer has a superior opportunity of being a good man. There would still be business enough.

"Never stir up litigation. A worse man can scarcely be found than one who does this. Who can be more nearly a fiend than he who habitually overhauls the register of deeds in search of defects in titles, whereon to stir up strife, and put money in his pockets? A moral tone ought to be infused into the profession, which should drive such men out of it. . . .

"There is a vague popular belief that lawyers are necessarily dishonest. I say vague, because when we consider to what extent confidence and honors are reposed in and conferred upon lawyers by the peo-ple, it appears improbable that their im-pression of dishonesty is very distinct and vivid. Yet the impression is common, al-most universal. Let no young man choos-ing law for a calling for a moment yield to the popular belief—resolve to be honest at all events; and if, in your own judgment, you cannot be an honest lawyer, resolve to be honest without being a lawyer. Choose some other occupation, rather than one in the choosing of which you do, in advance, consent to be a knave."

Lincoln was not one to give advice to which he himself paid no heed. He dis-couraged litigation. Whenever he could, he persuaded contesting parties to settle outside the court. He never took a case in which he suspected his client was not in the right. Because he hated to see anyone victimized, he took many cases from which he could expect no fee. Of such cases two are well known: one because it involved a famous figure in American history and the other because it illustrated dramatically his shrewdness and alertness as well as his honesty.

82

From a Currier and Ives print.

In the first case, his client was the great actor Joseph Jefferson, who was trying to bring good theater to the West. He and his company had received a permit from a certain town council to erect a theater. The last planks of the building were being hammered into place when bigots in the community, hearing of this invasion of "sin," put pressure on the town council to stop the show. The council resorted to a trick: they passed an ordinance requiring a $500 license fee for a theatrical exhibition. This was an enormous sum in those days, and it was known that Jefferson had put all his money in the construction of the theater.

Incensed by the trickery, injustice and intolerance behind the ordinance, Lincoln voluntarily stepped into the case. Appearing before the town council, he made its members ashamed of their chicanery and infused some of his own generous spirit into them. The license regulation was rescinded and the show was allowed to go on.

In the second case, Lincoln represented a young man charged with murder. He knew the accused and was convinced of his innocence. He knew also that if he did not take the case, the defendant's family was too poor to afford another lawyer. He knew, too, that the young man's case was regarded as hopeless. The only direct testimony that would be offered would be against him and it would be supported by evidence that the defendant and the murdered man had quarreled.

At the trial Lincoln seemed to be letting the prosecutor have it all his own way. He raised none of the customary legalistic objections. He did not once interrupt the prosecutor's confident presentation or his examination of the witness. Then Lincoln rose to cross-examine the witness who claimed he had seen the deed.

Lincoln: "Young man, do you realize you are under oath?"

Witness: "Yes, sir, I do."

Lincoln: "And that to lie is to commit perjury?"

Witness: "Yes, sir. But what I'm telling is the truth."

Lincoln: "You claim that on the night of the murder you were standing two hundred feet from the scene of the crime?"

Witness: "Yes, sir."

Lincoln: "Would you mind repeating just how you were able to be so certain that the perpetrator of this foul crime was the defendant?"

Witness: "Well, sir, as I said before, it was a full moon. It was almost as bright as day, and I saw young Will and Metzgar having an argument and pushing each other around. All of a sudden Will picked up a piece of iron and hit Metzgar over the head with it, and then he ran."

Lincoln: "And it was only because of the full moon high in the sky that you were able to see so well at that distance?"

Witness: "Yes, sir."

Lincoln: "If there had been no moon or a young moon, you would not have been able to see what happened at all. Is that not true?"

Witness: "Well . . . yes, sir, that's true."

Lincoln (sharply): "Just as I thought, young man! You have perjured yourself before this court. Your Honor, gentlemen of the jury, I submit that this witness, upon whose testimony the prosecution hopes to convict my innocent client, has lied."

Prosecutor: "I object, Your Honor. Mr. Lincoln must prove that statement."

Lincoln: "I will. The evidence and authority is the book I hold in my hand. It is an almanac in which it is clearly shown that, on the night and at the time the witness says the crime was committed, there was only a half-moon, and that instead of riding high in the sky, it was setting!"

Lincoln's victory in this case, which had seemed so hopeless, spread his name throughout the state. People talked about this honest, generous, wise and humorous lawyer. In frontier communities such men

"The Council of War." Lincoln with Grant and Stanton (Rogers Group) by John Rogers.

were turned to as leaders. Lincoln represented his neighbors for several terms in the State Legislature, and then his constituents sent him to Washington as their Congressman. There he took an independent course. He did not consider himself bound to the Whig Party, and consequently the party leaders found this freedom objectionable and rebuffed him. For some years following his term in Congress he stayed out of politics. Some people thought his political career was finished and that he should content himself with his growing law practice.

Then came an event that jolted him, along with millions of other conscientious Americans, out of his daily routine. The country had been held in an uneasy balance regarding the slavery issue by the Missouri Compromise. This had satisfied neither the North nor the South; but antislavery men like Lincoln, who put the preservation of the Union above anything else, had tolerated it on that account. Proslavery advocates, however, were constantly seeking ways to get around it. Finally, they induced Senator Stephen Douglas to sponsor the Kansas-Nebraska

Act. This nullified the Missouri Compromise. It seemed fair enough, leaving the determination of the slavery issue to the territories, yet it favored the pro-slavery interests, who sent out armed horsemen as fake settlers to terrorize the genuine settlers.

Lincoln emerged from his virtual retirement in Springfield and waged a magnificent campaign against the Kansas-Nebraska Act. The then still-pioneer Middle Western states were the ones most violently outraged by it. They were close to the territories affected and had first-hand knowledge of such raiding activities. In an attempt to placate these states Stephen Douglas embarked on a speaking tour. Lincoln challenged him to a series of debates. In these Douglas, a nationally known senator, suffered defeat after defeat at the hands of the obscure backwoods lawyer.

The news of these political debates spread across the country and transformed lawyer Lincoln into a national figure of consequence. Yet, at the opening day of the convention of the young Republican Party in 1860, few considered him a likely candidate for the chief office of the land. As the sessions went on, however, more and more delegates turned to him. And so was chosen as a Presidential nominee the man destined to preserve the Union and enlarge, by emancipation, the freedom and equality promised all its citizens in its Declaration of Independence.

WITH MALICE TOWARD NONE

(LINCOLN AS PRESIDENT)

Rarely has the head of a great country faced such overwhelming obstacles as Abraham Lincoln did as President.

During his campaign Southern leaders had threatened that their states would secede from the Union if he were elected. His ride from Illinois to Washington for the inauguration was partly a nightmare trip through hostile country. Some of the crowds at the towns where the train stopped were openly unfriendly, and even at station platforms where he was welcomed, there were a few who hooted and jeered at him.

Lincoln's route to the capital took him through Baltimore, Maryland, and as the presidential train approached that city, an anxious man urgently sought a personal interview with the President-elect. The man was Allan Pinkerton, a railroad detective who was to become the founder of a famous detective agency. He came to warn Lincoln of a plot to assassinate him in Baltimore.

Through a change in the schedule the would-be assassins were foiled. Instead of arriving in Baltimore on the hour that had been announced, Lincoln passed through the city in the middle of the night before. This, screamed his political enemies, lowered the dignity of his high office; this was an act of cowardice! And they harped upon it in an attempt to arouse public scorn.

On his arrival in Washington, one of Lincoln's immediate problems was to strengthen his wavering party. He had been a dark-horse candidate, and he had won because none of his better-known rivals would give way. To pacify the disappointed candidates Lincoln gave them high Cabinet posts. And so he began his administration with a motley Cabinet, some of the members of which resented him and considered him inferior to themselves.

He had hardly taken office when the Secessionists provoked the Civil War by firing on federal Fort Sumter in the harbor of Charleston, South Carolina. Lincoln immediately consulted his Cabinet about sending an expedition to relieve Fort Sumter. The Cabinet was six to one against the expedition. Some of those who were opposed felt that the attempt would be hopeless. All six thought that if fresh federal forces were to engage the South Carolina militia, the state would formally secede from the Union.

But to Lincoln, the firing on Fort Sumter was, in itself, an act of secession. Determined counteraction, he felt, was more likely to halt further steps toward secession than a passive policy of allowing the South's initial step to go unchecked. Therefore, although his Cabinet was almost unanimously opposed to the expedition, Lincoln took sole responsibility for the order relieving Fort Sumter.

And so the fearful war began. The Southern states had already begun to organize a separate Confederacy, and several states soon formally seceded from the Union.

Now we know that the North was stronger and would ultimately have won. But the immediate advantages were with the South. If Lincoln had not been so calm and resolute, had be given way to defeatism, as did so many in the North, history might have had a different tale to tell.

When hostilities opened, the South had most of the country's professional officers and most of its trained soldiers. One reason for this was that the two sections of the country held different ways of life. In the "good families" of the South, few men thought of other careers than running a plantation, going into politics or becoming Army officers. Consequently, a majority of the graduates of West Point had been Southerners. When a Southerner was educated beyond primary school, it was usually at a military academy.

There were, moreover, few cities in the South. People were accustomed to outdoor living, to camping and hunting. Many Southerners had gone West to Indian country, and many had become experienced Indian-fighters. Being geographically closer to Mexico and expecting to carve out new Southern states from the conquered Mexican territory, the South had sent many of its sons as volunteers in the war against Mexico.

Thus, when the Civil War began, the South had virtually a corner on the trained officers; also, most Southern recruits already knew how to handle guns and many had already gained battle experience. In contrast, the North had few professional Army officers, and many of its recruits barely had time for training before they went into battle against comparatively seasoned Southern troops.

Lincoln had offered the command of the Union armies to Robert E. Lee, who was personally against slavery. But Lee had put loyalty to his native state of Virginia above everything else. And so the nation's best general led the Confederate armies. It was almost two years before Lincoln found, in General Ulysses S. Grant, a commanding officer who could equal the best Southern commanders.

These first advantages brought the South a string of early victories. It was well over a year before the Northern Army could hold its own in a battle of any importance.

This was not all that Lincoln had to cope with. Military defeats were demoralizing many people of the North. They demanded that Lincoln make peace at any price. These "Copperheads," as they were called, not only opposed continuing the war; some even plotted with the enemy.

On the other hand, there were the all-out abolitionists who pressed for the immediate emancipation of the slaves. This, however, would have alienated the border states, in which there were many slaveholders, and might well have pushed them to the side of the Confederacy. Lincoln had to be patient under many angry protests and insults from Copperheads and abolitionists.

Then came the battle of Antietam, where the fact that the Northern army had held its lines could be considered a victory. And, on January 1, 1863, Lincoln, feeling that at last the North was strong enough to risk decisive action, issued the Emancipation Proclamation, formally ending slavery in the United States.

By that time the Northern forces had become battle-hardened, and Lincoln had found General Grant and other good commanders. Grant's victory at Vicksburg on the Mississippi was a turning-point. From then on, not even Lee could win major battles for the South. At Gettysburg, in Pennsylvania, Lee himself was driven from the field, and large Southern forces were never again to penetrate Northern territory.

Few battles in history exacted such a fearful cost in lives as did Gettysburg and few were so decisive. None has been so immortalized. Lincoln's memorial address was delivered on the battlefield of Gettysburg at the dedication of a national cemetery there, in November, 1863. Lincoln, with his many heavy burdens of state, could not spare the time to compose an elaborate oration. He had left that to Edward Everett, who worked up a resounding two-hour speech.

On the train ride from Washington to Gettysburg, with a borrowed pencil, on the back of an old envelope, Lincoln wrote down a brief speech of dedication which he had written out earlier in a rough draft. The few paragraphs did not look impressive, then. But they came from the heart and they spoke to the heart. They so perfectly expressed the feeling of the audience that applause seemed irreverent. Perhaps they were not heard distinctly by all those present—for some, his speech was over before they had properly settled themselves. But all over the nation, his speech, as given to their newspapers by the reporters at the ceremony, was read by the people of the country with emotion. Less than a page in length, it has become treasured by all Americans as an expression of the very soul of their nation. Many know the words by

President Lincoln with his son Tad.

heart.

"Fourscore and seven years ago our fathers brought forth upon this continent a new nation, conceived in liberty, and dedicated to the proposition that all men are created equal.

"Now we are engaged in a great civil war, testing whether that nation or any nation so conceived and so dedicated, can long endure. We are met on a great battlefield of that war. We have come to dedicate a portion of that field, as a final resting place for those who here gave their lives that that nation might live. It is altogether fitting and proper that we should do this.

"But, in a larger sense, we cannot dedicate—we cannot consecrate—we cannot hallow—this ground. The brave men, living and dead, who struggled here, have consecrated it, far above our poor power to add or detract. The world will little note, nor long remember what we say here, but it can never forget what they did here. It is for us the living, rather, to be dedicated here to the unfinished work which they who fought here have thus far so nobly advanced. It is rather for us to be here dedicated to the great task remaining before us—that from these honored dead we take increased devotion to that cause for which they gave the last full measure of devotion —that we here highly resolve that these dead shall not have died in vain—that this nation, under God, shall have a new birth of freedom—and that government of the people, by the people, for the people, shall not perish from the earth."

After Gettysburg, Lincoln's problem was no longer to sustain the courage of the faltering but to curb the rancor of the vengeful. Fainthearts had become fire-eaters who wanted to carry on the war to the utter destruction of the South.

Lincoln wanted to bring the bloody fighting to an end as soon as possible and on terms that would permit a harmonious and honorable reunion. When there were suggestions for peace negotiations on either side, Lincoln encouraged them. News of one such attempt leaked out, and a deputation of raging "bitter-enders" came to warn the President that he must have nothing to do with it. Lincoln calmly heard them out, watched them leave and then waited for word from Grant. At the general's headquarters there was a secret Confederate delegation headed by Alexander Stephens, Vice-President of the Confederacy. Grant's message announced a slim hope for peace if Lincoln could negotiate in person. Lincoln needed not another word. He rushed down to Grant's camp. For two days he was gone from the capital; no one knew where.

The peace negotiations did not succeed, but Stephens was so deeply impressed by Lincoln that he wrote afterward, "With Lincoln the Union rose to the sublimity of religious mysticism."

It had become only a matter of weeks now, before organized Confederate resistance would have to end. Some of Lee's own men were deserting, and no attempt was being made to hold them back, since they could no longer be fed or armed. Lee's surrender could be expected at any moment.

In the meantime, Lincoln had been re-elected. The nation was awaiting his second inaugural address. Would he announce harsh terms for the South—the gallows for its leaders, jail for its thousands of soldiers, fines, penalties, and garrisons? These were the demands of the vengeful-minded of the North.

But what Lincoln proposed in his plea to the people of the nation was that the South be welcomed back into the Union, like a brother into the family circle. In his second inaugural address were these inspiring lines:

"With malice toward none; with charity for all; with firmness in the right, as God gives us to see the right, let us strive on to finish the work we are in; to bind up the nation's wounds; to care for him who shall have borne the battle, and for his widow, and his orphan—to do all which may achieve and cherish a just and lasting peace among ourselves, and with all nations."

Had Lincoln lived to carry out his generous policy, the nation might have gone through the Reconstruction period with less rancor and tension. The heritage of war bitterness might have been less heavy. But a half-mad assassin made that impossible. The bullet of John Wilkes Booth prevented Lincoln's wisdom and humanity from being used to "bind up the nation's wounds."

Psychologists who have studied Booth's life believe that he was severely disturbed, if not insane. His activities were hardly conceived by a reasoning man. Wise and able Southern patriots like Alexander Stephens and Robert E. Lee genuinely mourned Lincoln's death. They knew that Booth had struck down the man who could have done most for the South. Lincoln's body was carried on a black-shrouded train across the country from Washington to Springfield, Illinois, where he was buried.

The journey was a national funeral cortege that continued for twelve days. At every stop, weeping crowds came to do him honor. The nation's grief was solemnly and sadly expressed by Walt Whitman in his memorial poem:

O Captain! my Captain! our fearful trip is done,
The ship has weather'd every rack, the prize we sought is won;
The port is near, the bells I hear, the people all exulting,
While follow eyes the steady keel, the vessel grim and daring:
But O heart! heart! heart!
O the bleeding drops of red,
Where on the deck my Captain lies,
Fallen cold and dead.

O Captain! my Captain! rise up and hear the bells;
Rise up—for you the flag is flung—for you the bugle trills,
For you bouquets and ribbon'd wreaths—for you the shores a-crowding,
For you they call, the swaying mass, their eager faces turning;
Here Captain! dear father!
This arm beneath your head!
It is some dream that on the deck,
You've fallen cold and dead.

My Captain does not answer, his lips are pale and still,
My father does not feel my arm, he has no pulse nor will,
The ship is anchor'd safe and sound, its voyage closed and done,
From fearful trip, the victor ship, comes in with object won:
Exult O shores, and ring O bells!
But I, with mournful tread,
Walk the deck my Captain lies,
Fallen cold and dead.

THE PRESIDENT AND THE CALCULATED RISK

(GROVER CLEVELAND)

The spring of 1893, shortly after Grover Cleveland's second inauguration, was a time of crisis in the United States. A special session of Congress had been called to resolve the issue of sound currency and inflation. Because of the disunity in the country over this issue, the President seemed to be all that stood in the way of national disaster. The people had full confidence in him. He was the one who would make things right.

On May 5 the President noticed a rough spot on the roof of his mouth. It became increasingly painful. On June 18 he had it examined by the White House physician, Dr. O'Reilly, who found that a malignant growth, extending from the teeth up the jawbone nearly to the eye, was threatening the Chief Executive's life. An immediate operation was imperative, yet had to be kept a complete secret. There would be widespread panic if it became known that the life of the most important man in America was in danger.

At Bellevue Hospital in New York City, Surgeon John F. Erdmann was getting ready to perform an operation. He was interrupted by his chief, Dr. Bryant. "Dr. Erdmann," said Bryant, "I'm going to perform a critical operation. I want you to assist me."

"Of course. When is it to be?" said the young surgeon.

"The date is not definite, but I must ask

you to make no engagements for the evening of June 30."

"Who is the patient?" asked Erdmann.

"Sorry, I can't tell you that either. But on the evening of the operation, a Dr. O'Reilly will call for you at your home."

On the night of June 30, the mysterious Dr. O'Reilly appeared at Dr. Erdmann's residence on 34th Street. He introduced himself and with no further ado asked Dr. Erdmann to accompany him to the Battery. There they boarded a launch which took them out to the yacht *Oneida,* anchored in midstream.

Dr. Erdmann got no replies to the questions he put to Dr. O'Reilly, except that he was to assist at a cancer operation, to be performed on board the ship.

When Dr. Erdmann was introduced to the other doctors, all distinguished specialists, his mystification only grew deeper. There was Dr. Janeway, a noted general practitioner; Dr. William Keen, a famous surgeon from Philadelphia; Dr. Hasbrouck, a New York dentist.

Shortly after they had all assembled in the main saloon, which had been set up with complete operating-room equipment, other people came aboard. The introductions were being made by Dr. Bryant, who was evidently in charge: "Dr. Janeway, Dr. Keen, Dr. Hasbrouck, Dr. Erdmann . . . Gentlemen, our patient—the President of the United States, Mr. Grover Cleveland!"

The yacht was anchored that night off 25th Street near Bellevue. The next morning it steamed up the East River into Long Island Sound, coming to anchor in a secluded cove.

The President, who had spent a fairly comfortable night without sedatives, was propped upon a chair against the mast. "Why this position?" he asked Dr. Bryant, who was supervising the arrangements.

"To lessen the danger of swallowing blood," was the grim reply.

"Anything you say," said the Chief Executive, as he settled back in the chair to receive the anaesthetics: first, nitrous-oxide gas, then ether. Before succumbing to the final effects, the President made this statement: "Gentlemen, this country is in a precarious condition. I've called a special session of Congress for August 7, thirty-seven days from now. I've got to be there . . . and you've got to see to it that I am. All right, gentlemen, your patient is ready."

As the anaesthetic took effect, Dr. Janeway kept close check on the patient's physical condition. Difficulty was experienced in rendering him unconscious. Cleveland's pulse remained strong. He was then fifty-six years old, very heavy, with a short, thick neck.

Dr. Hasbrouck first proceeded with his extraction, removing the patient's teeth on the upper left side. Dr. Bryant made the necessary incisions in the roof of the mouth, and then, working at top speed for thirty-one minutes, removed the entire left upper jaw and part of the palate. No external incision was necessary, nor was the eye-ball touched. At 1:55 P.M. the operation was completed. With sighs of relief the doctors put their patient to bed.

Dr. Erdmann, who had assisted at the operation, was also given the responsibility of watching over Cleveland. The President soon awoke and, with his mouth filled with cotton, dazedly mumbled, "Who-who you?"

"I'm Dr. Erdmann," was the reply.

"Erdmann?"

"Yes, Mr. President. Dr. John F. Erdmann."

Cleveland, his breathing stertorous, continued, "Where . . . where you from?"

"Chillicothe, Ohio," replied Erdmann.

"Chillicothe. Know a man in Chillicothe, name of Nibge?"

"Why, yes, I know him," came Erdmann's surprised response.

"Nibge, like everyone else, wants a federal job. Does he need a job?"

"I don't think so, sir. He's a successful druggist. He must be after more money, asking for a federal job," essayed Erdmann.

"Then he won't get a job from me," growled Cleveland. And with that he closed his eyes and went back to sleep.

When he awoke, Dr. Bryant was by his side, and assured him that no one in the capital knew about the operation aboard the *Oneida*.

"Bryant," said Cleveland thickly, "no one must know."

"We all understand, Mr. Cleveland. I can vouch for the medical men. This operation will remain a secret, but you may have to have a second operation," replied Dr. Bryant.

"But I *must* appear before Congress on August 7," protested Cleveland.

"Very well," replied Bryant. "Second operation or no . . . you will appear before Congress."

"God willing," breathed Cleveland fervently.

The operation was successful. On July 3, the President was up and about. The *Oneida* continued her cruise. On July 5 she dropped anchor in Buzzards Bay, and Cleveland was able to walk without difficulty from the launch to his summer home, "Gray Gables." On July 17, there was a brief second operation to burn out some granu-

lated tissue. The President recovered. Dr Kasson Gibson, a dentist from New York took an impression of President Cleveland' jaw and made a vulcanized rubber substi tute for the part that had been removed.

On August 7, Congress opened. Cleve land delivered a masterful speech. No on suspected what an ordeal he had been through only the month before. The speech did much to calm the partisans on both sides of the silver question. The economy of the country was safe.

As Dr. Erdmann many years late pointed out, "Mr. Cleveland was a man o great courage and patriotism. It took a lo of courage to reach the decision he made to undergo such an operation."

For his own safety it would have been better to have had the operation performed in a hospital under proper conditions, with full facilities available. But the President regarded the welfare of the country as par amount. He risked both the physical dan ger of the secret operation, and also the possible damage to his reputation if the news leaked out that he had helped to deceive the people. But he was ready to risk anything and everything for the sake of his country.

The faces of Washington, Jefferson, Lincoln and Theodore Roosevelt carved on the granite of Mount Rushmore (South Dakota) by Gutzon Borglum.

THE MAN WHO CARRIED A BIG STICK

(THEODORE ROOSEVELT)

The train rattled and puffed through the barren Badlands. It would soon reach the town of Medora, North Dakota. "Ordinarily," the conductor told his Medora-bound passenger, "we don't stop here. Last time we did, those Medora cowboys shot out all the windows of the train."

"Well, it's where I'm getting off, just the same," the passenger said. He stood up to take his baggage from the rack. "Give me a hand with this, will you, conductor? I haven't been too strong lately."

"Thought you looked a little peaked," the conductor said, helping him. "But do me a favor. The time before they shot out the windows, those crazy cowboys climbed under the dining-car and shot up through

it. Scared the passengers out of their wits. Now, if you'd just sort of jump off the train when we slow down, we'll toss your baggage after you."

"All right."

"And I'll give you a little free advice, Mister," the conductor added. "Those glasses you're wearin', and that derby hat —you'd better take 'em off. In Medora, glasses are sissy and a derby is just an open invitation to target practice."

Maybe the passenger should have taken his advice. As he jumped off the train, his hat blew off his head. When he picked it up, there were a couple of bullet-holes through the crown.

A warm introduction for the twenty-fifth President of the United States! But that was in 1885, exactly sixteen years before the man in the glasses and derby hat became the youngest President in United States history. His name was Theodore Roosevelt.

At twenty-five, Roosevelt had served three terms in the New York state legislature, but then political difficulties seemed to call a halt to his public career. And what the doctors had told him made it worse. "You're a very sick man, Mr. Roosevelt," they had said. So, he had come out West to Medora, to buy a ranch, punch cattle, hunt buffalo and work himself back to health. He meant to live in peace for the rest of his "useless" days.

Nine months later he sat in a ranch-house cabin, writing, by lamplight, to a friend in New York:

> Maltese Cross Ranchhouse
> Medora, North Dakota
> Date Uncertain—certain only
> of the temperature outside—
> 34 degrees below zero!

My dear Commissioner:

It's a long time since I've written you. Time in the Badlands stretches as far as space. I was soon at home in this country. I bought some cattle, built a little cabin, found a partner—a fine old Scotchman with blue eyes and mutton-chop whiskers. His name is Lindsay Sutherland, and—

His partner, Sutherland, interrupted him, "Supper, laddie!"

"Never felt hungrier—or stronger—in my life," said young Roosevelt as he took up his knife and buttered a hot biscuit. "I was just writing the Commissioner," he added. "I'm finished with public life. From now on, I'm looking out for just T.R."

At that moment someone knocked on the door. Three men entered the cabin, the wind blowing in after them. They stamped their feet and shook the snow from their overcoats.

Young Roosevelt stood up. Two of the men facing him had put the bullet-holes through his derby the day he arrived in Medora. The third man's name was Jake Saunders. He had come on "business."

"Mr. Roosevelt," said Saunders, "I been watching the way you're building up the Maltese Cross. Put quite a hunk of money in it, eh? Well, you've done a fine job, but you overlooked payin' for the land, which happens to belong to me. And those logs you used, they was cut from my trees."

Lindsay Sutherland spoke up angrily. "Nobody ever owned this land, Saunders. It was open range, free for the taking. It belonged to the man who used it. Saunders, you're a rotten, thievin'—"

Jake Saunders looked at one of the men he had brought with him. "Mr. Sutherland talks too much, Dutch." He gestured toward him, and Dutch slapped Lindsay Sutherland across the face.

"I always thought the Scotch was cool-headed folk, God-fearin' and debt-payin'," Jake Saunders said. Then he turned to Roosevelt. "I reckon you'd like to keep the work you put in here. And I'd sure like you to keep it—all legal-like, with a deed of sale—from me."

"What would it cost?"

"Well, from a nice polite fellow like *you*," Jake Saunders grinned, "no more than five hundred. I'll see you Monday night, in town."

That particular evening it was safer to be polite. But on Monday evening, Jake Saunders suffered a disappointment. Young Roosevelt was not in town. On Tuesday morning, Roosevelt and his partner found a piece of rope attached to the cabin door—and the rope had been tied to form a noose. Attached was a note: "We're giving you one more week to settle up."

On Wednesday, burning with anger, Theodore Roosevelt went into Medora to have a talk with Mr. Packard of the county newspaper. He found the editor in his office, busy getting out his paper. He listened calmly to what Roosevelt had to say.

"Of course Jake Saunders never owned that land," Packard replied. "And you're not the first he's held up this way."

Roosevelt said, "It seems to me, Packard, that those of us who want law and order around here should get together and do something about it."

"This is a big county," Packard said. "You could fit all of Massachusetts into it. But we've no real government and no sheriff within hundreds of miles. So the thieves and bullies rule it. Jake Saunders is the boss from here to Cannonball Creek. He's made everybody else pay."

"And if I *don't* pay?"

"Then a group of masked men will ride up to your cabin, accuse you of horse-stealing and hang you from the nearest cottonwood."

"Has that happened before?"

"It sure has."

"Then what would you advise me to do?"

"You have a choice," Packard said. "One: pay up. Two: leave town. And now, Mr. Roosevelt, if you'll excuse me, I have a paper to put out."

Young Roosevelt stood up. "Keep your paper open for another hour, Mr. Packard. I might make some headlines!"

He did—by knocking Jake Saunders to the floor of a local saloon. "And that," as Roosevelt wrote to a friend, "was my last encounter with Jake for some time. He wasn't seen by anyone . . . yet his actions were felt . . . by me and the rest of the peaceful ranchers . . . cattle stealing . . . pillaging . . . knavery of all kinds."

One day in the spring Packard appeared at the ranchhouse. The two partners greeted him.

"Things have grown so bad," Packard told them, "that something *must* be done."

"You bet things have grown bad," Lindsay Sutherland said. "They was bound to. And *you*, so free with that crawling ad-

vice you handed Mr. Roosevelt two months ago."

"What else could I have advised him?" Packard said. "To go get himself killed?" He turned to Roosevelt. "But it's different now; the ranchers are ready to take your advice. They all respect you hereabouts. You're an Easterner, but you ride the range in all weathers like anybody else. You're a serious cattleman. And you knocked Jake Saunders senseless. The ranchers know now that this section has got to have some decent government. And they're looking to you to get it."

The meeting was held in Medora. Packard was elected sheriff and Theodore Roosevelt his deputy. "The first step for each one of us," Roosevelt said, "is never to buy any stolen cattle. The second step is to support the sheriff with all our power. Remember, he only has as much authority as we citizens give him."

The first new act of violence occurred that very day. Jake Saunders and his crew attempted to set fire to the Maltese Cross.

97

In this they were unsuccessful, but they killed Lindsay Sutherland.

Now the county was aroused and a posse was formed to hunt Jake Saunders and his gang. The posse combed the coulees and the craters and pockmarks of the Badlands. After a week Saunders was tracked to a camp on the Little Missouri River.

"Here he comes," one of the men in the posse whispered. "He must've been out hunting himself some game. Look at him comin' so careless-like. Mr. Roosevelt, I won't shoot till you do. But if you don't mind, I'd like the honor."

"I'm not going to shoot," Roosevelt said. "And neither are you."

"But he killed your partner. And he'd sure kill you if—"

"He's going to jail," Roosevelt said. "And he'll have a trial—a fair trial with a judge and jury. That's what we guarantee a man in this country. That's what the meeting was for. Now put that rifle down."

Jake Saunders was captured alive.

Roosevelt wrote a letter to his friend in New York about his experience.

Well, my dear Commissioner, when I came out here, I meant to follow your advice and leave public life. But after a while, I began to realize how important justice is in this big country. Like all Americans I like big things: big prairies, big forests and mountains, big wheat fields, railroads, herds of cattle, big factories, big steamboats, and everything else. But if we are to grow bigger, and stay great, we must keep steadily in mind that no people were ever benefited by prosperity if they corrupted their virtues. For it's not what we *have* that will make us a great nation; it is the way in which we *use* it. And so, let this letter serve as something of a notice. Tomorrow I am leaving for the East to return to public life.

Hopefully,
Sheriff Teddy.

Teddy's great popularity and effectiveness carried over to the national scene. His lively spirit and amazing vigor stimulated the country, and people readily followed his lead. He got all the volunteers he wanted when he organized his "Rough Riders" to fight in the Spanish-American War. He got full public support in his campaign to "bust the trusts," and he got the world to pay attention when he enunciated the policy: "Speak softly and carry a big stick." He established the United States squarely and solidly in the front rank of great powers in international affairs. The globe became Sheriff Teddy's county!

Colonel Teddy with his Rough Riders on San Juan Hill.

FREEDOM'S WARRIORS

The American Soldier has been but one of the valiant champions of the nation's freedom. Others have fought with song and with speech, with printed page and with that most potent weapon, martyrdom. Whenever the ideals of the New World Republic have been endangered, uncompromising supporters have risen to protect them. Sometimes truth can be arrived at only when men are willing to sacrifice their lives for it, and Americans have stood ready for that fateful moment from the days of Nathan Hale to those of Sergeant Curtis Culin.

It is possible, sometimes, that a man may become a national hero in a cause which other men of stature regard as mistaken—as in the case of Robert E. Lee, who is held in affection and respect by every American though he led the armies of secession in our lamentable War-Between-the-States. Sometimes the roots of greatness lie in courageous campaigning against overwhelming popular opinions—as in the cases of Roger Williams, Henry David Thoreau and Susan B. Anthony. Through these and others, America has learned in the procession of the generations that minorities have the right to be heard, and that if a cause has but one small voice, it may yet prove to be that of justice and truth. The nation has also learned that it can depend for heroic action not only on its leaders but on the least of its citizens when opportunity offers itself.

THE FIGHTING MEN

THE *KNOWN* SOLDIER

(SERGEANT CURTIS CULIN)

In the past perhaps it was true that the victory in a battle, or in a war, went to the better general. Caesar, Napoleon, a host of other military leaders seem, on the basis of history's evidence, to have won because they had military genius, superior skill and judgment. But today the decision in a war depends on the genius of the nations involved. In a way, all the people of a country fight every battle.

It starts far back in the schoolrooms and the playgrounds, in the way people live and work together, achieve individuality and personal independence or learn unthinking obedience. In the nation's streets, in the offices, in the factories, in the legislatures, in the planning rooms—as well as in the general's headquarters—the preparations are made for the course of the battle before, finally, it is fought by the man in the trenches—the common soldier who has to do the job of fighting.

We do pay a great national tribute every year on Armistice Day to that fighting man. His monument is the Tomb of the Unknown Soldier in Washington, an expression of our respect and an acknowledgment of our great debt to the men who have died for their country on the field of battle. We don't know the name of the particular soldier who is buried there or what his exploits were. But we do know that, as a symbol, he stands for the many great deeds of the men and women in the

101

ranks who constitute the most important factor in our victories.

Thousands of these great deeds are known and recorded in the archives of the Army, Navy, Air Forces, Marine Corps, Coast Guard and other services. We can't print them all here, but to represent the contributions of all these war heroes and heroines, here is the story of one *known* soldier's contribution.

In France, on the morning of July 25, 1944, the American Army crashed forward in what history books were to call "the great St. Lo breakthrough." This victory enabled the Allies to break out of Normandy into the French plains beyond, in a sweep that did not slow down till they reached the Rhine.

Yet, less than a month before, that same mighty American Army had been stopped dead in its tracks in Normandy. A thousand tanks had growled to a halt, their massive power useless, stalled by an obstacle never intended for war—beautiful green hedgerows.

Sergeant Dobson peered out from the turret of his tank. Hedgerows. They loomed up ahead, tall, heavy green walls. Dobson had never seen anything quite like them, back in the States. . . . "Nothing to it, Joe," he called down cheerily to the driver sitting below him. "What's a couple of hedgerows to a tank, huh? Give it the gun, boy, and let's take it!"

The tank, an M5, ground forward, picking up speed, plunging toward this innocent-appearing obstacle. On the other side, the Nazi machine guns chattered, but Dobson was confident that his heavy, bullet-proof vehicle would scatter them like rabbits.

In his own tank, a few yards away, Sergeant Curtis Culin warned Dobson, over the inter-com radio, "It looks easy, Sarge, but don't be fooled! I ran into a couple earlier today. You'll pile up on it! *Don't try it, Dobson!*"

Sergeant Culin said later, "Dobson only laughed at me. Well, his tank hit that hedgerow solid — head on — and then stopped dead. That M5 was hung up on the wall, her belly forty-five degrees in the air. I signaled my driver to give our tank the gas and get there fast, but a Nazi hand-grenade beat us to it. Right in the hatch. Poor Dobson and his team inside never knew what happened."

Culin knew what happened and in a short time so did the entire Tank Corps. At its base a hedgerow is a mass of leaves, roots, stalks and dirt; atop, it is a thick mass of large shrubs and small trees. Six feet high and four feet thick, every hedgerow is a solid green wall. The Normandy farmers had spent hundreds of years building and growing them, to mark their boundaries. Our farmers accomplish the same purpose with barbed-wire fences. And now the Nazis sat behind the hedgerows, laughing at the halted American tanks.

As Sergeant Culin said, "The fact is, ever since we hit the beaches after D-Day, those babies got in our way, but good! They lined the roads all the way into St. Lo, and the Nazis were hoping, just itching, for us to go down those mined roads. They'd have us, then, for sure. But the fields were all broken up by the hedgerows. I guess there must have been ten thousand of them. They had us stopped cold."

The prospects for any advance looked bleak. "The way it looks we might as well pack up and go home," Sergeant Culin's tank-driver said.

But the sergeant walked around his tank, studying it. Then he looked up, squinting through the sunlit haze, at a steeple six miles away. That was St. Lo, where the Nazis had established their Chief Communications Center. Six miles: and all that lay between were the rolling fields—and those blankety-blank hedgerows. "The trouble is," Sergeant Culin said to the driver, "we've been ramming our tanks against them like billygoats." He

Aerial view of the Unknown Soldier's Monument.

patted the nose of the tank. "Look at the shape. Nothing sharp about this final drive. What happens when we're tearing along and bust into a hedgerow?"

"We bounce off," the driver said. "Or get hung up the way poor Dobson did."

"Right. But maybe, if we put something *sharp* in front—something that'll cut in—"

"You've got something there, Sarge," the driver said. "Why not talk it over with the major?"

Sergeant Culin did. And the major said thoughtfully, "Something sharp? Like a knife-blade?"

"No, sir," said Culin. "More like a fork. The contraption I've got in mind would bite into the hedge, loosen those roots from the dirt—maybe tear a hole right through them."

"It's worth a try." Ordinarily, his next step would have been to order the maintenance men to prepare a blueprint. But that would mean miles of red tape, and the idea might even have to go all the way to Washington for consideration and approval. All of which would take time; and in this war you were either quick or you were dead. "Culin," he said, "you want to try making one of those forks? Then hop to it!"

"But," as Sergeant Culin said later, "I needed heavy metal to make that fork—big tough hunks of steel—and there wasn't anything like it lying around in this man's army. I tried every ordnance depot in Normandy. Nothing. Then I figured maybe I could get the metal off one of our dead tanks.

"So, Gus and I drove out one night to where we could see the hulk of a damaged M5. We started to climb out, intending to hook a cable onto it and drag it away. Then we heard a plane coming toward us, fast and low. Was it one of ours, or a Nazi? We didn't wait to find out. We dove back into the hatch, and Gus slammed down on the gas until we were hidden under some trees. And just in time. That plane swooped down and started firing, but the funny thing was, he wasn't firing at us."

"Well, will you look at that!" Gus laughed. "He's hammering that dead M5 out there! He thinks it's *us*."

"Looks like we won't be able to pick up that tank tonight," Sergeant Culin said.

"Them Germans, they sure don't want us to win this war." This was Gus's favorite remark.

"They never did figure we'd get *this* far," Sergeant Culin said. Then he stopped. "*Beaches*. That's it, Gus! They never figured we'd get this far into Normandy. Why? Because they knew we'd never get past the beaches—because fifty yards off every beach, they'd planted the bottom with sharp metal spikes to rip our landing-craft to pieces. Gus, there's our *fork*, ready-made for us! All we've got to do is go down and get it."

Sergeant Culin had found the "contraption" he'd been searching for. But, beneath the water, the spikes were embedded in concrete blocks the size of a room. Before the metal could be brought up, it was necessary to blow the blocks apart. This the tank maintenance men did, and a week later Sergeant Culin was ready to run the first test.

When the signal was given, the test-tank —spikes welded to its face and braced with a steel bar—rumbled forward, picked up speed and charged toward the hedgerow. The sawtooth forks ripped up a whole section of the hedge and the tank roared through, leaving a huge open gap behind it.

Ten days later, the Battle of the Hedgerows came to an end. On the morning of July 25, a thousand American tanks, every last one of them equipped with Sgt. Curtis Culin's hedgerow forks, cut through the barrier of green death and captured St. Lo. Normandy was open. Thanks to an enlisted man's Yankee ingenuity, our armed forces had taken a gigantic step toward winning World War II.

FROM FAILURE TO SUCCESS IN THREE SAD YEARS

(ULYSSES SIMPSON GRANT)

At thirty-eight he was a miserable failure —he had proved inadequate at everything he had tried—farming, auctioneering, bill-collecting. He had been cashiered out of the U.S. Army as a drunkard. He was broke and had to come to his father for help, had to take a job in his father's store to make a meager living for his family.

Yet, within less than five years, he became one of the most renowned men in the world, one of the great heroes of American history. As commander of the Union forces he was the winning general of the Civil War, and his popularity was such that the people of the United States twice accorded him their highest honor, election to the Presidency of the United States. His career is an inspiration to all who have a hard row to hoe, to all who are "down" but will not give up and go "out."

His name, of course, was Ulysses Simpson Grant. Well, not exactly. He was christened Hiram Ulysses Grant, but the Congressman who appointed him to the U.S. Military Academy somehow made an error and entered his name as Ulysses Simpson Grant and that became his name, officially. At the Point, however, his friends called him Sam.

He was only eighteen when he was graduated from West Point, and great things were expected of the likable red-haired young man. He made good friends, and just before the Mexican War he became engaged to Julia Dent, sister of his friend Frederick Dent.

Grant leans on General Meade's shoulder, in a field conference of his staff. Bethesda Church, Virginia, 1864.

106

Photograph by Mathew Brady.

Second Lieutenant Sam Grant distinguished himself in that war with Mexico and was cited twice and brevetted to first lieutenant and then to captain. When the war was over he married Julia Dent, and his future in the Army seemed brighter than ever.

The brightneses began to dim when Grant was ordered to California. That meant separation for the newlyweds and loneliness for Sam Grant. He sought solace in drinking and more drinking, and before he found out that he was chasing an illusion, he was forced to resign from the Army.

That was in 1854. He returned to his family in St. Louis and tried to work his farm near that city. It wasn't good land, and though he labored almost incessantly on the acres he called Hardscrabble Farm, no living for him and his family was to be made from it.

Nothing he tried met with success, and finally he had to go once again for help to his father, Jesse, who gave him one more chance to make good, as a clerk in his leather store, the J. R. Grant Leather and Hardware Store in Galena, Illinois.

And so, one April day in 1860, when the steamer *Itasca* arrived in Galena, a middle-aged ex-soldier, not looking much like a West Pointer, helped his wife and four children down the gangplank. In Galena, the ex-soldier attended to his job and his family but otherwise kept pretty much to himself until the young men of Galena, with war in the air, organized a volunteer troop. Then the veteran was called upon to drill them.

Ten days after Fort Sumter fell, the Jo Daviess Guards, the Galena volunteer troop, left for Springfield. They reported to Governor Yates and Grant was given a commission as colonel of the 21st Infantry. The tide of fortune had turned for Hiram Ulysses Simpson Sam Grant.

The North needed trained and experienced officers, and soon Lincoln called Grant to Washington and gave him a command. Grant was daring and vigorous. At first the untrained men under him suffered heavy losses. Nevertheless, they had faith in him as a skilled officer who was always mindful of his men. He saw that they were trained properly and he never asked a man to do what he couldn't do himself.

In 1862 Grant captured Fort Henry and Fort Donelson. In 1863 came his great victory at Vicksburg, establishing him as one of the Union's superior generals.

Elsewhere in the war, affairs were going badly for the Union forces and in March, 1864, after Grant's victory at Chattanooga, Lincoln made him commander of all the Union forces. In little over a year, General Grant succeeded in destroying the main armies of the Confederacy. On April 9, 1865, he accepted Lee's surrender at Appomattox and sealed the victory of the Union. Only five years after U. S. Grant, a dejected failure, took a $600-a-year job in his father's store, he was the nation's hero.

Grant's career is probably the most dramatic demonstration in our history of the truths that there's nothing permanent about failure and that it's never too late to succeed.

RETREAT TO VICTORY

(SAM HOUSTON)

"I am besieged by Mexican troops. Santa Anna demands our surrender; otherwise our troops will be put to the sword. I call upon you in the name of liberty, patriotism and everything dear to Americans to come to our aid with dispatch."

So read the alarming message from Colonel Travis. At the Alamo, a Spanish Franciscan mission converted to a fort, the defenders numbered fewer than two hundred. Santa Anna was said to have well over seven thousand men behind him. Against such odds, how long could the Alamo hold out?

The message was the more alarming be-cause it had been on the way for ten days before it reached the settlement on the banks of the Brazos River. Here, a convention of American settlers had been in session for the past two weeks. Much had been accomplished. Texas had been declared a free and sovereign republic, independent of Mexican rule.

The great step had been taken, but all those who had voted for it were aware of the possible grave consequences of this act. The Mexican Republic and its President, Santa Anna, would declare them traitors and rebels, to be executed if captured. Now, with this news from the Alamo, what the

Sam Houston in the early fifties. Photograph by Mathew Brady.

Texans had expected had come, and sooner than they wished.

"I move this convention be adjourned immediately," a representative shouted. "We must arm and march to the aid of the Alamo!"

"Gentlemen!" Sam Houston called, holding up a hand to silence the cheering and the battle cries that rose from the convention floor and thundered against the rafters. "Gentlemen! Your attention, please!"

A tall man whose great dignity made him look even taller than his six feet two, Sam Houston stood quietly, waiting for the cheers to subside. Soldier, ex-Congressman, ex-Governor of Tennessee, he had been sent to troubled Texas by his friend Andrew Jackson, President of the United States.

"Sam," President Jackson had told him, "Texas should belong to the Union, not Mexico. And there are bigger things at stake than just Texas—the whole Southwest. You'll find Steve Austin at the head

of things out there. A good man, maybe too good to be dealing with that Mexican Santa Anna. You're a fighting man, Sam. Go on out and help 'em."

So Houston had come to Texas to aid in its fight for freedom, and the convention had just reaffirmed his position as General of the Texas armed forces.

"I know how you feel," he told the convention. "But this is not the time to go off half-cocked. Your place is here, gentlemen. Mine is to find an army. And, God willing, we'll save the Alamo!"

Brave words, spoken by a man of courage. But as he rode toward the Alamo, Sam Houston was doubtful. Behind him rode four hundred men. As volunteers flocked to join him, the number increased to five hundred—still a pitifully small force to put against Santa Anna's thousands. What had happened in the ten days it took that message to arrive? The Alamo, a roofless, crumbling structure, was a poor place to defend. Colonel Travis was there, and Davy Crockett, and Jim Bowie—all good fighters. Yet how could even such men prevail against Santa Anna's might? Only a miracle could have kept the defenders alive.

Houston's fears were confirmed. Several miles before his forces reached the Alamo, his scouts came upon a woman riding furiously toward them on horseback. Her eyes still showed the horror through which she had lived.

"Too late," she told Houston. "Colonel Travis—Crockett—all the men—killed. Butchered. We stood them off for six days. Then they swarmed over the wall. . . . Only the women and children were spared. And Santa Anna—he put me on this horse—sent me to tell you. 'Remember the Alamo,' he said."

"We'll remember it," Sam Houston said grimly. "And Santa Anna will never forget it."

That night, the Texans ate their rations cold. No fires burned in the silent camp, lest sparks or flames be seen by Santa

The Alamo.

Anna's scouts.

One or two of the officers were for giving up the struggle. "If we fight," Major Smith said, "Santa Anna will wipe us out, General. We don't stand a chance."

"Keep up that kind of talk," Houston said, "and I'll break you down to a private, Major."

"But how can five hundred men drive off seven thousand?"

"The Mexicans haven't trapped us yet. And Texas is a powerful big place to fight in, Major."

Big talk, the major thought to himself. Mighty big talk. And later, when a Mexican spy was dragged into camp, that's just what it appeared—big talk and nothing more.

"Just picked up a rattlesnake wiggling into camp," said Baker, the scout. He hauled the Mexican up to General Houston. "Come on, speak up, feller. You tell the general what you just told me."

The Mexican stammered, "Santa Anna— he come this way—four divisions—he will kill you all—he is right behind you—"

"Shall I hang him or shoot him, sir?" Baker asked.

"No hurry," Houston said. And he turned to Major Smith. "It appears you were right, Major. It's no use. We can't fight seven thousand. We'd better get out of here, make for the border before it's too late."

"Now that makes sense," Major Smith agreed.

Baker, the scout, asked, "What do we do with this Mexican spy?"

"Kick him out of camp," Houston said.

"Yes, sir, but—"

"Kick him out of camp," Houston repeated wildly, "before I up and change my mind and have him strung up!"

Astonished, Baker obeyed the order.

Major Smith said nervously, "Well, General, I'll give the command to break camp. With that Mexican loose, we'd better light out of here quick."

"Major, do I look insane?"

"What, sir?"

"We're going to retreat. And when that spy tells Santa Anna—that's what I spared him for, Major—when he tells Santa Anna, he'll chase after us. We'll give him a run, a run he'll never forget. And then, when and where he least expects it, we'll strike!"

So the Texans beat a sham retreat, with Santa Anna's thousands hot on their trail. "Victory is certain!" Sam Houston said to his men. "Remember the Alamo!" But, as he backed them up to the border, many grew fearful and deserted his ranks. Others thought it was not a sham retreat, but a disgraceful flight. Among the officers murmurs rose, and demands for explanations. "If those explanations aren't satisfactory, General Houston must go," said the officers. "Either we fight," they said, "or disband and run for safety over the border, as some of the volunteers are doing."

But Houston gave no other explanations. "Retreat," he said, "and more retreat, until our moment comes."

Retreat and more retreat, and then the moment came. On the thirty-eighth day, Sam Houston gave the command to halt. Santa Anna had made camp at the San Jacinto River. "Only one of his four divisions is with him," said Houston. "He's cocky. He thinks we're beat, boys. He thinks it's only a matter of time before he mops us up. He's so cocky that at three o'clock he'll be taking his afternoon nap. And his men will take their siesta, too. We'll catch 'em asleep."

And that's how it was done. Before the Mexicans could rouse themselves from their afternoon siesta, the Texans were upon them. Santa Anna himself was captured, wearing a blue smock and red carpet-slippers. With his capture, the Mexican Army was vanquished. It rode off Texas soil and never returned.

Thus was Texas freed—by a general who ran away.

From a painting by C. Y. Turner.

WATER GIRL

(MOLLY PITCHER)

Was Molly Pitcher, a heroine of the Revolutionary War, a legendary character, or was she a real person? For a long time historians could not say for sure, but her life has now been carefully traced and here is this brave girl's story.

Most people know her only as the heroine of the Battle of Monmouth, which was fought on June 28, 1778, between the troops of General Washington and the British forces under General Clinton. They know that when her husband, one of Washing-

ton's artillerymen, was wounded, she took his place at his gun and kept the piece firing until victory was won. But they know very little else about her.

Molly was born in Carlisle, Pennsylvania, the daughter of John Ludwig of that village, who christened her Mary. While she was working as a housemaid in the home of Squire William Irvine she met and married John Hays, who had a barbershop across the way from her employer's home. Soon after their marriage the Revolutionary War broke out. Young John Hays joined the Army as a private under the command of Mary's former employer, now General Irvine. His regiment spent the terrible winter of 1777–78 with General Washington at Valley Forge.

Mary went back to work in the Irvine household. The news from Valley Forge was discouraging, and Mary was deeply concerned about how her husband was faring. She heard that the troops at Valley Forge were without proper food, clothing or shelter and that nothing was being done to supply them. Finally, she could stand it no longer.

She went to Mrs. Irvine and burst into tears. "Here we are in a warm house and well fed, while poor John goes hungry and cold in that camp. I must go to him."

"But how could you make the journey, child?" asked Mrs. Irvine. "You know, it's more than a hundred miles over the mountains. Not even supply wagons can get through."

"I'm strong," was Mary's reply. "If you'll lend me a rifle I can make it, Mrs. Irvine, on foot if need be."

And make it she did. After sixteen days of trudging through snow and cold, sometimes through drifts four feet high, she arrived at Valley Forge. Like many other wives of soldiers of that period, she joined her husband in the Army and made herself useful, cooking and washing. Indeed, one wonders what would have happened to Washington's men during that crucial winter if these valiant women had not been there to bolster up their husbands' morale.

Then came the summer of 1778, one of the hottest on record. Mary was right at the front with her husband's artillery company. It was on the scorching day of June 28 that she was to win her lasting nickname.

General Clinton's troops attacked with a heavy artillery barrage. The Americans replied with their own cannon, John Hays' company giving a good account of themselves right at the point of the heaviest fighting. But the heat was so intense and the battle so fierce that many soldiers fainted and many were incapacitated by thirst.

Without saying a word to her husband Mary seized a pitcher and went to fetch water from a spring not far from the front lines.

She hurried back to her husband's company, where John was busy keeping the guns firing. All day this brave girl kept bringing water to the soldiers. Above the din of battle could be heard cries of "Molly!" "More water!" "Over here!"

"Coming," she would call back. "Here, hold out your cup. Take a drink, soldier. Never mind the cup, you can drink out of the pitcher." And off she would go to another thirsty soldier. All day long she raced back and forth with the precious water.

"Molly—pitcher—over here next," the soldiers kept calling. And so she won a new name on the battlefield—Molly Pitcher.

"Coming as soon as I can, soldier," was her cheerful reply. So it went all through the fighting that day. "Molly, pitcher." "Molly!" "Over here, Molly, pitcher."

On one of her return trips from the spring Molly was terrified to see her husband fall wounded. She quickly bound up the wound with the hem of her petticoat. Then, since there was no one left to load his cannon, she took his place. She knew how to load the gun as well as any man, and she kept it firing during the rest of the battle.

When night fell, with victory assured for the Americans, Molly was at last able to rest and attend to her wounded husband's needs. The next day, to her surprise, she was called up to be decorated for her valor by General Washington himself, in front of all the assembled troops. Her husband lay nearby on a cot which had been fetched in order that he might watch the ceremony.

Molly Pitcher at the Battle of Monmouth.

After the Battle of Monmouth, one of the most decisive of the Revolution, Mary returned to Carlisle with her husband. There he died several years later. After that she married one of his fellow soldiers, a man named McCauley. She was to outlive him also.

Many years later her native state of Pennsylvania passed a special act of the legislature granting her financial aid for the rest of her life for her services to the Revolutionary cause.

Memorials have been erected in honor of Molly Pitcher at Carlisle and at Monmouth Battlefield in New Jersey. Real gratitude for her deeds, however, has been best expressed in the minds and hearts of those Americans who have also made courageous sacrifices for their country in time of need, emulating heroic Molly Pitcher.

"OUR COUNTRY, RIGHT OR WRONG"

(STEPHEN DECATUR)

It was a strange place for the American flag to be flying, outside a grim prison in Tripoli. The "Stars and Stripes" hung limply in the blaze of African sunlight. At the base of the flagpole stood a prison guard, an axe in his hands, his eyes on his ruler, who stood a few yards away.

The sultan, or bashaw, of Tripoli in that year of 1801 was looking at someone else, a man dressed in the uniform of the American Navy. The uniform was dirty and disheveled, as if it had been slept in for many weeks, as indeed it had. Since the capture of his ship by the bashaw's navy, Captain Bainbridge had been held in a dungeon cut deep in the rock. And now, though he stood erect, the captain's face was haggard.

"When the flagpole falls," the sultan informed him, "your country and mine, Captain, will be at war." Still smiling, he raised his hand, giving the signal for the guard to begin chopping.

The first stroke of the axe cut deep in the pole, shaking it. Atop the pole, the cloth fluttered, its fifteen stars agleam in the sunlight. A minute later, those stars no longer gleamed. Beneath the fallen flagpole, the American flag lay crumpled in the dust. And the sultan, his humor satisfied, ordered Captain Bainbridge returned to his dungeon.

The sultan felt he could afford to laugh. From every ship that sailed the Mediterranean along the North African coast, his fleet extracted tribute. "Oh, no," the sultan demurred. "Not tribute. Merely a fee. Our navy, you see, provides protection for your merchantmen in the Mediterranean. Without our help, your ships would be the prey of those terrible Barbary pirates."

But the other nations knew the sultan to be the greatest pirate of them all. English, French, Spanish or Dutch might be angered by this payment of tribute, but they felt that for the time being, at least, they could afford it. Especially since the sultan acted on the principle: "The weaker the state, the higher the tribute." Who were these puny fifteen United States to protest against so reasonable an arrangement? Yet protest they did. And to demonstrate that protest they had boldly sailed their tiny fleet into Mediterranean waters.

"These Yankees," he marveled, "are really, you know, quite mad. Already we have captured their flagship, the *Philadelphia*, with its Captain Bainbridge. But would you believe it? Their ships continue to skulk about in our waters. One might almost imagine they *desire* us to blow them to the bottom of the sea, and impress their crews as slaves. Not that one can make much profit on *that* transaction. They make such poor slaves, one might as well kill them at once. And this fellow, this Captain Bainbridge, do you know what he said to me as the flagpole fell? 'Freedom,' he said, 'has a peculiar toughness, Your Highness. It lends the state a great strength.' Imagine that, if you will!"

Had he been able to observe Captain Bainbridge at that moment, the sultan would have laughed even louder. In his foul prison cell, in almost total darkness, Bainbridge was writing a message, using lemon juice for ink. And a short time later that note, smuggled out by a friend in the Danish consulate, found its way into the hands of the commander of the American fleet, Commodore Preble.

"Invisible ink?" Lieutenant Decatur inquired.

"No, lemon juice," Commodore Preble replied, passing him the note. "I held it

Stephen Decatur

117

over a lamp, to bring out the writing."

Decatur read the message aloud: " 'Implore . . . you . . . to send . . . in . . . a party . . . to burn . . . my ship.' "

Commodore Preble said, "Bainbridge ran the *Philadelphia* aground on an uncharted reef. It's in the harbor, under the guns of the Tripolitan shore batteries. And she's well guarded—at least two hundred of the enemy aboard, with thirty-six of our own cannon ready to be used against us. What Bainbridge asks us to do is impossible."

"Impossible, sir?"

"Suicide."

"That ship I captured a few weeks ago," Decatur said. "The Tripolitan ketch, the *Mastico*. Remember, sir?"

"Well, what about it?"

"With a band of picked marines, sir, perhaps I could slip her into the harbor, tie onto the *Philadelphia* and set her afire, before the guards knew what was going on."

Commodore Preble tried not to look eager. "Nonsense, Mister Decatur! You've never been inside that harbor."

"But I have a pilot to conduct me, sir, a Sicilian who knows the waters hereabouts."

"Nonsense," the commodore repeated. But, he thought, tonight the moon will be in the first quarter and if the weather continues this way, he'd have the advantage of clouds.

That night, with a hundred volunteers—marines and sailors of the American fleet—Lieutenant Decatur set out to wipe the mocking smile off the face of the sultan of Tripoli. Before dawn he had returned.

"Lieutenant Decatur reporting, Commodore."

"The *Philadelphia?*"

"Destroyed, sir."

"And your own losses, Lieutenant?"

"One man slightly wounded, sir. The shore batteries opened up and put a cannonball through the mainsail of the ketch.

Otherwise, we're quite in order."

"You've earned yourself a rest. My compliments to your men. You may inform them they will be given double rations of grog."

"If you'll excuse me, sir," Decatur said, "I don't believe we have time for that rest. In Tripoli, they won't believe we did this job with only one ketch. They know our ships are standing out here. They'll be after us for sure."

Commodore Preble nodded. "They outnumber us. We don't stand much chance, do we, Mr. Decatur, unless we make a run for it?"

"I have an idea, sir."

"Another one of your wild ideas? The bashaw believes we Americans are mad, and the more I look at you fellows of this younger generation, the more I'm inclined to agree with His Thieving Highness."

"A simple stratagem," Decatur said. "It would cost us only one ship. But it might mean disposing of the whole pirate fleet."

"God help me!" the Commodore cried. "The bashaw *is* right! Mister Decatur, isn't *one* miracle a night enough for you?"

Later that day, under a broiling Mediterranean sun, a ship sailed into the harbor of Tripoli. It flew the British colors, but to the Tripolitan port inspector who sailed out to meet it, it appeared suspiciously like an American frigate.

"Ship ahoy!" one of the inspector's men shouted. "What . . . ship . . . are . . . you?"

"*Royal Arms* . . . British merchantman . . . cargo of cotton. . . ."

The Tripolitan inspector climbed aboard warily. But, as he glanced around, his breathing came more easily. No cannon on deck, no armament at all. And a half-dozen sailors peacefully at work. The inspector smiled. "A thousand pardons for this intrusion, sir. We were assailed with the notion that this might be an American ship. A foolish error, eh?"

"Now that you have realized your mistake," Stephen Decatur said stiffly, "per-

Stephen Decatur in a hand-to-hand fight at Tripoli.

haps you will be good enough to—"

"Cotton, did you say? A cargo of cotton?"

"From Liverpool," Decatur said impatiently, his face still burning with anger. "You wish to see our papers? Sir, this is a humiliation that will not be lightly thought of by the British Crown, I can assure you—"

"But no!" the inspector cried. "I do not plan to inspect the cargo. I am here simply to escort you safely into the harbor. A formality, you understand." He nodded toward the sailors on deck. "These men—they are all of your crew? It seems so small a crew for the long voyage from Liverpool."

"One watch," Decatur explained irritably. "The others are below—"

"Just so, just so," the inspector said hastily. "You must forgive my inquisitiveness, Captain. The Americans, you understand. They are giving us trouble. They are proving most stubborn about paying the necessary fees and duties, you see, and—"

"We are in the harbor lanes, sir," a seaman called to Decatur.

Shading his eyes against the sun, Decatur squinted across the water toward a nearby fleet of ships. "The sultan's navy?"

"The biggest part of it, yes," the inspector said proudly. "We like to keep the lower harbor clear for merchantmen, like yourself, ships that pay the fee—"

"Of course," Decatur said. Then he called out: "Three points to leeward!"

"But no!" the inspector cried, touching Decatur's arm. "That will carry you into the midst of the fleet!"

"Exactly," Decatur agreed. Raising his voice again, he cried, "All hands, man the lifeboats! Lash the wheel! And Mister Morris!"

From one of the hatches, a seaman answered, "Ready on the fuse, sir!"

"Light it!" Decatur called. "And let's get out of here!"

A minute later, the bewildered port inspector found himself sitting in a lifeboat, surrounded by a crew of sailors rowing frantically away from an abandoned ship. "But, Captain!" he shouted. "What ghastly joke is this?"

"A joke your precious sultan won't enjoy." Decatur laughed. "Row harder, boys! We're almost clear now!"

Behind them, the abandoned frigate drifted lazily into the midst of the sultan's fleet, in her hold not a cargo of cotton, but a cargo of gunpowder, with a lighted fuse attached. With a burst of flames, the frigate exploded.

No, it was not a joke for the sultan to enjoy. For, in that explosion, most of his fleet was destroyed. Nor, later, did the sultan relish having to pay two hundred thousand dollars worth of indemnities, or being ordered to release all American prisoners from his prisons. Least of all did he enjoy signing the treaty that guaranteed his permanent respect to the honor and integrity of the United States. Of course, he had no intention of abiding by that treaty. The Americans were mad, quite mad if they thought he would. He rebuilt his fleet and went into the tribute-exacting business once again.

It was not until 1815 that Stephen Decatur, in command of a larger and more impressive United States Navy, finally convinced him of the error of his ways.

On the medal: THE·GIFT / OF / PEOPLE / UNITED / TO·THE / AND·MEN / ASIATIC / UNDER·THE / OF·COM / GEORGE / THE / OF·THE / STATES / OFFICERS / OF·THE / SQUADRON / COMMAND / MODORE / DEWEY / 1899

THE VICTORIES AT MANILA BAY

(GEORGE DEWEY)

When Commodore George Dewey stepped aboard the *Gaelic* at San Francisco, his orders were: "Proceed to Japan and take command of the United States Asiatic Squadron."

This was in December of 1897. America was not then reckoned a major world power. Compared with the navies of other nations, her fleets were unimpressive.

"Two years away from home," one of Dewey's lieutenants mourned. "And eight thousand miles. We'll miss all the excitement—if we do go to war with Spain. The major part of the Spanish fleet is in the Caribbean. There's not likely to be much ac-

tion out here in the Pacific."

Commodore Dewey's comment was, "You'll get your excitement, Lieutenant. The first round will be fought in the Philippines. That's not the general opinion in the Navy, of course, but it's *my* opinion—and Theodore Roosevelt's."

The new year of 1898 brought an insurrection in Cuba and an uprising against Spanish rule in the Philippines. War between Spain and America seemed even more imminent. Now, if the cannons roared, their flames might light the waters of both oceans.

That was in the mind of the German

Prince Henry when he said, "Be seated, gentlemen, please. The glasses are being refilled."

The scene was the harbor of Hong Kong, aboard the battleship *Deutschland*, where Commodore Dewey was attending a dinner given by the Imperial German Asiatic Squadron. Toasts were being made to the countries represented by the various officers present. The British anthem had just been played.

Prince Henry turned to Commodore Dewey. "Do you expect, Commodore, that you Americans will beat these Spaniards?"

"I wasn't aware," Dewey said guardedly, "that there was a state of war between the Spaniards and ourselves."

"But soon, eh?" Prince Henry said. "And when it comes, what will you do, Commodore?"

"Move into Manila Bay. And clean out the Spanish fleet in twenty-four hours."

Prince Henry laughed. "But the Bay is heavily mined."

"So I have heard," said Dewey. "But an admiral under whom I once had the honor to serve, once said, 'Damn the torpedoes, full speed ahead!'"

The German prince laughed again, then rose to his feet. The stewards had brought brimming champagne glasses, and now Prince Henry lifted his. "Gentlemen, I propose another toast—to the Czar of Russia. . . ."

"Your Highness!" Commodore Dewey protested. "I intend no disrespect to the ruler of Russia, but, in accordance with diplomatic custom, I believe I outrank the commander of the Russian fleet. Therefore, the first toast—"

Prince Henry smiled, but his eyes were cold. "Of course. I was confused. Gentlemen—a toast—to the President of the United States."

The assembled officers drank.

"And now," Prince Henry nodded to the band, "the national anthem of the United States."

But, as the ship's band played, Dewey's jaw tightened. His face flushed with anger; he strode from the dining room, followed by his officers.

The German band had played "Hail, Columbia," not "The Star-Spangled Banner." There could be no doubt of it; a direct insult to the United States had been intended. This indicated, further, that if the United States went to war with Spain, the Germans would work for the defeat of the American Asiatic fleet.

The day after Dewey received word that hostilities between the United States and Spain had, in fact, broken out, Prince Henry sent a cable to Berlin: "The U.S. fleet sailed this morning for the Philippines. The Philippines are in revolt against Spain, and would be glad to place themselves under protection of a European power, particularly Germany. I await instructions."

Meanwhile, the American fleet plowed on through the South Pacific, led by Dewey's flagship, the *Olympia*. As they neared the Philippines, Dewey gave the order: "Tell Captain Gridley to set his course for Manila Bay."

"We'll arrive after dark, sir," Lieutenant Brumby pointed out. "And then—"

"We go straight in."

"But, Commodore, if I may make a suggestion, sir . . ." And when Dewey nodded, he continued, "We don't know these waters, sir, and—"

"We'll take soundings as we go."

"But, sir," Brumby said worriedly, "those minefields! It's said the Bay has the most elaborate set-up of any harbor in the Pacific."

"Those minefields," Dewey said. "Every naval man in the Far East talks about them. All that talk makes me suspect something, Lieutenant Brumby."

"What, sir?"

"Those minefields don't exist."

Midnight—and the hills of Manila loomed in the darkness, close above the

American fleet. Slowly, without lights, the ships pushed deeper into the danger area. Aboard the *Olympia,* the men were tense. In the darkness, the ships of the Asiatic Squadron could collide, ram one another. While below, in the murky water, lay possibly the greatest menace of all . . . silent . . . waiting . . . loaded with death. . . .

"This goin' in without lights is chancy," a sailor murmured. He leaned against the tarpaulin of one of the hatches.

Beside him, another sailor peered upward, seeing Commodore Dewey silhouetted on the bridge. "I think the skipper's plenty worried about those minefields, too."

"Any second now, and boom—" The first sailor shivered. Then he stopped talking. For Dewey's voice called out quietly from aloft, "It might interest you men to know that I'm going below—for a nap. We passed those so-called minefields ten minutes ago."

That morning, at dawn, May 1, 1898, Dewey gave the instructions heard round the world: "You may fire when ready, Gridley." And almost instantly the American guns roared. Taken unawares, the Spanish ships went down—the *Reina Christina,* the *Isla de Cuba,* the *Castilla,* the *Isla de Luzon*—one by one, eight in all. By noon all were destroyed.

Afterward, Dewey blockaded the port of Manila. No ship, whatever her nationality, could enter or depart without his permission.

Dewey Triumphal Arch "In Greeting To Our Admiral."

Then something happened that the calm skipper, now promoted to Admiral, had been expecting.

"I don't like the smell of it," Captain Gridley said one night. Standing beside Dewey on the bridge, he squinted across the moonlit waters of the Bay. To port, the *Deutschland* lay at anchor. Alongside, uncomfortably close, were the *Kaiserin Augusta*, the *Cormorant*, the *Princess Wilhelm*, the *Kaiser* and half a dozen other ships of the German Asiatic Squadron. "Looks like the whole bloomin' lot of 'em, sir. And they outgun us two to one."

"We are not at war with Germany," Dewey said grimly.

"You'd think we were, the way they've been disregarding the blockade—ignoring our signals—sending out those searchlight beams at night—encouraging the enemy—"

"We'll stop all that," Dewey said.

"But when, sir?"

His answer came a few minutes later. In the darkness, off the port bow, a small craft came racing. To Captain Gridley it appeared to be a torpedo boat. He ordered the searchlights played on it. "Pick up that launch to port!"

"Hail them!" Dewey ordered.

A moment later, Lieutenant Grumby said, "They don't answer, sir. And she's headed this way full speed!"

"Put a shot across her bow!"

A six-pound cannon barked, but the launch kept coming. The six-pounder barked again—this time to hit. The shot missed, but the launch stopped. One of its crew waved the German flag. When the launch pulled up alongside the *Olympia*, it was Admiral von Dietrich who climbed aboard.

"We thought you might be a Spanish torpedo boat," Dewey explained. "You should have shown your colors, Admiral."

Von Dietrich was enraged. "I await your apologies for this incident and a number of other matters. You have stopped and boarded all neutral vessels entering the Bay. You—"

"It is not only my right," said Dewey, "but my duty."

"You have assigned us positions in the harbor that prevent our maneuvering—"

"You are not supposed to maneuver, sir."

"You prevent my launches from communicating with the Imperial German Consul at Manila. You turn back my transport when all I wish is for a few German soldiers to land at Manila and stretch their legs in a harmless drill. And now, you add to these outrages by firing on myself, in my own launch, which carries not even one machine gun."

"Tell me," Dewey said. "Does Your Excellency know it is my fleet and not his which is blockading this port?"

"Of course."

"And is Your Excellency aware that he has no rights here whatsoever, except such as I choose to allow? And does Your Excellency realize he *cannot* move, he *cannot* maneuver, he *cannot* communicate except by my express permission? Tell me, has the Imperial German government decided to make war on the United States? Is that her intention?" His voice rose to a shout. "Do you want war with the United States? You are very near it, sir. And you can have it! You can have it as soon as you like!"

At dawn the next morning, shielding his eyes from the glare of the rising sun, Dewey watched as the German ships sailed off and disappeared beyond the horizon.

"Let me congratulate you, sir," Captain Gridley said. "They're skulking off with their tails between their legs. I don't imagine we'll see them for a long while to come."

"Perhaps," George Dewey said. "But eventually we will be seeing them again, Captain. And the United States will need a bigger Navy than this one when we do."

Admiral Dewey had a way of calling his shots.

FATHER OF THE AMERICAN NAVY

(JOHN PAUL JONES)

At first, his name was simply John Paul. Born in Scotland in 1747, he went to sea as a cabin-boy at the age of twelve and by the time he was nineteen he was captain of his own ship. In 1773, he touched at the port of Tobago in the West Indies. As his ship lay at anchor, he learned that one of the sailors was urging other members of the crew to mutiny. Paul called this sailor before him, but his attempt to reason with him failed. The sailor, in a rage, leaped across the cabin with his knife-blade flashing, and Paul was forced to draw his sword. In the fight that ensued Paul killed the sailor.

Even though Captain Paul had slain the sailor in self-defense, and even though the British Navy permitted no leniency in the punishment of mutineers, the captain's friends urged him to take flight.

"You have too many enemies in high places," said one. "You rose to a captaincy too rapidly and you have been too head-strong and obstinate in your dealings with the stick-in-the-muds in London. If you go on trial charged with murder, your enemies will do their best to convict you and then let you rot in jail."

Several days later, a ship out of the West Indies stopped at Edenton, North Carolina, to unload some cargo belonging to Wylie Jones, a local planter. Darkness had fallen before the ship could be maneuvered alongside the pier. As Jones went aboard to talk with the captain, he was almost knocked off his feet by a young man hastily leaving the ship. The young man, in fact, seemed to reach instinctively for his pistol, then laughed lightly and said, "I'm sorry, sir."

Jones watched the young man go off down the dock in the direction of the lights from the tavern.

"Who is he?" Jones asked the captai[n]

"I don't really know," said the captai[n] "He calls himself Smith and he came [o]n at Tobago. But he seems to know ever[y]thing there is to know about ships."

The stranger's knowledge of shippi[ng] interested Wylie Jones. He finished h[is] business with the captain as quickly as [he] could and went to seek out the strang[er] in the tavern. He found the young m[an] sitting in the darkest corner, eati[ng] supper.

"I'm Wylie Jones," the planter intr[o]duced himself, "and I hear you kn[ow] everything there is to know about shi[p]ping. That interests me a great deal, if [it's] true."

"I'm John Paul," said the stranger, "a[nd] I *do* know something about shipping."

"You told the captain your name w[as] Smith," said Jones. "Tell me, Mr. Pa[ul], what happened in Tobago."

John liked the directness of the m[an] and invited him to sit down. Before [the] evening was over, he had told Wylie [his] story, and Wylie, in turn, had been dra[wn] out about his plantation affairs and ab[out] his plans for the future in the Colon[ies] particularly plans for a navy. In their [dis]cussion Jones kept returning to the ru[mor] that a revolt was brewing.

"Are you testing my opinion?" J[ohn] Paul asked the planter. "Let me tell [you] that I don't like this talk about fight[ing] against the Crown. It's treason, [you] know!"

"Our quarrel is not with England," s[aid] Wylie. "Our quarrel is with a small gr[oup] in power who won't grant us the ri[ghts] of free men. But enough of this. You m[ust] come out to my plantation with me [and] be my guest. You will be welcome th[ere] until you have made your new plans."

126

John Paul stayed on at the Jones's plantation for several months, and during this time Jones tried to impart to him a sense of the American spirit.

"A new, free spirit," he described it, "and the future of this country depends on its unhampered development. The size and resources of this country are just not made to wait on the pleasure and dis-pleasure of the King's ignorant ministers."

One evening both John Paul and Wylie Jones were attending a ball at the Reynolds' plantation in Virginia.

"That young protégé of yours, Wylie, is quite a handsome lad," observed Reynolds.

"Yes, and he'd make a fine captain in the navy," said Wylie pointedly.

In the midst of the festivities, a courier arrived with a letter for Reynolds. The moment he had finished reading it, Reynolds stopped the music and asked all the men to step into the library with him.

"Gentlemen," said Reynolds, crumpling the letter in his fist, "two days ago, some hot-headed fools destroyed a cargo of tea, dumped it overboard into Boston Harbor. I ask you, is this not rebellion?"

"Not necessarily," said Wylie. "Let us consider what prompted this action."

"That tea belonged to His Majesty," said Reynolds. "It was destined for the Colonies—and the duty therefrom to go to the Crown!"

"Duty to the Crown, yes," said Wylie Jones, "but without proper representation of the Colonies!"

"Gentlemen, it's time we renewed our allegiance to the King," said Reynolds. "Fill your glasses with wine, please. And now, gentlemen—to the King!"

Wylie Jones was the only man in the room who did not join in the toast. Everybody stared as he walked away. John Paul, catching up with his friend at the door, pulled him about to look in his face.

"Do you know what you're doing, Wylie?" he asked. "Are you really a traitor?"

"Whatever I am, John, I'm not a hypocrite," said Wylie quietly. "I know absolutely what I'm doing. Good-by for now, John. Think about me and the future of this country, will you? You're a great sailor, and the freedom-loving people of the Colonies have a real need for your services."

For many months, John Paul rode up and down the Atlantic seaboard, trying to comprehend the ferment in the air. "Treason—treason—treason—that's all it is," he kept saying to himself. But gradually a new vision took shape before him.

It was put together out of many little things. There were the words of the tavernkeeper, who had said to him, "It isn't the dying, it's the living that counts, sir— living free in the country that you yourself built." There were the words of the girl at the blacksmith's shop: "I'll have to shoe your horse, sir. My father's off with those that are getting ready to fight. He says we should elect our own government so we can all have a voice in it."

At last, John Paul became convinced of the justice of the Colonial cause. He offered his services to the Continental Navy and was made a lieutenant immediately. Before going to his first assignment he paid a visit to Wylie Jones.

"I knew you would return," said Wylie, "and wearing that naval uniform."

"I don't know what lies ahead for me, Wylie," said John, "but whatever it is, I want you to be part of it. You not only befriended me and gave me a home; you also helped me find a country, a country I can now believe in with all my heart. I want, therefore, to adopt your name. Not just John Paul but John Paul Jones, in the service of the Continental Navy."

In a very short time, the outnumbered poorly-equipped Continental Navy under the brilliant leadership of John Paul Jones was to beat the powerful British Navy at its own game. The news of his daring raids against British shipping and of his victories at sea inspired the fighting Americans and gave them new courage. The battle of his *Bonhomme Richard* against the British *Serapis* is one of the great sea fights of history. The British blockade was broken, and many British ships were captured and added to the American fleet.

When peace finally came, he argued strongly against reducing the fleet and urged Congress to form training academies for future officers. He also recommended that qualified men be sent abroad to study naval policies and tactics. John Paul Jones not only fought a war; he was the architect of America's navy. His contribution to his adopted country was a salute to its future naval forces.

Bonhomme Richard, commanded by John Paul Jones, defeats the British *Serapis*.

PRESIDENT ROBERT E. LEE

"A traitor!" they called him then.

"One of America's best-loved heroes!" they call him now.

He was superintendent of the U.S. Military Academy at West Point in the early 1850's, teaching young Americans the arts of war. Ten years later he gave some of the same young men practical lessons in brilliant generalship as he fought and de-feated them at Richmond, Bull Run, Fredericksburg and Chancellorsville.

He was a devoted American patriot, yet he did his level best to divide and thus destroy the American Union of states. But if you know the kind of man he was, you will understand why now, more than ninety years after the War Between the States, all Americans honor and respect the name of Robert E. Lee.

He fought brilliantly at Gettysburg, but the odds against him were too great and he lost that crucial battle. For two years after the defeat at Gettysburg, the Confederate Army retreated. Short of men and supplies, its position had become hopeless. Finally, General Lee agreed to meet with General Grant at Appomattox. His officers tried to persuade him to disperse the remaining Confederate forces into guerrilla bands. But although Lee knew that he might prolong the war, he no longer believed the Confederacy could win it. He refused to see his men turned into marauders. More sad years would be required for the country to recover from the tragic war that had burned and destroyed the very land over which it was fought.

The wait for Robert E. Lee to emerge from the McLean House at Appomattox seemed to his men like a bad dream. It *was* a bad dream, they felt, when he appeared alone and wearily mounted his horse, Traveler. "Men," he said, "we have fought the war together . . . I have done my best for you as you have for me. You will all be paroled. Officers are to retain their side-arms. Officers and men may keep their horses. You will need them when you get home."

"Don't say it!" cried one of the soldiers. "We'll fight 'em yet."

Lee raised his hand, commanding silence. "My boys, no one of you is defeated! You have fought gallantly and honorably. Our surrender is an honorable one. But now you must go to your homes, as I go to mine, take up again the care of your families, prepare the soil for the future. It will not be easy, but if you face the peace bravely, as you have gone into battle, we shall win a victory after all."

Turning his horse, he rode slowly away, his decision to end the war weighing heavy on his shoulders.

Robert E. Lee returned to find his beloved Virginia countryside looted and burned. People were hungry. There was no work. And after the assassination of President Lincoln, the federals were everywhere, watching, looking for trouble. Lee heard that he himself would soon be tried for treason. But worst of all were the fires of resentment and hatred which still burned in the hearts of his fellow Southerners. He could well understand it, but he knew that as long as they dominated men's thoughts the South would remain a wasteland. Now that the war was over, the young people must turn their backs on the dark days and begin rebuilding.

His own allegiances had been sorely tried during these years. He had not originally been an advocate of secession. In 1861, when the Southern states threatened to secede from the Union, he had been living near Washington, D.C., a colonel in the federal army. President Lincoln had offered him the command of a large army to be sent South in order to enforce federal law. He had replied that he was willing to sacrifice everything for the Union—except his honor. He was a Virginian. He could not take part in an invasion of the Southern states. He had to stand by his own people—his native state—giving to them not only his sword, if need be, but his very life.

Now that the war had been fought—and lost—Lee decided to return to his ruined plantation and set an example by becoming a farmer. He had given the best years of his life to the struggle. He was old and tired now, and, with a charge of treason threatening him, his name was under a cloud. It was up to the younger men, his son's generation, to make the peace work. Yet he soon realized that the young people of the South—as well as the North—the soldiers who went into the Army as boys —had no training for anything but war. This was impressed upon him when he was approached by a group of his former officers. Despite the formal articles of surrender at Appomattox, they were organizing the nucleus of a new fighting force. There were already guerrillas in the Carolinas whom they could join. Nobody was going to make them—the proud sons of the South—accept military occupation!

But Lee refused to join the underground army. Instead, he gave up his idea of farming in order to return to public life as President of Washington College at Lexington, Virginia. When he assumed his post, he found a rundown college damaged by the war. There were no funds and only a handful of students. But it was better than nothing. In time, the enrollment would grow and the education they received would help them in the giant task of Reconstruction.

From all around, people came to talk with President Lee, a paroled prisoner, yet treated with the highest respect. He saw everyone, whether it was a student coming to enroll or not. A young man entered his office one day, saying, "You spoke to me at Chancellorsville, General Lee."

"Of course," answered Lee. "I remember. You wanted a leave and I had to reject it. Well, now you have it. You can go home."

"I've been home," he replied bitterly. "They burnt it to the ground. They took everything. Didn't even leave enough so's I can work the fields."

His former general reminded him that everyone faced hardships. He musn't let them defeat him. There was too much work to be done.

"Oh, I'll find work, General Lee," the youth answered. "But not here. I'm leaving the South. I can't see any reason to stay

131

General Robert E. Lee. Painting by M. S. Nachtreid.

after what's been done to us. I just thought you might want to know—"

Lee shook his head sadly. "No, I don't want to know that. We fought like men. Now, let us accept defeat like men. You ask how we can hold up our heads? By being proud. Go back and rebuild your home. Hew logs and put them together if you must. But go back. And be tolerant. You can't work for Virginia by leaving her."

In reviewing the curriculum of the college he decided that courses such as Latin and Greek could no longer fulfill the expanding needs of his students. They must be given a chance to learn more practical things, like chemistry, commerce, journalism. The young men at Washington College must also learn to assume responsibility before they went out into the world.

Lee also insisted on self-government for the student body. It was not an easy thing to achieve. Students from the North had also enrolled at the college. Every time a new Yankee came on the campus, he found the "unreconstructed" Southerners giving the Rebel yell and waving battle flags. The faculty objected that there was not enough discipline; there must be *certain* rules and regulations. But Lee refused. "We are a democracy here," he said. "My boys are on their honor, learning to live as citizens in the larger democracy of our nation. They will be treated like the gentlemen they are —Northerners *and* Southerners."

But, of course, some outbreaks occurred between the students. "Wouldn't you know it'd be a Yankee'd take the last chair! . . . Go on, take it, y'carpetbagger. You've taken everything else. . . ."

". . . You say it's a ball. I say a strike. And I oughta know. I played against your side all through the siege of Richmond, and you know who won *that* little game. . . ."

Tension mounted until it erupted into open warfare. Lee visited one of the Southern boys in the infirmary where he was taken with cuts and bruises. "You know," he told the youth, "there's a controversy going on in the North. They're bringing strong pressure to bear against us, claiming General Lee is training a new crop of Rebels. I never before felt such an accusation worthy of a reply. Now, I'm beginning to wonder if they might not be right."

Three years after Appomattox, Lee felt that he had succeeded in making his point. The college already had students from all over the United States. After the early struggles which had taken place on the campus, the young men had finally learned how to live together more harmoniously. This achievement might not appear to be remarkable to those who remembered Robert E. Lee as a brilliant general, but to President Lee it meant that the new generation would be better able to guard the hard-won peace. For Lee was a military man who loved peace and hated war.

Near the end of his life, Lee mounted old Traveler, the horse that had once carried him through gunfire and smoke, and rode out into the countryside to a place where he could gaze down on the college he had helped to rebuild. Of course one man could do but little in his own lifetime, but after his death there would be others, he knew, others he had trained well to carry on the work of rebuilding a united nation.

THE PATRIOTS

"Liberty does not consist . . . in mere general declarations of the rights of men. It consists in the translation of those declarations into definite action."

WOODROW WILSON, 1914.

THE MIDNIGHT RIDER

(PAUL REVERE)

"One if by land. Two if by sea."

These words echo in our minds when we hear the name of Paul Revere. We see a figure on horseback, galloping through the night, calling out, "The British are coming!" Perhaps we even remember a stanza or two of Longfellow's poem:

"Listen my children and you shall hear
Of the midnight ride of Paul Revere. . . .

"A hurry of hoofs in a village street,
A shape in the moonlight, a bulk in the dark. . . .
And beneath from the pebbles, in passing, a spark
Struck out by a steed flying fearless and fleet."

Paul Revere. A patriot on horseback, yes, but also an artist and craftsman whose designs were to become treasured heirlooms. He was to found one of America's great industries.

But how did men see him while he lived? That Boston patriot, Dr. Joseph Warren, for one. What might he say of him? He was Paul Revere's friend and admirer—"A dark, stocky, sturdy figure of a man. Paul was of French stock. His hands were strong. A craftsman's hands. Strength —that was the keynote of Paul's mind and body. Above all, he was trustworthy, utterly trustworthy."

Dr. Warren had good reason to value trustworthiness. Along with such Massachusetts leaders as Samuel Adams, John Hancock and Isaiah Thomas, he was active in the colonists' growing movement toward rebellion against the British. One April evening as he started toward Revere's shop, he knew the threatening explosion could not be far off.

Apparently, the redcoats were up to something, too. Only last night, in Boston Harbor, the small boats on the British transports had been lowered and made ready for action. At any moment, those boats might be filled with armed soldiers. The most ominous sign of all was that the British grenadiers and light infantry had been ordered off guard duty.

The bell above the shop door tinkled as Dr. Warren entered Revere's shop and found its owner still at work. Warren looked around cautiously.

"Clemmens has gone to supper," Revere assured him. "We can talk freely." Ike Clemmens, whom Revere employed as an engraver, was a Tory.

"Sam Adams and John Hancock have gone to Lexington," Dr. Warren said. "So has John Adams. Unfortunately, General Gage, the British commander, seems to

Paul Revere arouses the Minute Men.

have learned of this. Gage will certainly try to seize them, as well as our military stores at Concord."

"Hancock and Adams must be warned," said Revere.

"Yes," Dr. Warren agreed. "Will you go to them, Paul?

Paul nodded.

"And then to Concord," Doctor Warren went on. "All our cannon and ammunition must be hidden deep in the swamps, where the British can't find them. On your way back, stop to see Colonel William Conant in Charlestown. Tell him if the British make a move, we'll give him warning. Signal lanterns will be hung in the belfry of Christ Church. One lantern if the British march by land. Two lanterns if they embark in the boats for Cambridge."

Not long after that night, Dr. Warren, only thirty-four, was to die at Bunker Hill, slain by a British musketball. Revere lived on for many years, but people remembered his midnight ride to warn the patriots that the British were coming. They couldn't stop talking about it. His wife, Rachel, would pretend to be annoyed, but her pride in her husband showed through.

"That precious ride again!" she sometimes exclaimed. "Will I never hear the end of it? I'll tell you this, though—I tried to stop him."

Then she might explain, "Paul was a widower with six children when I married him. And I had one of my own. So that night, when Paul told me he must ride a *second* time, I thought of our seven children—

Boston Massacre Broadside. Engraving by Paul Revere.

"Oh, have I confused you when I say a *second* ride? Well, he had already gone to Lexington and warned Adams and Hancock, then on to Concord and home. After that, if the British moved, he was to inform Bob Newman, the sexton at Christ Church, from whose belfry the warning lantern would hang. Then Paul was to ride *again,* this time ahead of the British. That first ride was bad enough, but the second! Why, it was almost like asking Paul to put his head into a noose! If the British caught him, I'd be a widow—with seven mouths to feed.

"So I said, 'Why is it *you're* the one who is always asked to risk his neck?'

" 'Not me alone,' he said. 'Billy Dawes is riding tonight. And he goes the most dangerous way, by land across the Neck. And Josh Bentley and Tom Richardson will row me over to Charlestown—'

" 'Under the guns of the enemy fleet?' I was half-weeping. 'Oh, no, Paul!'

" 'Don't you fret. We'll be quiet about it, Rachel,' he said. With that he gave me a kiss and was out the door before I could argue any more.

"It was but a short time after he departed that someone came rapping on the door with the news that the British had posted men on the road to Lexington to stop any warning rider! And Paul had known that before he left!

"Well, I don't suppose *I would* have stopped him, even if I could have. For if you love a man like Paul, you don't come between him and the doing of what he believes is right."

In later years, Paul wrote about that fateful night when he, Josh Bentley and Tom Richardson shoved a boat into the water at full tide. The oars were muffled in a flannel petticoat borrowed from Richardson's sweetheart, the petticoat still warm—said Paul—when they ripped it apart to bind the blades. Past His Majesty's ship the *Somerset,* with her sixty-four guns, they let the tide take them gently onto the Charlestown shore. Here, Colonel Conant waited, holding the reins of a horse.

"Jim Larkin's finest," the colonel said, giving the horse a pat, "and Charlestown's best. Good luck to you, Revere!"

Good luck . . . perhaps Paul had it, that night. But he also had courage and devotion to his country's cause.

For most of us, that's the Paul Revere story, and that's all we know about Revere. But he was to enjoy forty-three prosperous years. They were also years of service to his country.

When the Continental Congress needed someone to engrave and print its paper currency, it turned to Revere. When Massachusetts needed a commander for the militia defending Boston, Revere accepted the dangerous position. When cannon were needed, it was Paul Revere who, in a short time, learned how to make them.

And when peace came, and the Second Church required a new bell, it was Paul who cast it. From his Boston shop, beautiful silver work—museum pieces today—continued to pour. More and more children came to him and Rachel.

In 1798, Revere wrote to the Secretary of the Navy, suggesting he be allowed to make copper sheathing for ships of war. But how could he do this, he was asked, since only the British knew the secret of making sheet copper. In the second place, America did not have the rolling mills that would be necessary. Well, in the first place, Revere said, about this "British secret"—"I do not believe it's a secret at all. We'll experiment until we find out how to make it. And in the second place—I'll build the mills myself, even if I have to borrow the money."

Let the log of the U.S.S. *Constitution* speak for his craftsmanship: "June 26, 1803. The carpenters gave nine cheers, which was answered by the seamen and caulkers, because they had in fourteen days completed coppering the ship with copper *made in the United States of America!"*

THE BATTLE HYMN OF THE REPUBLIC

(JULIA WARD HOWE)

In the street before a proud Boston mansion surrounded by ancient and beautiful oaks, a violent drama was being enacted. Julia Ward Howe watched the scene below with an increasing sense of horror. The U.S. marshal and his deputies had been combing the neighborhood for an elderly escaped Negro slave. He had been working up North for several years as a waiter, but his former owner had traced his whereabouts and was now demanding his return. According to the recently passed Fugitive Slave Law—this was 1856—armed force, if necessary, could be used to restore such human property to the lawful owner.

Julia saw the deputies fanning out across the grounds of the house next door. Suddenly, she saw the Negro, a panting old man, running downhill with a deputy after him.

"If he don't stop before he gets to the corner, shoot to kill!" rang out the marshal's voice. Holding her breath, Julia turned away from the window. She heard herself counting, "One—two—three—four." And then it came—the awful crack of the deputies' pistols aimed at their fleeing human target.

That evening at dinner, Julia's husband, Dr. Samuel Gridley Howe, observed that she had barely tasted her food.

"Julia, my dear, are you ill?" he asked.

"Oh, I don't dare become ill," she answered. "You have too many sick people to take care of already. But the country, Sam, the country is terribly sick. What I saw today took away my appetite. I saw the marshal and his men chase an escaped Negro. . . . Then I heard them shoot him down."

"I knew about it, Julia," said her husband gently. "I hoped you would be spared the knowledge of it."

"But I don't want to be spared the knowledge of anything," cried Julia. "You and I, we call ourselves abolitionists. But that isn't enough. We must speak out. We must *do* something soon. Tonight I feel that my life is being wasted. What have I done—I've written a few mediocre poems."

"But, my dear," protested Samuel, "good poems are never a waste of time. And I go by Dr. Holmes' opinion. He considers you one of the finest poets writing in America today."

"I can't help comparing my feeble words and those spoken by John Brown. Remember that speech he made the other afternoon? That was the poetry our time needs. There was genuine fire in it. Oh, Sam, if I could capture only a little of that fire in one significant poem. . . ."

A few days later, Julia again heard John Brown speak. He had been asked to address a meeting of abolitionists at one of the fine houses in Boston. Once more the intensity of the man's vision had inspired everyone. After most of the people had gone and John Brown was standing alone, Julia summoned the courage to speak to him.

"I'm Julia Ward Howe, Mr. Brown," said Julia. "I'm a writer, but perhaps you have never heard of me."

"Julia Ward Howe? Of course I have heard of you," said John Brown heartily, as he extended his hand.

"I mentioned that I was a writer," went on Julia, "only because I wanted to tell you that since hearing you speak, I can no longer feel I am accomplishing anything with my writing."

"Words have won great battles," said John Brown.

"Not my kind of words," said Julia. "What we need now are words with an-

Julia Ward Howe.

other beat, words that can express the real agony that our country is going through. When I hear you speak, I hear such words!"

"I am getting old, Mrs. Howe," said John Brown. "The arms of death are closing round me. I shall have to leave God's work behind me—unfinished. I wish I could make you see your own work as God has given me the power to see mine!"

"What do you want me to see?" asked Julia earnestly.

"Glory!" exclaimed John Brown. "Glory beyond this corporeal frame. Mine eyes have seen it, madam. If it is God's will, you, too, shall see it when the time comes. The days of wrath are at hand. It will take rivers of blood to wash away the sins of slavery!"

John Brown. Painting by John Steuart Curry.

"I shall never forget your words," said Julia, pressing his hand.

Three years later, in 1859, Julia was again inspired by his prophetic words. This time he was speaking for the last time—just before his death. His attempt to rouse the slaves in revolt against their masters had failed, and he was to be hanged for treason.

"Had I interfered in the manner which, I admit, has been fairly proved," he said to the court which convicted him, "had I so interfered in behalf of the powerful, the educated, the so-called great or in behalf of any of their friends, and suffered and sacrificed what I have in this interference, it would have been deemed right. But because I did what I have done in the name of those who were helpless and oppressed, it has been called by another name."

Within two years of his death many of the Southern states had seceded from the Union, and the American people were engaged in a grim conflict.

Early in November, 1861, the Governor of Massachusetts asked Dr. Howe to go down to Washington. He wanted a thorough check of the wounded men from the state, and he wanted to be sure that they were receiving the proper care. When Dr. Howe accepted the assignment, Julia insisted on accompanying him.

"But Washington is a battle-torn city, Julia," remonstrated Howe. "You will have to look on terrible things."

"That's exactly what I *must* do," said Julia. "My eyes have been straining to see what John Brown saw so easily—the things that lifted him up and made him strong. Those soldiers leaving town this morning—some of whom we know—did you hear what they were singing as they marched off to the war? 'John Brown's body lies a-mouldering in the grave'—that's what they

were singing. They've put their own words to that old camp-meeting tune, and it's become the marching song of the nation. John Brown's spirit is leading them!"

At the end of their first day in Washington, Julia was standing at the window of their room in Willard's Hotel.

"You must try to get some rest," said Dr. Howe. "After all, you went everywhere today that I did, and *I'm* exhausted."

"I couldn't possibly sleep," said Julia. "I keep thinking of the spirit of those wounded men—so ready to go back again to face death, some of them for the third or even fourth time. John Brown said to me that I must look for glory beyond this corporeal frame. 'Mine eyes have seen it, madam,' he said. Mine eyes—mine eyes . . .'"

Out of this echo of John Brown's words, Julia Ward Howe suddenly was able to fashion her stirring words for the old camp-meeting tune.

"Mine eyes have seen the glory of the
    coming of the Lord;
He is trampling out the vintage where
    the grapes of wrath are stored;
He hath loosed the fateful lightning of
    His terrible swift sword:
His truth is marching on. . . ."

Julia called her poem "The Battle Hymn of the Republic" and sent it to her friend and neighbor, James Russell Lowell, then editor of the *Atlantic Monthly*. He published it in the February issue. Within a few weeks, everyone in the North knew the poem by heart. Union soldiers now sang her words as they marched off to war. And Julia Ward Howe's vigorous "Battle Hymn of the Republic" has become part of America's heritage of strength and greatness.

141

THE NATIONAL ANTHEM

(FRANCIS SCOTT KEY)

One of the darkest hours in American history came on the night of August 24, 1814, when the British burned the city of Washington. President and Mrs. Madison had barely managed to escape from the White House before the British marines set fire to it. The cabinet was in flight, and the citizens of the city, with all the belongings they could salvage, were jamming the roads of the countryside.

From the windows of his home in nearby Georgetown, Francis Scott Key looked down upon the burning capital. The road before the house was filled with people, old and young, hurrying off in the direction of Baltimore.

Key, who had distinguished himself as a constitutional lawyer in many cases tried before the U.S. Supreme Court, knew almost every person of importance in Washington, and he was deeply concerned about the safety of his friends. He hurried out to see what he could do to help. Almost at once he came upon his neighbor, Colonel John Skinner, who was trying to keep some order in the crowd. From Skinner he learned that the Americans would rally at Baltimore and make a stand at Fort McHenry. As they spoke, a man rode up to inform Colonel Skinner that the British were on their way to arrest Dr. Beanes.

"Dr. Beanes is my close friend," exclaimed Francis, "and he's an old man. What do the British want with him?"

"They say he had some British soldiers arrested and they're going to make an example of him," said the man.

Key and Colonel Skinner rode down to the doctor's house in the burning city as fast as they could, but he had already been seized when they arrived. After conferring with Secretary of War James Monroe, the two men then embarked, under a flag of truce, for the flagship of Admiral Cockburn's fleet, then ready to open fire on Fort McHenry.

Key pointed out to the admiral that Dr. Beanes had been absolutely impartial in his treatment of the wounded, quite as many British as Americans having received his expert care.

"For that I'll release him to you," said the admiral, "although I remain of the opinion that I should have this scoundrel hanged from a yardarm. It's true, you know, that he urged a group of his townsmen to throw some of our British soldiers into jail. And now I shall have to inform you, Mr. Key, and you, Colonel Skinner, that I shall detain you both, along with Dr. Beanes, during the bombardment of Fort McHenry. This is to prevent you from informing your friends about our exact position. After we have captured Baltimore we will put you ashore."

"Aren't you taking a lot for granted, Admiral?" asked Key.

"Look through that porthole, Mr. Key," he replied. "See that flag over the battlements of Fort McHenry?"

"Yes," said Key, "it looks rather proud flying there in the sunset."

"Well, Mr. Key," said Admiral Cockburn as he walked away, "proud as it may look to you now, it won't be there in the morning. So take a good, last look at it."

For safekeeping, the three Americans were rowed away from the center of attack and put aboard the British ship *Surprise*. It was to be a sleepless night for all three of them, standing near the gunwale of the enemy ship and trying to catch sight of their country's flag over Fort McHenry in the bursts of gunfire. The British frigates reeled as they sent broadside after broadside thundering across the harbor. It did not seem possible that the American fort could hold out. At last the dawn came.

Peering through a telescope, in the dim early light, Key cried out exultantly, "Our flag is still flying!"

The British attack on Fort McHenry had been repulsed.

Key and his companions were sent ashore. While resting in a hotel, Key revised certain notes he had jotted down during that memorable night, and fashioned them into the ringing verses of "The Star-Spangled Banner."

Within a few hours, handbills of the poem circulated throughout Baltimore. Neither the author's name nor the tune to which the words were to be sung was given. However, before the day was out, everyone in Baltimore knew that Francis Scott Key had written the words and that they were to be sung to the tune of "To Anacreon in Heaven." This tune was so familiar that everyone in the colonies knew it and so old that many of the older Americans remembered singing it long ago in England.

"Oh, say, can you see, by the dawn's
   early light,
 What so proudly we hailed at the
   twilight's last gleaming—"

Even before Francis Scott Key's death on January 11, 1843, "The Star-Spangled Banner" had come to be regarded by all Americans as their national anthem. However, it was not until March 3, 1931, that it was officially so designated by an act of Congress.

The flag which "still waved" over Fort McHenry, and inspired *The Star Spangled Banner.*

THE CHAMPIONS OF HUMAN RIGHTS

"Driven from every other corner of the earth, freedom of thought and the right of private judgment in matters of conscience direct their course to this happy country as their last asylum."

SAMUEL ADAMS, 1776.

FREEDOM OF WORSHIP

(ROGER WILLIAMS)

"I ask you this," the white man pleaded. "Put aside your tomahawks. Silence your war drums. Smoke the peace pipe with all my people."

The Indian, Miantonomo, hereditary chief of the Narragansetts, was silent for a while. Roger Williams was interceding for the very people who had driven him out of Massachusetts. The Indian could not understand. He asked, "Why you good to people who hurt you?"

Williams replied, "Whatever they have done to me, they are still my people." And he went on, "I do not seek to preach to you. The only way I can explain this to you is in the words of my Lord, Jesus Christ. He taught us to forgive our enemies. He said return good for evil. Do unto others as you would have them do unto you."

As Miantonomo knew, this was not the statement of a man who lacked courage. Indeed, Roger Williams was prepared always to fight for what he believed. Had he not been prepared, a few years earlier, during that summer of 1635 in Plymouth, when he had stood up to deliver his sermon? The atmosphere in the small, square, log meetinghouse was hushed. From among the worshipers, Mary had gazed up anxiously into his face, waited with pounding heart. Be a little careful, my dear husband, she had prayed, for they'll stop at nothing to hurt you.

He, careful? The phrases that issued then from bold-jawed Roger Williams grew bolder and bolder. "We know," he cried, "that nine rulers of this colony are ministers of the established church in Massachu-setts Bay. They not only govern the church, but the Colony as well. A few brief years ago, when we landed at Plymouth, it was our intention to avoid a union of church and state. We have failed. Already we have religious intolerance again. We must worship God their way, not according to the dictates of our own consciences. Brethren, this tyranny must come to an end. God shall be worshiped by each man according to his will. Be he Jew or Turk or anti-Christian, every man must have the same right to live among us. Intolerance is not the mark of a true believer in Christ, our Lord. In this or any Christian civilization tolerance and freedom must be the sentinels!"

The Massachusetts Bay authorities had answered this challenge by summoning Roger Williams to appear before the General Court in Boston. "Roger Williams, in addition to preaching sermons which are open heresy, you stand accused of holding that His Majesty does not own these lands which make up our Colony."

"This land," answered Williams, "belongs in truth to those who first possessed it—the Indians. No one—and least of all a Christian monarch—has the right to seize it from them."

This heretic would destroy the Colony! Mr. Dudley was particularly vehement in his denunciation. "We sentence you, Roger Williams, to banishment within six weeks."

So he prepared to depart, to take his wife and their child, christened Freeborne, into the wilderness.

The authorities meanwhile had debated the danger of Williams' presence in the country. This Roger Williams—did he not have friends, followers? Might not some of these faithful follow him into the wilderness? And there, might he not set up a colony of his own, a colony of heretics and rebels that would be a thorn in the side of the Massachusetts Bay government? A warrant was issued for Williams' arrest. "They plan to carry you back to England in chains," a friend warned. "You must leave immediately. You know the Indians —go live with them."

"This is God's will," Williams told his wife. "Trust in His Providence. I will find a place, then send for you."

Day by day he traveled through the forest in swirling blizzards. Cold, half-starved and feverish, he staggered along the faint Indian trails. Waiting alone through the long winter months, his wife Mary wondered—was he well, alive; had he been fortunate; had he met with friendly Indians, or—?

Providence had not deserted Roger Williams. The Narragansett Indians were friendly. And when, in the spring, Mary and the child joined him, Williams had already established a tiny settlement in Rhode Island. One by one his followers arrived. Along Narragansett Bay log cabins sprang up. This place, called Providence, was to be a haven for the oppressed, a place of tolerance, where all men and women could worship as they saw fit, where freedom would be practiced. Freedom of thought, opinion, conscience. . . .

"Plymouth and Boston seem so far away now," Mary said. But they were nearer than she knew. One day a rider appeared, bearing news: the Pequot and Narragansett Indians were rising, ready to make war on the colonists. "Our troops on the upper Connecticut," the rider said, "burned a Pequot village or two, in revenge for the slaying of one of our traders. So Mr. Dudley sent me to you for help."

"Mr. Dudley!" Mary remembered Dudley's voice, ringing out in the courtroom: "Brethren, this heretic would destroy the Massachusetts Bay Colony!" and Roger's voice answering, "It is not I, Mr. Dudley, who will destroy this Colony, but you. All of you!"

"Then this is God's judgment!" Mary cried.

"Nay, Mary," Roger Williams said. "It is not for us to judge our enemies." He turned to the messenger. "Take word back that I will do what I can. The Narragansett Indians are my friends. They helped me in my most difficult hour, and when we bought our land from them, they promised peace between us."

Then he sought out Miantonomo, the sachem of the Narragansetts. "Yes," Miantonomo said, "we trust you, Roger Williams. Have you not let us follow our own gods? You do not force your religion upon us, as do the others. But you are different. We trust no other white man."

"I promise you," Williams said, "it will be a just peace."

"Your word is good, brother. I will hold council with my warriors." But the Pequot Indians, Miantonomo said, would probably not listen to peace talk.

Miantonomo kept his word. But, just as he had warned, the Pequots took to the warpath in a struggle that lasted for years.

Branding Roger Williams' Rhode Island settlement a menace to both church and Crown, the New England colonies banded together against the Indians. They formed a league of defense, excluding Providence. In these desperate straits, there were those in Providence who said, "Massachusetts, Plymouth, New Haven, Connecticut, are all in the league. They will not allow us to trade or travel among them or to use their harbors. Our crops will rot on our hands. We must find a way to cooperate with

Roger Williams finds a haven with the Indians.

them. We must compromise, or we are lost."

"No," said other voices. "Providence stands for the freedom to think as we please. We cannot surrender that freedom, and surrender is what they demand."

Then someone else stood up, saying, "We are outcasts. The other colonies would gladly trade with us, but for one reason. And that reason is Roger Williams. We must give Williams up. Only by giving him up will we save ourselves."

"Brethren," Roger Williams said, "you may be right. At least, here you have the right to speak as you believe. We all have that right. But I have an opinion also. The other colonies refuse to deal with us. Why? Because we have no legal basis. We need a charter from the Crown, a free and absolute charter of civil government. With your permission, I will sail for England and request that charter."

"But if you should fail?"

"Then I shall go to Boston and give myself up."

Many months later, a ship from England sailed into Boston Harbor and dropped anchor. Tired and worn from the long voyage, Roger Williams stepped down the gangplank, into the arms of his waiting wife—and a circle of bayonets.

"Roger Williams," Mr. Dudley said, "you were warned never to step foot in this Colony again. You escaped us once. This time you will not. You are under arrest."

"Better read this first," Roger Williams answered, handing Dudley a letter. "From the leaders of Parliament."

Dudley read it. "'In recognition of Roger Williams' good affections . . . sufferings by the oppressors of God's people . . . his Indian labors . . .' Why, this is a letter of safe-conduct!"

"So you cannot hold me," Williams said. "And now, read this." And he gave Dudley another document, a larger one this time, a charter of freedom for the Providence Colony, granted by Parliament.

This, as Roger Williams said, was more than a charter of freedom for Providence. He declared, "For liberty is a God-given right, as natural as the air we breathe. Liberty is hardly got and as hardly kept, but someday even these colonies will be free —and all America, too. And—God willing, all the world may yet be free."

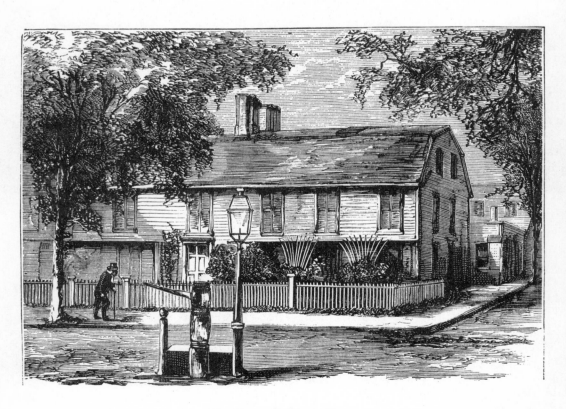

The Roger Williams House.

THE CHAMPION OF COMMON SENSE

(TOM PAINE)

Among the several trades at which Tom Paine had tried his hand in his native England were weaving, corset-making and shoemaking. He came upon literature—the field in which he would win immortality—almost by chance. At the same time, he found the flame that was to consume his entire life—the cause of human rights.

Paine was, in the 1770's, an exciseman, or tax collector. In this calling another great writer of his time, Robert Burns, was also to suffer and starve. Although the cost of living had been steadily rising, excisemen were then being paid not a penny more than the rate established nearly a hundred years before. The salary fixed then had remained an unalterable part of the statute on excises.

Deciding that a century was a long enough time to wait, the excisemen sent a delegation to the King's ministers to petition for a salary increase. This petition had been written by Thomas Paine, and the excisemen had been so impressed by its eloquence that they had chosen him as their delegate to present it. They felt sure that such a reasonable and moving statement of their case would persuade the ministers.

They were to learn that sometimes men of power have unreasoning minds and hard hearts. The petition was refused, and Paine was dismissed from the excise service as a mutinous fellow.

At that time in London there was another petitioner to the King's ministers. He also was to win immortality as a writer (and in many other ways). His life also was to be devoted to the cause of liberty. He had come all the way from the remote wilderness of America to present the grievances of the colonists. His name was Benjamin Franklin.

Franklin was treated somewhat more politely than Paine; in any case, he could not be dismissed from his job. But the King and his ministers thought it as presumptuous of the American colonists to demand that the Crown treat them as free men as it was for the lowly excisemen to seek better pay. Franklin, too, was rebuffed; at great cost, it was to turn out, to the King and his ministers.

While Franklin was in England, some of the greatest Englishmen of the time, and Frenchmen, as well, became his friends. One of the least conspicuous of them was that other petitioner Tom Paine. Jobless and not knowing where to turn, Paine sought Franklin's advice. Oliver Goldsmith had shown Paine's petition to Franklin, who had recognized in it the mark of a great journalist and pamphleteer. He said, "Go to America, Mr. Paine. There your free sentiments will be welcomed. That country has need of pens like yours." This advice strengthened the resolve that had already formed in Paine's mind. Soon he was on the high seas, sailing to America.

There he settled in Philadelphia, where he was hired as the editor of the *Pennsylvania Magazine*. He immediately justified Franklin's confidence in his journalistic gifts. In three months, under Paine's editorship, the magazine tripled its circulation.

Had this career been all Paine sought in life, he could have become one of the most successful journalists in history. But for him, the future good of mankind meant more than a career. When someone told him that he was only inviting trouble by his course, Paine replied, "If there must be trouble, let it be in my day, that my child may have peace."

In America, the cause of human rights

that had impelled Paine to put such emotion into his petition for the excisemen found new and greater expression. Like Paine, many aroused men in America were seeking freedom. Paine would write the burning words that would serve to light their path.

Early in 1775, there appeared a pamphlet entitled *Common Sense* that was read and discussed in every home in America where there was someone who could read. It did more to sway the American people toward the cause of independence than any other piece of writing. Washington himself acknowledged that he had been influenced by it, and he had it read and reread to all his troops as a morale builder: "Bring the doctrine of reconciliation to the touchstone of nature, and then tell me whether you can hereafter love, honor, and faithfully serve the power that hath carried fire and sword into your land? . . . But if you say, you can still pass the violations over, then I ask, hath your house been burnt? . . . your property destroyed? . . . your wife and children destitute? . . . Have you lost a parent or a child? . . . If you have not, then are you not a judge of those who have. But if you have, and can still shake hands with the murderers, then are you unworthy the name of husband, father, friend, or lover . . . you have the heart of a coward, and the spirit of a sycophant."

The pamphlet had a powerful effect on the Roberdeau family in Philadelphia, where Paine was a constant visitor. Rich and respectable, the Roberdeaus were partisans of freedom. Their daughter Irene had fallen in love with Paine and he with her. Their son Jaime Roberdeau had become his ardent disciple, ready to follow Paine in all that he did.

Naturally, Irene wanted a home and a family. She tried to keep Paine in Philadelphia, arguing that his best weapon in the fight for freedom should be his pen, not his sword. The other Roberdeaus also sought to keep Paine in Philadelphia because they knew that if Paine joined Washington's troops, their son Jaime would go with him.

Paine believed, however, that words should be translated into action. He joined Washington's army—and lost Irene. And Jaime went with him—to die at Valley Forge.

The first winter Washington's army spent was fully as hard as that which followed at Valley Forge. One bitter day Paine appeared at the Roberdeaus' mansion in Philadelphia. He looked pale and emaciated and was shivering. But the light that burned in his eyes was not fever; it was the light of another inspiration that was now to sustain the spirit of the American fighters for freedom as, earlier, his *Common Sense* had kindled it.

Paine asked Roberdeau to ransack Philadelphia to find him a hundred pounds of paper. In those days paper had become very scarce. Roberdeau's patriotism triumphed over his resentment of the request, and he managed somehow to find the paper for Paine. On it was printed another of Paine's great pamphlets, *The Crisis*. Its words rang throughout America and helped to keep men's spirits from faltering.

"These are the times that try men's souls. The summer soldier and the sunshine patriot will, in this crisis, shrink from the service of their country; but he that stands it *now*, deserves the love and thanks of man and woman. Tyranny, like hell, is not easily conquered. . . . What we obtain too cheap, we esteem too lightly: it is dearness only that gives everything its value. . . . By perseverance and fortitude we have the prospect of a glorious issue; by cowardice and submission, the sad choice of a variety of evils—a ravaged country—a depopulated city—habitations without safety, and slavery without hope. . . .

"Let it be told to the future world, that in the depth of winter, when nothing but hope and virtue could survive, that the city and country, alarmed at one common dan-

Tom Paine in 1792, about the time when he wrote the influential "Rights of Man," a copy of which is shown at the left.

ger, came forth to meet and to repulse it."

The following winter at Valley Forge was desperate for the ragged Continentals. The British had captured Philadelphia and the Continental Congress had had to flee and set up another temporary capital. In the frozen camp death came to young Jaime Roberdeau, perhaps from the hazards of exposure and malnutrition that decimated Washington's troops.

During this winter the words of Paine's *The Crisis* were reread. Again they helped to strengthen wavering spirits.

But fortunes changed in the following summer. Washington won a great victory at Monmouth. This, coming after the Battle of Saratoga, where Burgoyne had been forced to surrender, changed the course of the war.

The French, who had hesitated to extend open aid to the Americans while they were losing, now openly supplied money and arms and prepared to send a military and naval expedition as well. Freedom was winning in America. . . .

Some say that it was the disappointment of Irene Roberdeau's marriage to another man that sent Paine wandering from the country he had helped to set free, but we may accept his own explanation. He gave it to Franklin and Jefferson and other patriot friends who tried to keep his talents for their country. Now that America had become an independent nation, they said, why not remain here and enjoy the newly-won freedom?

And Paine replied: "Where freedom is not, there is my country!"

And so, to the end of his life, Paine remained a champion of the rights of humanity, wherever they had to be fought for. And for this he is remembered throughout the world, though it was in America that his best and most fruitful work was done.

> "These are the times that try men's souls. The summer soldier and the sunshine patriot will, in this crisis, shrink from the service of his country, but he that stands it now deserves the love and thanks of man and woman."

HE LED THE WAY TO REUNION

(HORACE GREELEY)

"Go west, young man, and grow up with the country," said Horace Greeley, and most Americans remember him just for that bit of advice. Some recall also that he was a great editor—of the New York *Tribune*—and that he ran for President against Grant in 1872, when he used the slogan "Turn the rascals out!" But hardly anyone nowadays remembers what was probably the greatest service Horace Greeley ever did for our country.

In the spring of 1865, when almost anyone could see that the Civil War was nearing its end, Abraham Lincoln asked Greeley to come to see him at the White House. It was not the first time the President had issued such an invitation to the influential editor who had been very helpful in getting him nominated and then elected President. But somehow Greeley had never before accepted any of Lincoln's invitations.

"I wanted to keep my independence. I wanted to feel free to point out Lincoln's mistakes, to criticize him or the administration as I saw fit," Greeley explained to a young employee, to whom he was giving final instructions as he prepared to board the train to Washington.

"But then," the young man said, "why did you accept *this* invitation, sir?"

"Well, I—hmmm—why, I don't rightly *know* why. Hmmm. Something—I don't know. I just did." Greeley's voice trailed off as the train started to move.

When Greeley walked into Lincoln's office he was visibly shocked by the President's appearance.

"Have I changed so much, my friend?"

said Lincoln.

"Well, it's been four years. I imagine we've both changed, a little."

The President spoke. "Greeley, I asked you down here for one reason. Soon this terrible war will be over, and we'll be one nation once again." He paused. "But what kind of a nation?"

"I'm not sure I understand you, sir."

"We took up arms for one reason—to preserve the Union. And with victory, it will have been restored—at least geographically, and legally. But otherwise, I'm greatly afraid, the breach will be wider than ever. Even before the last Confederate flag is lowered, there'll be an outcry from the North for—well, it'll be called 'justice.' In this case, the more proper term is 'revenge.' And revenge can breed only bitterness, and bitterness only more revenge. It's a frightful, endless process, Greeley. We've got to try to stop it, *before* it begins."

"*We*, Mr. President?"

"I hope so, Greeley. Because I seem to remember a rhyme: 'What's Greeley's opinion on Monday is *public* opinion by Sunday.' When you became an abolitionist, millions followed you. When you called for the hanging of Jeff Davis—well, it's said that ten thousand men enlisted, the sooner to gratify your desire in the matter."

"And now, sir, you'd have me reverse myself, and swallow my own words?"

"They were words for war, and they helped us to win. But they're not words which will contribute to a fruitful peace."

"But what *about* Jefferson Davis, sir? What will happen to him?"

"Privately, I hope he never falls into our hands."

"A good many Northerners believe that he is a rebel, and should so be tried for treason."

"To what end, Greeley? So North and South can fight the war all over again, in a courtroom?"

"Jefferson Davis should not be punished?" Greeley was incredulous.

"No. Let history judge him for us; we have a peace to win. Help us, Horace, please. Use that tremendous power of yours for charity. For magnanimity, in triumph."

"With all respect, sir, that which you call my power derives solely from my independence."

"And something else—Horace—your integrity. I thank heaven for it. There are already too few men in this world on whose integrity I'd stake my life."

"I thank you, sir, profoundly. And I shall consider what you have said to me, before taking a stand."

That was in March. On April 9, Lee surrendered at Appomattox Court House and the war was over. On the night of April 14, Abraham Lincoln was shot by an assassin at Ford's Theater and he died on the morning of April 15. The country's cries of grief were mixed with its cries for vengeance.

"Jeff Davis! Hang Jeff Davis! He's responsible! He's the one!" the hotheads shouted.

Davis and many Confederate leaders had gone into hiding or had fled across the Mississippi. A $100,000 reward was offered for his arrest and within a week the Confederacy's President was captured, brought to Fortress Monroe in Virginia and put in chains. Feeling ran high, and most of the newspapers fanned the flames of passion. "Murderer," "Traitor," "Arch-Rebel," "Hang him." But the *Tribune* was silent, while its staff champed at the bit, impatient to swell the chorus. Finally an assistant spoke to the editor.

"What is it, Greeley?" he said. "What's troubling you? You haven't been your old self, not since—come to think of it, not since you went down to Washington to see the President! You've never told me, Horace. What happened?"

"Nothing—he just looked tired—terribly tired. Poor Abe. If he'd only lived he'd . . . However, the Almighty must have had—other plans." He stopped suddenly, and his eyes widened. "Samuel, could it *be*—could it *be*?"

"Could what be? What are you talking about?"

"Could it be, Samuel, that I, Horace

154

Greeley, am included in those—other plans? Why did I accept Lincoln's invitation last March after refusing him for years? Why, tell me—why?"

The assistant smiled. "Well, if you didn't know—"

"If *I* didn't know—and I did not—then only the Almighty knew! And the Almighty knew something else, Samuel. He knew that Abe Lincoln's time on earth was brief and if I hadn't gone to Washington when I did—yes, of course. Oh, what a fool I've been—not to have realized . . . Now, got your pencil and paper? Good! Sit over there and take this down. Editorial entitled—let me see—entitled 'Magnanimity in Triumph.' Earnest I speak out at this moment to plead against passions certain to be fierce and intolerant. I plead for humanity, for forgiveness of all who have trespassed against us . . . In a reunited nation there can be no place for revenge, for malice, for injustice born in anger. The time has come when charity must replace bitterness, when the spirit of brotherhood must vanquish vindictiveness. And so at last I speak out to state that which I believe with all my heart—Jefferson Davis *must be set free!*"

That was the beginning of Greeley's crusade, which lasted for many months, but it was a costly crusade for Greeley. He lost influence, his popularity waned, and his friends said he would have to stop the crusade if he wanted to keep his chances of winning the Presidency in 1868, or even of becoming Senator.

Davis was still untried by any court, still a prisoner in Fortress Monroe, still an obstacle to the friendly reunion of North and South, when one day a visitor was announced to Greeley. It was Mrs. Jefferson Davis. She came to the point quickly.

"Mr. Greeley, I asked the President if my husband couldn't possibly be released on bail. He said he *might* allow it, but only if I could find a group of distinguished Northerners who would be willing to go down to Richmond and sign Mr. Davis' bail bond."

"Humph! *That* would get the President *nicely off the hook!*"

"And he said—and he said that you—Horace Greeley, would have to be one of them."

"And it would put *me right on it,* eh?"

"Oh, Mr. Greeley, if only you could *see* my husband—you *couldn't* refuse me. You couldn't. It would break your heart, to see him now. He's not even sixty, but these two terrible years in that frightful prison have—he's an *old man* now, Mr. Greeley. An *old man.* His hair is white now and his hands are so thin and wrinkled—and he's sick, terribly sick, and he'll *die,* Mr. Greeley, unless—"

"Mrs. Davis, I think I should tell you that your husband's welfare does not greatly concern me. I have never laid eyes on the man. He was my bitter enemy for four long years."

"Oh," she said, softly. "Oh, I see. I'm

Jeff Davis greets Horace Greeley.

extremely sorry, sir, for having taken up so much of your time. If you'll excuse me, I'll—"

"Madam, please sit down. If I've offended you, I'm sorry. I merely wished to make it perfectly clear to you that it is not from sentiment, or soft-heartedness, that I intend to sign your husband's bond. With me, it is—"

"What? Oh—oh, Mr. Greeley. Oh, Mr. Greeley," she said brokenly.

"It is solely and purely a matter of principle. I have said, and I believe, that before this nation can be reunited, Jefferson Davis must be set free. And so believing, I must sign his bond."

Horace Greeley knew full well what this decision meant to his political activities and how it threatened his future in public life. He knew how hard it would be to get a score of other distinguished Northerners to sign this bond with him. But he felt he had been given a mission by Abraham Lincoln, if not by God Himself, and he determined to do what he knew was right.

A few weeks later, together with Mr. Cornelius Vanderbilt of New York, Mr. Gerrit Smith of New York, Mr. Aristides Welsh of Pennsylvania, Mr. Benjamin Wood, Mr. Augustus Schell and fourteen others, Greeley stood before the bar in a crowded federal courtroom in Richmond, Virginia. One by one, they stepped forward and signed the bail bond for Jefferson Davis. And when all had signed, the greatest barrier to friendly reunion had been removed. Jefferson Davis was freed. But think for a minute—what if the President of the Confederacy had been executed? Suppose Jeff Davis had been hanged?

At great cost to himself, Horace Greeley defied public opinion when he knew he was right. What he purchased at this great cost to himself—a quicker, better, friendlier, more enduring peace in the Union—was, is and will continue to be of inestimable value to us all.

THE GREAT FEMINIST

(SUSAN B. ANTHONY)

This is the story of Susan B. Anthony, who was called "the Napoleon of the women's suffrage movement." Her enduring monument is the equal right to vote which she helped to win for American women.

When Susan began her fight for full citizenship for women, the very idea of women having equal rights with men was looked upon either as comic or sinful. A woman who wished to vote or hold public office or speak out at a public meeting or manage her own money was considered unwomanly or abnormal. For the rare man who thought a woman should have such rights, public disapproval was equally harsh. He was looked down upon as effeminate, weak-willed and probably weak-minded.

When the American feminist leaders—courageous and brilliant women like Lucretia Mott and Elizabeth Cady Stanton—began their fight, their first object was to win property rights for women. At that time a woman did not legally own even her personal effects unless she had been left alone in the world and had no husband, father or brother. If she had a father or husband as "protector" of this property, he could pawn even her heirlooms or jewels, sell them or give them away. If the woman took him to court, the case would be dismissed. If a woman of property married, what she owned came into the hands of her husband. Title did not even revert to her if he died; he could will the property to whomever he pleased.

In the reforms that followed the Civil War, these property rights for women were secured. Mississippi led the procession by being the first state to make it lawful for a woman to write a will. Other states quickly followed, and by the sev-

enties property rights for women had been written into most of the statute books.

The next campaign was for political rights for women. This was to be a longer and a harder struggle. The leading figure was that courageous, resourceful and determined woman, Susan B. Anthony.

Susan came of a well-to-do family in upstate New York, where her father was a textile manufacturer. In those days it was not the usual thing to send a daughter to college, but Mr. Anthony did. Nevertheless, he was a conventional father who shared the ideas of his time. He had educated his daughter to "polish" her so that when she married she could become a glittering salon ornament.

When Susan returned from college, Mr. Anthony expected her to inspect the eligible young bachelors of her social standing and, from among them, choose a proper husband. But, instead of discussing plans with him for a coming-out party, she asked him to help her find a job! His Susan had been stimulated to think for herself.

He learned also that Elizabeth Cady Stanton had delivered a lecture in the college on women's rights, and had inspired Susan with the determination to fight for those rights. Mr. Anthony's reply to Susan's request for help in finding a job was—"Preposterous, my dear. Women don't work."

"But they do, Father," replied Susan. "You yourself employ women in your factory."

"That's different," he said, annoyed. "They are not women of your class."

"If our country is truly a democracy," said Susan, "there should be no classes, no discrimination against women, no inequalities. Father, I want you to give me a job in your factory."

The exasperated Mr. Anthony retired to mull it over. Yes, he would give Susan a job in his factory. He would let her tend the looms; that monotonous and exhausting work would soon knock this romantic nonsense out of her.

But Susan's will was strong enough not to collapse under drudgery. Indeed, the realization that her job was the sort of work reserved for women, and at much lower pay than comparable work for men, strengthened her determination to see such injustices ended.

One evening the loom girls went to a secret meeting to hear Mrs. Elizabeth Cady Stanton. Susan accompanied them, and Mrs. Stanton recognized her. After the meeting, she asked Susan, "What are you doing here?"

"I am working in my father's factory," Susan replied. "I thought that doing the kind of work women do would equip me better for the fight for women's rights."

Mrs. Stanton, however, believed that Susan would be most useful to the cause as a teacher, for in the classroom she would be better able to influence the young people who would be the future molders of opinion.

And so, on Mrs. Stanton's advice, Susan became a teacher. But not for long.

At a convention of the New York State Teachers' Association, to which her fellow teachers had elected her a delegate, Susan caused a sensation. To the horror of her elders, she demanded the right to join in a discussion on the dignity of the teaching profession. Women teachers at that time were supposed to consider it enough of a privilege to sit and listen quietly to words of wisdom from the male teachers.

Worn down by her insistence, the chairman finally yielded the floor to Susan, but only for one minute.

"Thank you, Mr. Chairman," said Susan. "One minute is ample for what I have to say. You ask why the teaching profession is not as highly thought of as medicine or law. I'll tell you. Women who are not considered bright enough to be doctors or lawyers are nevertheless considered bright enough to teach the nation's youth. If you want to improve your station in life, all you fine gentlemen, I suggest you join the woman's suffrage movement."

This simple statement drew scandalized headlines in the papers. After reading them, the principal of Susan's school promptly fired her.

Now Susan felt that her training period was over. She plunged into action, and to the year of her death, at eighty-six, she remained in action.

She led a group of women into a barber shop in Rochester, New York, where a local election board was registering voters for a forthcoming election. She badgered the clerks into registering her, but they warned her that if she tried to vote she would be arrested. On election day, she led the march of another band of women into the polling booth. The dumfounded officials did not know what to do and allowed Susan to vote, although repeating the warning that she would be arrested for it.

Two weeks later, a United States marshal did arrest her. When she refused to

Susan B. Anthony. Photograph by Mathew Brady.

pay bail, her lawyer managed to have her released on a writ of habeas corpus. Susan's lawyer had a difficut task. His defense was directed toward the expectation of as light a sentence as possible, but his client's objective was to make her case serve as an illumination of injustice. For that purpose she welcomed court appearances, heavy fines, jail and other hardships.

In June, 1872, her case came to trial. Instead of letting the jury decide the question, the judge ordered a directed verdict of guilty. Then, according to custom, he asked, "Has the prisoner anything to say why sentence shall not be pronounced?"

"Yes," Susan replied, "I have a good deal to say. My natural rights as a human being, my political rights as a citizen of this country, even my judicial rights as a prisoner at the bar, are all being violated. You have degraded me from the status of a citizen to that of a subject. Your denial of my right to a trial by a jury of my equals is an offense against law. Not one of these jurymen, native or foreign-born, rich or poor, educated or ignorant, sober or drunk, is my peer. *Each is my political superior.* Therefore I do not ask for clemency, but a course that will do you far more harm, the full rigor of your self-constituted, so-called law!"

The infuriated judge did as she asked. He imposed the severest penalty the law permitted—a heavy fine and payment of the costs of prosecution. Susan refused to pay them, which meant a prison term.

There was one other way to escape jail —to appeal for a Presidential pardon. This Susan refused to do. She would not ask to be pardoned for something she did not consider a wrong. Her friends, however, asked for pardon in her behalf, and the President granted it.

The years of struggle for women's rights went on. Susan gained more and more friends and supporters, not only by her perseverance and courage, but by her good humor and good sense. By the time the nineteenth century came to an end, women had won the vote in many of the states, largely through Susan's efforts.

On the first day of the new century, a number of newspapers which at one time had reviled her now made respectful allusion to the fact that with the new century Susan would be entering her eightieth year. One of them observed editorially: "As we enter a new century, the twentieth century, a valiant fighter of old is approaching her eightieth year. And the whole nation takes this occasion to honor the spirit of Susan B. Anthony."

For Susan, the fact that she was eighty did not suggest retirement. Instead she took on still another task.

In England, women's suffrage had not done as well as in America. Lady Aberdeen, the English suffragette leader, had asked Susan to come to England to help out. Susan consented because, as she said, "If I can help the movement in England, it will help us here."

One of the reasons why the women's rights movement lagged in England was that Queen Victoria had publicly opposed it. Susan's plan was to wangle an audience with the Queen. If she were received at Buckingham Palace, the English people might feel that the cause of women's suffrage had become respectable and merited their thoughtful consideration.

The Queen was curious about this indomitable American woman and was eager to meet her. She invited Susan to the Palace. There the two distinguished old ladies had a friendly and candid chat.

Susan dwelt on the inconsistency of a Queen's ruling a mighty empire and taking the position that women were unfit to vote. Victoria replied that she ruled not out of choice, but out of duty. When her husband had been alive, she had gladly let herself be ruled by him.

"Then circumstances do arise," said Susan, "when a woman can no longer depend upon a man, and then, as you have proven, she *need* not depend upon a man. She can do well enough, depending on herself."

Susan's expectations proved correct. The fact that she had been received at the Palace enhanced the prestige of the women's suffrage movement not only in England, but in America as well.

Six years later, Susan died, but her work went on. In 1913, the day before the inauguration of President Woodrow Wilson, advocates of women's suffrage paraded in Washington and Wilson indicated his sympathy. In 1918, in an address to Congress honoring the contributions women had made in World War I, he concluded: "The least tribute we can pay them is to make them the equals of men in political rights, as they have proved themselves their equals in every field of practical work they have entered, whether for themselves or their country."

Although, despite Wilson's support, the amendment granting women full political rights was defeated at that time, it passed both Houses of Congress a few months later. Two more years were required however, before the necessary number of states ratified it. The last battle of Susan B. Anthony's great campaign was finally won when, in 1920, enfranchised women voters of America lawfully cast their votes for the candidates of their choice.

THE MEN OF VISION

Men who are willing to risk their lives in trying the unknown which lies ahead have ever been among America's most treasured citizens. Some have found their goals in a physical world and traveled to them through desert and canyon, over prairie and mountain, until the vast land has held no secret from its people. Others have been the leaders of expansion, finding homes for west-walking families and fertile lands to support them.

The frontiers of science have beckoned to others—to doctors who, in laboratory and hospital, have exercised imagination and patience until their labors have resulted in the saving of millions of human lives; to probers who have tested the earth and obtained a knowledge that will bring to men treasures of soil and water to lessen hunger and thirst throughout all countries; to astronomers who have probed the secrets of a universe so great that nations, and worlds, like ours seem minuscule in size and importance.

In the great universities of America, in the laboratories of foundations established by public-spirited citizens, in government-administered institutions, the great search for new truths continues. Each year sees other barriers crumble as men, inspired by the examples of the past, look ahead and make ready the road for the march of humanity toward safer and happier living.

THE EXPLORERS

"Columbus found a world, and had no chart
Save one that faith deciphered in the skies
To trust the soul's invincible surmise
Was all his science, and his only art."

GEORGE SANTAYANA, *O World.*

HE WON THE PACIFIC NORTHWEST
FOR THE UNITED STATES

(CAPTAIN ROBERT GRAY)

The longer they sailed against the line of breakers, the more his crew thought him a madman—for risking the *Columbia*, their lives and his own, in an attempt to discover a river. More than likely it was not a river at all, but merely Deception Bay, as the British called it.

Yet he wasn't a reckless man, Captain Robert Gray. Certainly the Boston Marine Association would not have called him in, along with Captain Kendricks, in 1787, had he not established himself as a mariner.

"Let me explain," Mr. Barrell said, speaking for the other businessmen who composed the Association. "Captain Cook, the Britisher, in his report of a recent voyage to the Pacific Coast, tells us that the natives in that region trap sea otters. Their pelts are worth from eighty to a hundred dollars apiece. We can secure these pelts by trading manufactured articles such as knives, axes and cheap jewelry for them. A rich harvest for whatever ship gets there first. And we," Mr. Barrell continued, looking keenly at Kendricks and Gray, "with your help, intend to get there first. But, gentlemen, you will not return immediately to Boston with those furs. Rather, from the Pacific Coast, you will sail for

China, where you will trade each pelt for a chest of tea."

"A dollar knife for a hundred-dollar pelt," Captain Gray mused. "And a hundred-dollar pelt for a two-hundred-dollar chest of tea." A worthwhile voyage, if successful.

"Aye," Captain Kendricks said. Older than Gray, more experienced, he seemed the logical man to command the expedition. "And it's up to us—"

Mr. Barrell held up his hand. "But there is something more, sirs—something more that we would like you to accomplish. Those western lands on the Pacific Coast— we would like you to claim them for our country. Oh, it's true that the Spaniards, the English and the French claim the terrain as their own and have split it among themselves. But perhaps we can establish a better claim. If, for instance, you gentlemen can discover a river, a large important river, then the United States, in claiming that river, can stake undisputed claim to all the land it drains. We should be in possession, in short, of the Pacific Northwest."

Almost three long years later the *Columbia*, captained by Robert Gray, came limping back to Boston harbor. But Gray had little about which to rejoice. In his exploration of the Pacific Coast he had not found the river. And what was worse, instead of the several thousand chests of tea the Marine Association expected to find in the hold, there were only six hundred. A small return for such high hopes, so Gray could expect only a chilly welcome.

When the *Columbia* had set out on the voyage alongside the *Lady Washington*, which was commanded by Kendricks, it had seemed, even to Gray, that Kendricks was the man to lead the expedition. Kendricks, however, had little enthusiasm for the exploration venture. He doubted that any river existed there. And he was not so honest nor so able as the Marine Association believed.

The *Columbia's* own three-year voyage might have been shortened by a year, Gray thought, and the *Columbia's* hold filled with tea. Yet they *had* made a vigorous, if unsuccessful, attempt to find that Northwest river. Certainly Kendricks must have long since returned. Trust *him* to tell a good story.

So, as the *Columbia* sailed slowly into Boston harbor, Captain Gray was thinking *This is probably the last ship I'll command for a long, long time.*

At first he paid little heed to the sound of a cannon on the shore. Then, when the cannon boomed again, he looked up. A small boat was just drawing alongside. *Boom!* went the cannon again and then Mr. Barrell, the Marine Association spokesman, was climbing up the rope ladder and leaping aboard.

What was he smiling about? Why was he laughing? Why was he clapping him on the back? Well, he won't keep that smile for long, thought Gray. When I tell him about the tea—

But what was Barrell saying? The booming cannon made his words faint.

"What did you say, sir?" Gray asked.

"Can't you hear, man?" Mr. Barrell cried, pointing to the fort where the cannon boomed. "You're famous, man, you're famous! Magellan, Cook, and now Captain Gray. You're the first American to carry our flag all the way around the world!"

Yes, defeat had given place to victory. Captain Robert Gray was a celebrated man, a man who had brought honor to his country. Even the disappointed shipowners were impressed and they decided to back Captain Gray in another expedition, this time in sole command.

So in September, 1790, the *Columbia* put out once more for the Northwest Coast. And this time, it seemed, Captain Gray was in luck.

One day in June of 1791, while cruising along the Pacific Coast, latitude 46° 10' north, the ship's lookout cried, "Yonder, off the starboard prow—a break in the land!" And there *was* a break in the land. Calling out for the ship to bear in close, Gray gazed eagerly at the approaching indentation. It must be the river he sought. And yet, those breakers foaming across it—

"It's not a river, sir," the mate said. "Only a bay, I'm afraid, sir."

"Bear in closer," Gray commanded. "And lower the pinnace. We'll send it ahead to feel out the way."

Grumbling, eight men climbed into the pinnace and were lowered away. Rowing hard, they led the *Columbia* toward the indentation. The water grew shallow, then shallower still. Seven fathoms deep, then five, then three, then one-half fathom three. Too shallow for the *Columbia!* From below came a sound of scraping and shrieking as her keel rubbed against a reef.

"Hard aport!" Gray shouted. Or was it too late? Would she founder? No, in a moment she floated free.

For nine days, the *Columbia* fought in vain to pass the line of breakers and go in through the mouth of what Captain Gray, despite the disbelief of his crew, was sure was a river. After many near disasters he gave up. He had done what he could

164

Captain Robert Gray.

The indentation would remain a riddle.

So he sailed away, and for the next few months the *Columbia* cruised up and down the coast, exploring, doing whatever trading it could with the Indians, while Gray tried to forget that indentation, that tantalizing break in the shore.

Then, early the next spring, cruising near the mysterious indentation again, the *Columbia* met another ship, the British *Discovery*. The two captains paid their respects to each other.

"No," the British captain said finally, as they stood talking on the *Discovery's* deck, "I'm afraid we've made no discoveries of note. We've been up and down this coast for nearly 250 leagues. We'd like to find that river before you do, of course," and he smiled, "but we've seen no opening of any importance. Unless," he added, nodding toward the indentation, "you count *that*." And he laughed.

"Yes," Gray said. "We spent nine days last summer, trying to get in there. I'm surprised you haven't tried—"

But the British captain was laughing. The joke seemed to be enormous.

"You mean you've tried?" Gray asked. "And weren't any more successful than we?"

"Tried?" the other man said. "Why, man, we call that Deception Bay. It was named by our Captain Meares, a few years ago. Meares tried to get in and almost lost his ship. And now you're telling me you had a go at it, too?" His laughter rose again. Imagine it—this American repeating Meares' mistake!

Stung by this mirth, Gray set his course south. Deception Bay! Was he the fool the British captain thought he was? Was it really only a bay? No, no, it was the mouth of a river; Gray was sure of it.

On the morning of May 11, he was once more off the foaming indentation. Swinging out to sea in a circle, he set the prow of the *Columbia* squarely toward the line of breakers. This time he was going in. Noth-

ing would stop him.

"Breakers dead ahead!" the lookout called.

The *Columbia* surged forward, the wind filling her sails. Seven fathoms, five, then three—

"We'll smash on the reef!" the mate shouted.

"Two cables' lengths," the lookout called. "Breakers dead ahead. One cable's length."

"Captain," said the mate, "we've gone too shallow. The crew are afraid—"

Gray said quietly, "We'll ride the next comber in. Helmsman, hold your course. Watch for it."

"Aye, aye, sir." Was the captain mad? The breakers roared around them, battering the bow. And then, from below, as he had heard it several months before, repeated as if in a recurring nightmare—the sound of the keel touching bottom. His hand held steady at the wheel but the helmsman thought, *We're done for, sure!*

"We're going to hit!" the mate shouted.

But behind them, an approaching wave rolled forward, lifting the ship like a giant hand and carrying her forward. And then—they were through.

"Bring her up into the wind," Gray called. "Stand by to drop anchor."

And now the test. "Over the side with a bucket," Gray ordered. And as a seaman followed his command, Gray held his breath. When the bucket rose again, filled, what would be dripping over its sides? The longed-for, sweet river water? Or salty sea water, proving him a fool who had endangered his ship and the lives of his men.

He filled a dipper and drank. The water was fresh.

It is called the Columbia, this great river, named after Gray's ship. Its discovery gave the United States of America an iron-bound claim to the rich Oregon country, a claim which Great Britain formally recognized in the Oregon Treaty of 1846. And its lands are now three states—Oregon, Washington and Idaho.

166

THE WAY WEST

(LEWIS AND CLARK)

The will to explore is part of the American tradition, quite naturally, for our very beginnings stem from the great explorations of Columbus, Balboa, Cabot, Hudson, Champlain and other famous navigators. Probably the most daring and productive of them all was the Lewis and Clark expedition, an enterprise first proposed by Thomas Jefferson. It was organized during the winter of 1803 and set out the following spring. After two years spent in searching out and mapping pathways to the Pacific, it brought back the knowledge needed for hardy farmers and artisans to begin the conquest of our western wilderness.

The expedition is so closely associated with the Louisiana Purchase that most people mistakenly believe it to have been organized to map out the vast new territories acquired from Napoleon.

A survey of the American West had long been a cherished plan of Jefferson's. His own *Description of Virginia* (when he wrote the book, Virginia included much territory to the west of the state) remains an excellent source-book of early discovery and exploration in America. Throughout his life he remained passionately interested in exploration of the unknown West.

Early in 1803 Jefferson sent a message to Congress urging such a survey. He was successful in securing a Congressional appropriation for the venture. To get the expedition started with the least delay, he used his personal influence to secure French passports for its members.

In the meantime Napoleon was planning another far-flung campaign and needed ready cash to equip it. On hearing of his plans, Jefferson immediately sent American negotiators to make an offer for the "useless wilderness," as Napoleon re-

Meriwether Lewis.

garded the Louisiana country. Strange as it may seem, many Congressmen held the same opinion as the French Emperor, and it required all of Jefferson's political skill to overcome their objections. Finally, he was enabled to take advantage of one of the greatest real-estate bargains in history. Thus, by the time the passports for the members of the Lewis and Clark expedition arrived, they were no longer needed. The explorers were now to travel through American territory.

The Louisiana Purchase had the effect, however, of centering a spotlight on this expedition. Now its discoveries would mean the opening up of new lands to American settlers. From the beginnings of the expedition to its triumphant conclusion, the whole nation followed its course eagerly.

To head the expedition Jefferson selected his young secretary, Meriwether Lewis. He made this choice because Lewis had shown himself to be competent and resourceful, but still more because the young man shared his own passionate interest in exploration. In turn, Lewis made a wise choice of an associate commander, the man with whom his name is forever linked, William Clark. Clark had had considerable experience in traversing the wilderness during the Revolutionary War. His brother was the famous General George Rogers Clark, who had won and held the western borderlands all through the Revolution.

During the winter of 1803–1804, Lewis and Clark recruited their party. All told, it came to forty-five—forty-four men and one woman. The latter was the Indian wife of Charboneau, a French trapper who had been hired as interpreter and guide. She turned out to be as useful as any man in the expedition.

Her name was Sacajawea, which meant "bird-woman." She had belonged to the Shoshone tribe but had been kidnapped in childhood by their tribal enemies, the Blackfeet Indians. Among these she had lived in slavery until Charboneau bought her and married her. Sacajawea knew the country better than Charboneau and became the expedition's most reliable guide.

Some of the men grumbled, saying that a woman was bound to bring bad luck. They grumbled still more when she showed signs of pregnancy. If there had been any place to leave her, the grumblers would probably have demanded that she be deposited there for her confinement.

They were to be glad to have her and her papoose among them, however, when the seemingly impassable Rockies appeared. For it was Sacajawea who made it possible for them to cross the Rockies and reach their goal—the western ocean. Jefferson's name was always thereafter to be linked with those of Lewis and Clark, and if a fourth name may be added, it should be that of Sacajawea.

In the winter of 1803–1804, the expedition assembled in Illinois, near the confluence of the Missouri and the Mississippi. There the men were trained, and the last supplies were made ready for loading. On March 14, when observations showed that the ice on the Missouri River had melted, the canoes were launched upriver.

Four days later the explorers reached the village of La Charette, the last western outpost of civilization. There they met the most famous of American pioneers, Daniel Boone. Then seventy years old, he was half-inclined to join the expedition, but he explained, regretfully, official duties kept him back. He was La Charette's chief magistrate.

From La Charette the expedition continued upstream on the Missouri. From then on, no clearing could be seen, and they were lucky to find an Indian path or a deer trail whenever they left a river roadway. Nature opposed them with every obstacle at its command—tempests, tangled forests, flooded rivers, wild animals, fierce summer heat and still fiercer cold, unknown insects whose bites brought agonizing and sometimes fatal fevers—and, finally, the menacing ramparts of the Rockies.

Late in the summer of 1805, the expedition reached the foothills. Before them rose the seemingly endless wall of rock, with snow-capped peaks piercing the clouds. Each search for a pass ended at a towering crag or precipice, and the men began to lose heart. It was reported that the local Indians would not reveal the

William Clark.

pass they were known to use, for their lives depended on keeping it secret.

Sacajawea kept reconnoitering. Finally, she came upon a band of her own Shoshone tribesmen. Among them, by good fortune, was her own brother. Through his influence and Sacajawea's persuasion, the Shoshones were talked out of their precious secret. They not only led the expedition to the pass, but they helped provide transport to carry the party and their gear through it.

The next objective was the Columbia River, which flows into its main channel through a number of tributaries. Three of these, called as a group the Forks of the Columbia, were among the discoveries of the expedition. The two leaders named them after Jefferson and his Secretary of State and Secretary of the Treasury, James Madison and Albert Gallatin.

Building canoes, the party then proceeded down the Jefferson fork and entered the main stream of the Columbia

169

River. Not long afterward, they reached their ultimate goal: the mouth of this great river, where its waters enter the Pacific. There they built a fort in which they wintered. Then, in the spring of 1806, they ranged along the coast, scanning the ocean for signs of a ship.

Had they found a vessel, they could have made the return journey in the comparative comfort of a sea voyage. Failing to sight a ship, they decided to return overland. Converting this necessity into further opportunity for exploration, they carried out two separate tours of discovery.

The party was split into two groups. Lewis took command of one, and Clark of the other. After additional explorations, these groups were reunited at the mouth of the Yellowstone.

The expedition arrived in St. Louis on September 23, 1806. As soon as it became known that the explorers had made their way to the Pacific Ocean and back, the whole nation echoed the impressive announcement. The expedition was hailed in newspapers, on the floor of Congress and in the pulpits. Every one of its members was rewarded for his part in it with large grants of the new lands. The leaders who had given such proofs of good management were appointed to administrative posts, where they could use the knowledge they had gained.

Unfortunately, Lewis' promising life was cut short. Appointed Governor of the Northern Louisiana Territory in 1807, he had spent two years working on his journals of the expedition. In 1809, on his way back East to arrange for their publication, he met with sudden death in a remote inn along the notorious Natchez Trace, a wilderness pathway infested by outlaws. Nothing certain is known, but it is supposed that he was murdered.

Clark was more fortunate. Like Lewis, he received a high governmost post, that of Superintendent of Indian Affairs. His office was in St. Louis. Pressed by the advancing white settlements, many of the Indian tribes, often against great odds, put up a stubborn resistance. When he considered it necessary, Clark led military expeditions against them, but he won greater fame as a peacemaker. His knowledge of Indian ways made him a successful negotiator.

Among Clark's other achievements was the founding of Paducah, Kentucky, which was laid out according to his plan. Our maps preserve his memory in the Clark Fork of the Columbia River, a tributary which he discovered.

Like Lewis, Clark had kept a diary. A skillful draftsman with a talent for drawing, he had made the expedition's maps. His sketches served as an added pictorial record. This material, together with the record compiled by Lewis and other members of the expedition, was published in a work of several volumes. Historians who have turned to them as source material have paid further tribute to Clark as an accomplished editor.

These books were promptly used, almost like charts of buried treasure, by leaders of immigrant parties which swarmed into the new lands that Lewis and Clark had traversed. For historians, anthropologists and other scholars they have continued to provide a precious store of information on the early state of our country before it was broken by the plow and the pick.

Today, a century and a half later, we can look back with awe at the achievement of their great expedition. The wilderness has become a fertile and prosperous land studded with great cities because of the rare leadership and courage of Meriwether Lewis and William Clark, the devotion and skill of Sacajawea, and the vision of Thomas Jefferson, who set them on their westward path.

THE PATHFINDER

(JOHN CHARLES FRÉMONT)

It was a fine day for sailing off the South Carolina coast near Charleston. The sun sparkled on the water and lazy waves lapped the sides of the small boat. The boy Charley, at the tiller, could see no cause for worry. He was looking forward to reaching that little island near Edisto where he and his two young companions would beach the boat and then go exploring. What if everybody knew about the island? "We'll make believe," Charley said, "we're discovering it for the first time. We'll keep records all the way. Henry, you'll make a list of the plants and the trees. I'll draw the maps. And Cecilia, you can help us both."

Yes, sir, Charley thought, we'll make it a regular exploring expedition. But he was getting uneasy. For one thing, the wind was dying down and the boat was losing speed. And over there was Drunken Dick, a rock ledge beneath the water. If the wind dwindled completely, the tide and the currents would seize the little craft and drag it in toward that line of dangerous foam. . . .

"Hey, that's better," Henry cried, as a puff of wind filled the sails. But he had spoken too soon. The breeze skipped away, and above the mast a seagull cried hoarsely, mocking the flattened sails.

"Break out the oars!" Charley ordered, imitating a sea captain he'd heard. "We'll have to row."

But Henry had forgotten to bring the oars. Charley made a mental note: when you go off exploring, remember to take all of the equipment you may need. Check on it. Then double-check, for the lack of proper equipment can mean the expedition's failure. It can even mean disaster. . . .

Not far away, the breakers roared over Drunken Dick, and a strong current was driving them upon it.

Can we jump for it, Charley wondered, and swim? Not that. The sea seemed alive with whirlpools. There was one chance: if he could just steer clear of that outer ledge—

The perspiration stood out on his forehead, but his hand was steady on the tiller. Cecilia screamed as the breakers of Drunken Dick foamed dead ahead.

"Whew!" Henry cried, a minute later. "That was a close one, Charley! I thought we were goners!"

Charley had been christened John. Born January 21, 1813, John C. Frémont's parentage was both unique and distinguished. His father, Charles Fremon, a surname later Americanized as "Frémont," was an adventurous French immigrant. His mother, Ann Beverly Whiting, was a descendant of a Washington family.

John Charles Frémont began his career teaching mathematics, but as soon as he could, he found work that might lead to exploring. In 1837, working for the U.S. Topographical Surveying Corps, he accompanied an expedition to western Georgia. Its aim was to arouse public interest and attract settlers to that area. With his knowledge of astronomy, botany and geology, young Frémont was able to prepare a report, complete with maps, such as the government officials had never seen. In Washington, his recognition was immediate.

To some people in Washington political society, Frémont's explorations were romantic. No romance about it, Frémont protested. "Scientific labor is just hard, conscientious work. And to mean anything, it must be practical, useful to the country." For that reason, he told Martin Van Buren, then the President, he was interested in the opening of the West. If the country were ever to develop as it should, new trails would have to be blazed along the safest, surest routes.

In 1838, in company with Joseph Nicholas Nicollet, a famous French explorer, Frémont set out to survey the great plateau country around the headwaters of the upper Mississippi and Missouri Rivers. They carried a chronometer, a sextant, a telescope, a collapsible boat and, a device especially prized by Frémont, a barometer. This instrument had only recently come into use. It indicated atmospheric pressure and could be used for forecasting the weather and for measuring elevations.

Some time later, after he had reported to Washington on the plateau country, Frémont spoke of that barometer to Kit Carson, the great pioneer scout. They were sitting around a western campfire that night, the logs blazing. Around them, the other members of the expedition lay exhausted. Tomorrow they would rise and ride forward, their horses carrying them over the endless plains, the mountain ranges. For this was Frémont's most ambitious expedition, an exploration of the entire western frontier, including a survey of the Oregon Trail. If they were successful, it would mean new territories and trails for thousands of people moving westward, new routes over which future tracks would be laid, over which transcontinental trains would someday thunder.

This night, swapping yarns with Kit Carson, listening to the murmur of the Deschutes River flowing past the camp, Frémont was reminded of another river and of the barometer he'd almost lost. "We were on the Owl, a pretty treacherous river in the spring. We ran into rapids and the boat smashed up against the rocks, tipping us overboard. Our instruments, fortunately, were snug, locked up in a case, and I yelled to Nicollet to grab them. Well, as it turned out, they were all right, undamaged despite getting banged around that way. Except for one, the—"

Kit Carson spat in the fire. "How about you, Cap'n? Was *you* all right?"

Frémont laughed. "Well, like Nicollet, I was a bit wet, but we came off with only a few bruises. Nicollet dragged me out. As I say, the barometer got a bath, too, and a pounding on the rocks. Its cistern had been broken, so I—"

Stiffening, Kit Carson threw up a hand warning him to be silent, and stood up. Except for the crackling fire and the river rushing past, the night seemed quiet. Carson padded off into the darkness. When he returned to the fire, his face was angry. The horses were gone, stolen by Indians. And—he hated to have to tell Frémont—the saddlebags containing the instruments and the reports were gone also.

Frémont was thrown into despair. Without the reports and instruments, he said, the expedition was useless. Then, a few nights later an old Indian woman came stumbling into the camp, attracted by the fire. She had been left to die in the forest, Kit Carson explained. This was the way the Indians of these parts disposed of old squaws. He questioned her further. Yes, her people had the horses; they were encamped only a few hills away. "Big feast tonight for the chief," she said.

After the feast, Kit Carson told Frémont, those Indians would sleep like the dead, if he knew their habits. A good chance for the Frémont party to retrieve the horses.

Still, it would be mighty risky, creeping into that Indian camp. "If we get caught, they'll skin us alive."

"We *must* have those papers, those instruments," Frémont said.

"You and your danged instruments," Carson snorted. "*I'm* thinkin' of the horses."

Later, riding back from the still-sleeping Indian camp, with the horses and their valuable loads, Carson chuckled: "Cap'n, I want to say—that was the neatest bit of horse-thievin' I've ever seen."

"They left the saddlebags right on the horses," Frémont marveled. "Thank God, everything's here, intact."

In the gray light of dawn, the Frémont

Frémont camps in a pass in the Sierra Mojada.

173

party resumed its march, blazing new trails throughout the mountainous territory of the West. Slowly, Frémont led his expedition across the towering Sierra Range, whose soaring peaks had never before been studied by a scientist. And at last, on March 6, 1844, the expedition rested on a small foothill overlooking the Sacramento Valley, golden and crimson in the sunset. California lay spread out before them.

This was Frémont's crowning achievement as an American explorer. His reports hastened California's admission into the Union, and "The Pathfinder," as they called

Charley Frémont, became civil governor of the territory. He was its first U.S. Senator when California became a state in 1850, and when he was only forty-three he received the Republican Party's first nomination for the Presidency.

On a hilltop overlooking the Sacramento Valley, Kit Carson had said to him, before they descended, "Cap'n, I have a feeling someday, thanks to you, this whole region out here'll be filled with people. And I want to apologize for laughin' at your scientific doodads. I been thinkin'—I guess they got some use after all."

Frémont addresses the Indians at Fort Laramie.

THE TOP OF THE WORLD

(ROBERT E. PEARY)

At Almy Bay, in the Far North, the signs were ominous. It was February. Commander Robert E. Peary had left his ship early December, bound for Fort Conger on the fringe of the Arctic Sea. Since this trip was to be merely a preliminary to the full-scale expedition to the North Pole, he had taken only a few Eskimos along with him. December had passed into January. The time of the full moon, the only time for traveling during the long Arctic night, had come. The men aboard Peary's ship, the *Windward*, watched the moon grow larger, reach its fullness and then fade. February—where was Commander Peary? "Ah, well," Captain Bob Bartlett said, standing on the deck of the *Windward*, which served as a base camp for the main party of the expedition, "if there's any man that can take care of himself in these parts, it's Commander Peary. Did you know the Eskimos call him Pearyarksoah? In their language that means the Great Peary. And that's not a name a man acquires easily."

"But I wish we knew more of their language," someone else said, for two of the Eskimos who had accompanied Peary had come straggling back into camp. They had deserted. But where? And why?

"An independent lot, these Eskimos," said Captain Bartlett. "And they like it easy. They've no taste for working hard. That trip to Fort Conger is a rough one."

No, the desertion of the two Eskimos was, in itself, not too ominous a sign. But

175

Bartlett was more worried than he let on. Over the years, since 1886, when he had first come North on a leave of absence from the Navy, Robert E. Peary had acquired a great knowledge of these grim, icy wastelands. And he had already accomplished a great deal, filling in the blank spaces on the maps and proving that Greenland was an island. On one of his Arctic trips with his wife, their child had been born—the "Snow Baby," the first white child born so far north.

Yes, Captain Bartlett thought, if any man was equipped with the experience and courage, the stamina, to survive the hazards of Arctic exploration, it was Commander Peary. Yet, where was he now? Between the decks of the *Windward* and Fort Conger lay a thousand miles of harsh coast. If he was lost, no searching party would ever find Peary; the trails would be wiped out, covered by snow and ice. Years from now, perhaps, someone might blunder across his body, frozen in a block of ice.

February passed into March; the passing of time was the most ominous sign of all. And then, one day, Commander Peary returned. But there was little cause for jubilation on the *Windward*. As the dog-team panted up to the side of the ship, the men aboard looked down at the Eskimo piloting the sledge. "Pearyarksoah," the Eskimo called, pointing to the fur-wrapped bundle in the sledge. He could not walk from the sledge. They carried him on board.

It had happened, the Eskimo said, "one day before you say Merry Christmas."

"Cut off his boots," the ship's doctor ordered. And then, "Good Heavens!"

From the bed where he lay, Peary looked up at him, "Will you have to amputate, Doctor?"

"Frozen from the knee down," the doctor said. "Gangrene may set in."

"If it means amputating my legs," Peary said, "then I'll take my chances with gangrene."

"Well, the legs—perhaps we can save them, Commander. But your feet. . . ." Squeezing, prodding, his fingers went over Peary's feet, first the right, then the left. "Can you feel that? And that?"

"I can feel the big toes," Peary said, "but—"

"But not the little ones, eh? Well, it's not quite as bad as I had thought. Still, we'd better work fast."

"All right," Commander Peary said. "The little ones will have to go. But mind you, I want your word—no *more* than that."

"You have it," the doctor said.

A few weeks later, on his toeless feet, Commander Peary was again driving his sled dogs toward the Pole. It seemed crucially important to him that an American should be the first to reach the North Pole and claim the territory around it for the United States. Once more, however, he failed to reach it. Still, with each attempt he was penetrating deeper into the unknown Arctic wastes.

These explorations and discoveries were bringing him fame, but he had not achieved his real purpose. On July 8, 1908, after a trip home, he sailed northward again, this time in a specially built ship, sturdy and broad-beamed to withstand the impact of the Arctic ice floes. With Captain Bartlett at the helm and dozens of seasoned Arctic men aboard, the ship pushed and edged and cracked its way north, fighting through ice floes to Cape Sheridan.

Weeks of careful preparation followed. The dash for the Pole must be made before spring, when the ice would begin to melt and split and deep wide fissures would appear, making the way impassable. And everything must be planned, down to the last detail. Any carelessness or oversight might mean not the life of one man but the lives of all.

Then one cold morning—the sledge loaded, the dogs panting in their traces, ready for the run—Peary called the men of the expedition into the cabin of the ship.

Peary plants the American flag at the North Pole. Painting by Dean Cornwell.

"I see no reason," he told them, "to delay another hour. The cold is holding, but there's no telling how much longer it will do so. Now let us review our plans. We leave in six groups."

One group, he went on, would lead the column, breaking trail for the first hundred miles, then leave its surplus supplies on the ice and return to the base camp, the ship. The second group would continue from the point where the first group left off for the next hundred miles, then turn back. "Then Marvin will lead to about the 86th parallel, where MacMillan will take over from him and carry on. And, finally, if all goes well, Captain Bartlett, you will lead us to the 88th parallel."

"Aye," said Captain Bartlett.

"With all you men breaking the trail," Peary said, "and carrying supplies to the various depots along the route, my dog-teams ought to be fresh enough for the final run. But, with all our preparations, you men know as well as I how tricky the Arctic is. An open lead of water in the ice may keep any or all of us from going on, or worse still, from coming back. Until now, most of our explorations have been on land. There was always a chance to fight our way back, as long as our physical endurance held out. But out there, on the pack ice, escape may be cut off at any time. From the moment we leave this ship, the failure of one may mean the end of us all."

So began a journey unparalleled in the annals of exploration. Up, up toward the top of the world, these men fought their way. Across a sea of treacherous ice, crushed and piled in mountainous ridges, and in between them, the leads, valleys of new ice which, without warning, might open and plunge men, dogs and sleds into the icy darkness of the Arctic Sea.

And one by one, each of the groups left supplies as planned—Dr. Goodsell, Borup, MacMillan, Marvin. . . .

As Captain Bartlett said later, "I left Peary close to the eighty-eighth meridian, about one hundred and thirty miles from the North Pole. It was a fine, clear day, about thirty degrees below zero. There was little sentiment in our parting—the commander was not a sentimental man.

"Moreover, everything seemed auspicious. Peary was now within easy reach of the Pole, and the last march we had made together had taken us over big level floes. The Eskimos were confident and happy. The moon was on the wane, making the chances of bad weather or strong tides less and less each day. Peary had the pick of the dogs, sleds and the Eskimos and grub enough for months. After entering my observation I gave him a copy, keeping one for myself. We loaded our sleds and then we had some tea, some pemmican and a few biscuits. As I shook Peary's hand, I felt sure that we would meet again, back at the ship. I shook each of the Eskimos by the hand and, laughing, said, 'North Pole emungwa tima'—that is, 'North Pole not far now.' Then we were off southward to our ship. Our job was to keep our trail open, so that Peary would have easy traveling on the way back."

Captain Bartlett was not wrong. Peary planted the American flag at the North Pole. And beside the flag, he left a bottle with a notice inside, reading: "90 Degrees North Latitude—North Pole. April sixth, nineteen hundred and nine. I have today hoisted the national ensign of the United States of America at this place, which my observations indicate to be the North Polar Axis of the earth, and have formally taken possession of the entire region, and adjacent, for and in the name of the President of the United States of America. I leave this record and the United States flag in possession. Signed, Robert E. Peary, Commander, United States Navy."

And as Ootah, the Eskimo, remarked on the return journey, "The devil is asleep or having trouble with his wife—or we should never have come back so easily."

178

BREAKERS OF THE WESTWARD TRAIL

"Conquering, holding, daring, venturing as we go the unknown way,
Pioneers! O Pioneers!"

WALT WHITMAN, *Pioneers! O Pioneers.*

THE FIRST FRONTIER

(DANIEL BOONE)

Dan'l Boone, he was the one. Yup, he was the first frontiersman. Perfessional, that is. First lots o' ways, and best, too.

Nowadays folks talk o' the *last* frontier. Use words like Middle West, Middle Border, Far West and Wild West. Know what the West used to be? Know what the *first* Wild West was? Kentucky. That's right, Kentucky. Used to be a wilderness, and the first white women in Kentucky were this Dan'l Boone's wife and daughter, Rebecca and Jemima.

Guess in the beginning there wa'nt no frontier at all. That string o' mountains, folks call 'em different names in different places—Adirondacks, White Mountains, Green Mountains, Poconos, Blue Ridge, Great Smokies—them mountains kinda kept the people down near the seacoast until this Boone opened up the way. That was in '75, just when we were gettin' up on our hind legs to fight the British.

This Boone blazed a trail through them mountains to the wilderness—they call that trail the "Wilderness Road" now—and found the sweetest land you ever saw, twenty million acres of it. Indians called it "Ken-ta-kee," meanin' "among the meadows," so we called it "Kentucky,"

or "Kaintuck" for short. Boone claimed it, paid the Cherokee Indians for it, built a fort and made a settlement there. Named it Boonesborough.

There's, oh, a thousand stories I could

179

tell about Daniel Boone. He knew the animals like he was an animal, the birds like a bird, and the Indians like he was one of them. He could read the signs in the woods like no one else. He'd take a deep breath and tell you things you 'n I could never guess. "Gonna rain," he'd say when there was not a cloud in the sky. It'd rain. "Indians!" he'd say, and in a little while we'd top a rise and see the smoke of their fire 'way, 'way off.

There's plenty can tell things from footprints and busted twigs and trampled grass. Those are easy signs. Dan'l could tell things when there was no sound, but oughter be. And when there was sounds, he seemed to know what the birds was saying and even the insecks. He knew what it meant when some leaves and buds was dry and others wet. I guess that was 'cause he loved the woods and the wilds and

everything in 'em. He got along fine with all the tribes and they all gave him their respeck. 'Cept for that, he might've been killed when he was only forty-one 'stead of livin' to be eighty-four.

That's the best story about Dan'l Boone. 'Twas in '78. The redskins had been tricked by the redcoats, who'd been tricked by that turncoat Jim Girty. One day that winter, word came that there was a war party out; they'd scalped ten men at Licking Creek, they were burning homes all over the valley and they were headed for Boonesborough. There weren't nearly enough men in the fort to hold 'em off and Dan'l Boone knew that. No chance to beat the Indians, no sense runnin' away.

So what did Dan'l do? He just went out all alone to powwow with Blackfish, the Indian chief. He made Blackfish ashamed to be even thinkin' of burnin' Boonesbor-

"Daniel Boone Escorting Pioneers." Painting by George Caleb Bingham.

Daniel Boone's arrival in Kentucky. Painting by Ward Lockwood.

ough and drivin' out women and children from their homes in the cold wintertime. Blackfish said, "Boone, you speak truth. Blackfish will not burn Boone's town in winter. We come back in spring. We take Boone and go see Colonel Hamilton in Detroit. I have spoken." When they got to Detroit, this Colonel Hamilton wanted to get hold of Boone. But Blackfish wouldn't let him go. "Blackfish adopt Boone. Worth a hunnert men. Make him Shawnee blood-brother," he said.

They washed him in the river, painted him red all over, and gave him a reg'lar haircut—all cut off 'cept a scalp lock. Well, Dan'l didn't like that, o' course, and told 'em so, and it didn't take him long to escape. He made his way back to Boonesborough, a hunnert and sixty miles, in five days, and then he got that there fort good and ready. He knew that five hunnert Indians and British were a-comin'. They worked on the stockade, built new blockhouses and got their rifles and ammunition all set.

Then the British and Indians came. It was the damnedest attack Kaintuck ever saw, but Boone stood 'em off day and night for ten days. And then the varmints run off, licked.

Boone didn't stay in Kentucky. There was gettin' to be too many people there for him, after a while. He moved West, then West agin and agin, sort of settin' the style for the country, lookin' always for the fresh new land, makin' new frontiers all the time. Yup, he was the first—and the best.

"Daniel Boone Protects His Family."

FOUNDING FATHER OF TEXAS

(STEPHEN AUSTIN)

In 1820, it was a long and trying journey from Arkansas to Texas, where the Spanish flag still flew. There were the usual hardships of the trail—and there were the Plains Indians, particularly the Comanches, to dodge or fight. Moses Austin, already past the prime of life, found the going hard.

In Arkansas, hundreds of people, awaiting his return, knew their future rode with him. If he were successful, the Spanish governor of the Texas territory would grant him acres of rich land. Then these restless hundreds would pull up stakes, load their wagons and follow their Moses into this new promised land. Among them was Moses' son Stephen, prepared to depart at any moment for Louisiana, where he would recruit additional settlers for the western trek.

No one saw any reason why the news should not be good. The Spaniards were welcoming settlers who would develop the land and, what was more, fight off the warlike Comanches. Those hard-riding warriors were a constant menace to Spanish rule, and the *Americanos* had proved their ability as Indian-fighters.

When news of the land grant came, Stephen Austin immediately set out for Louisiana, where he recruited his party. However, on reaching Nacogdoches, the Texas town where he was to join his father, he was met by his mother. She was alone.

Moses Austin was dead. The trip home from Texas had been too much for him. "Pneumonia," Stephen's mother said. "He was wishing he could see you again, son, but he knew he never would. Before he died, he said he wanted you to carry on— to lead the settlers West to take up the Spanish grant."

"It's a mighty big job," Stephen said doubtfully. He reckoned himself a man, but the responsibilities he was about to undertake might well overwhelm a leader who was only twenty-seven. And his task seemed even more staggering when he received fresh news from below the Rio Grande.

"A thousand pardons," a Mexican rider panted, as he rode into Nacogdoches. "I had an urgent message for Señor Moses Austin. But now that I hear he is dead—"

"You can give me the message," Stephen replied. "I am his son. I shall take his place."

"Then you have not heard of the revolution in Mexico? We have driven out the Spanish. Mexico is now a new republic, Señor. I come as a friend to warn you. The new government may not recognize the grant of land the Spanish authorities made to your father."

"But they must," said Stephen. "Mexico will need settlers to hold Texas against the Indians, even more than Spain did. And I've got to have that grant. Hundreds of families have given up their homes to follow us."

"Most unfortunate," the rider said. "But I am afraid—"

From Nacogdoches to Mexico City— eight hundred miles—was a long and dangerous journey on horseback over deserts and mountains. But Stephen Austin, having made his decision, did not hesitate.

In Mexico City, he made contact with the officials of the new government. The land grant was confirmed.

By 1830, American settlers in Texas numbered some thirty-five thousand. Austin's colony, a vast coastal tract bounded by the Brazos and Colorado rivers, had prospered, despite the raiding and plundering of the Comanches.

But in Mexico conditions were chaotic.

Stephen Austin.

Texas became the pawn of every political faction. All the land grants were threatened, and the Austin grant was no exception. Beset by these uncertainties, the Americans submitted a petition to the Mexican government, requesting permission to set up their own local government, collect their own taxes and organize their own defenses against the Indians.

And once again, bearing the Americans' petition, Stephen Austin rode toward Mexico City. This journey, said many of the settlers, would be a futile one. "Petitioning the Mexicans won't do any good . . . we ain't never gonna be sure our homesteads won't be taken away and our cattle confiscated 'til we run those Mexicans across the Rio Grande and set up a free country for ourselves."

When Stephen Austin arrived in Mexico City, however, he was still hopeful of obtaining a peaceful settlement. Months went by, but he could get no definite action from the authorities. Knowing the needs and the temper of his compatriots in Texas, he wrote to them, advising them to go ahead

184

with their plans, but counseling patience.

Then one day Austin was summoned to appear before a Mexican military tribunal. The charges against him were treason and incitement to insurrection.

"Señor Austin, a letter which you sent to Texas has been intercepted. In it, we have found that you urge your fellow Americans to set up an independent state. Do you deny this?"

"No, I do not. But—"

"You confess to treason?"

"No. I have come here with a petition for reforms—"

"Say no more, Señor. This letter, and your own confession, convict you. For this, you should be shot, but you are fortunate in having friends in Mexico City who think it unwise. Instead you will go to prison."

Austin spent over a year in the Mexican prison. Finally, friends secured his release under bond. Six months later, wrecked in health and prematurely aged by his ordeal, he was permitted to return to Texas. Austin took with him the promises of Mexican officials that something would be done to reform the government. But by now he was convinced that the only salvation of Texas was independence.

On May 2, 1836, a convention of Texans met at a settlement on the Brazos River. Texas was declared a free state—a sovereign and independent republic. The next step would be to draw up a constitution.

Before this could be done, a bombshell burst upon the convention. The Alamo, an abandoned mission turned into a fort by the American settlers, was under attack. Thousands of Mexican troops, led by the Mexican general Santa Anna, were storming the walls. Altogether, counting the women and children, there were only a hundred and fifty Texans to hold off upwards of seven thousand Mexican soldiers.

"If we don't move mighty fast," General Sam Houston said to Austin, "we won't be needing a constitution. Santa Anna will take the Alamo, then ride on up here to take care of *us*. The convention has just confirmed me as general of the armed forces of Texas. But how many fighting men do I have? Four hundred—"

"We must form a government that the nations of the world will recognize," said Austin. "Otherwise, we'll be considered nothing but a band of rebels."

"That's your job," Sam Houston said.

"You'd better go to Washington right away, Austin," said Burnet, the provisional governor of Texas. "They know you up there. Recognition is what we need. If Washington recognizes us as a free and independent republic, other countries will go along."

"In the meantime," Houston said ruefully, "I'd better be getting on. Seems I've got to show Santa Anna what the Republic of Texas can do with four hundred men. I'll be damned if I know *how* we're gonna do it, Steve, but don't tell anybody I said so."

But Sam Houston did show the Mexican forces what Texas could do. With his hastily recruited and poorly armed forces he defeated and captured Santa Anna. In Washington, meanwhile, Austin had obtained recognition of Texas by most of the great nations of the world. Texas became the Lone Star Republic.

But the pioneers of Texas were Americans; their destiny was bound up with that of the United States. Nine years later, they took their place in the Union. And the name of Stephen Austin is beloved in his state as the "Father of Texas."

Sutter's Fort (Old Barracks).

HOW TO FIND GOLD

(JOHN A. SUTTER)

It is remarkable how many discoveries and inventions appear to have been made *purely by chance*. But when you examine the facts, you'll find in about every case that the elements of thought, hard work, perseverance, character and ability are much more responsible for the success than plain good luck. In the sports world they say, "Luck is on the side of the better team," a truth that applies to all aspects of life.

The discovery of gold in California is one of the most dramatic instances of "chance." The facts are simple: John A. Sutter owned a large tract of land in the Sacramento Valley of California. He commissioned James Wilson Marshall to build a sawmill for him on the American fork of the Sacramento River. In the course of building the tailrace of the mill Marshall discovered gold. "The gravel's full of it," he said that day in January (the 24th), 1848, when he reported his find to Sutter. News of the discovery leaked out quickly and spread like a prairie fire, and the fabulous Gold Rush to California resulted.

Was the whole thing just plain luck? How did Sutter happen to be on hand in California? How did he get possession of all that land? Why was he doing any construction at all in the wilds of the almost uninhabited Sacramento Valley, so far from the coast? The answers cover many years and many miles.

Sutter's trail goes back more than 7,000 miles to Switzerland. Johann August Sutter, born in Germany of Swiss parents in 1803, decided at the age of thirty-one to set out for the New World to seek his fortune. He left his family in Switzerland and took ship for New York.

Arriving in America, he considered what he should do. He thought there were better opportunities and a better life in the West, and soon he was traveling as a trader over the Santa Fe Trail in the Southwest. Always alert and enterprising, he made friends wherever he went, and wherever he went his friends told him of the rich lands and golden sunlight of California. He determined to go there and eventually, by a roundabout way, he reached Monterey, the capital of California, which was then Mexican territory. With the letters of introduction and recommendation that he had received from his friends, he went to see the governor and obtained a grant of land such as the government had been making to selected responsible people.

The land that Sutter chose was the beautiful, fertile Sacramento Valley, and he won the grant by pointing out that it was very far away and therefore rather undesirable to most, and by promising to keep order there and develop the area so that it would serve as an outpost, protecting the lands along the coast.

Only Indians were living in the Valley when Sutter and his men came there. With firmness and justice, he gained the confidence of the Indians and they helped the white men to build homes, plant fields and tend herds of cattle and sheep. But though trees were plentiful, lumber was scarce and very expensive. Either the timber had to be hewed and smoothed by hand, a very slow process, or it had to be transported many, many miles from the coast.

San Francisco in 1848.

"Very well," said Sutter, "we'll build our own sawmill and make our own lumber." He hired Marshall—and the rest is history. And the recipe for history, as you can see from this story, is made up of many ingredients: take some hard work and enterprise; shake well with courage, thought and imagination; season with judgment and understanding; add a dash of good luck. Serves all of mankind.

187

Gold mining at Sutter's Mill. Painting by Dean Cornwell.

HE LED THE WAY

(KIT CARSON)

The trembling of a twig, the quality of a breeze, the shading of a voice—any of these could make the difference between disaster and success for an expedition into the wide, wild West in the days when that country was new and unexplored. There waited Indians who would scalp you, others who'd help you. There were wild animals and reptiles—mountain lions, wolves, bears, rattlesnakes—that could tear you apart or kill you with their poison, others that you needed for food, leather, clothing. There were almost impenetrable forests, raging torrents, steep heart-breaking mountain peaks and many another hazard. And, in the beginning, there were no roads or paths except once in a while a faint Indian trail.

If you were going West then, you had to have someone to lead the way, someone who had been there before, who knew the country, knew how to deal with the Indian tribes, was a crack shot, with a quick "draw." Even so, unless you employed a very good guide, you and your band might wind up, without your hair, as food for the birds or as skeletons in the desert. If you were lucky, you got Kit Carson to lead the way. He was the best.

Christopher ("Kit") Carson was seventeen when he ran away from his home in Missouri (he had been born in Kentucky)

189

and joined Captain Charley Bent's 1826 caravan to Santa Fe. There he met Ewing Young, the famous trapper and "mountain man," and joined Young's expedition to the Gila mountains, to hunt fur-bearing animals and to fight the Apaches. When Young decided to push on to California, young Kit was one of the few chosen to go along. He had become a sure shot, an expert in the woods and on the trail, and he was "mighty easy" to like. He had an adventurous spirit, a vagabond heart, and he roamed all over the West in the following years.

When John Charles Frémont planned his western exploration, there was no doubt as to who should be his guide—it had to be Kit Carson. Kit led Frémont's expeditions of 1842, 1843 and 1845 to the Rockies, Oregon and California by way of Great Salt Lake. On many occasions he proved how true it is that the guide makes the difference.

Kit Carson led many other expeditions to open the West, and to make the route less dangerous. He drove a flock of 6,650 sheep overland to California in 1853, and when the Civil War broke out he promptly offered his services to the Union forces, in which he became a brigadier-general.

Carson City and Carson Valley in Nevada are among the many places named for the great pioneer scout who made the advance into the Great West a little easier, and the country's growth a little faster, a little better.

Kit Carson's home in Taos, New Mexico.

190

"Every great advance in science has issued from a new audacity in imagination."
JOHN DEWEY, 1927.

THE MAN WHO UNDERSTOOD MADNESS

(BENJAMIN RUSH)

Philadelphia, 1789.

"Father, who is that strange-looking man?"

"Where, Lucille?"

"In the street, over near the horse-trough, Father. He's dressed in rags, like a scarecrow. Oh, look! He's drinking from the trough, just like a horse. Ugh! That water is so dirty. *I* wouldn't. Father, he's looking at me—and those eyes—his eyes are so—"

"Don't be afraid, Lucille. I'm here. But don't ever let me catch you going near him. That's Mad Joseph. He's possessed."

"Possessed, Father?"

"By the devil, my child."

* * *

Philadelphia, 1789—the largest, most comfortable city in the newly born United States of America. But in a darkened room of the Philadelphia Hospital, a doctor looks down upon the figure of a man lying on a rude cot.

"Owen!"

"Yes, Doctor?"

"What's this patient doing here, in this overcrowded ward? And why is he pushed back into this corner? And why is he lying on that hard cot?"

"Oh, don't let that bother you, Doctor. That's Mad Joseph. The devil's been at work in his brain so long, shifting things about, I don't imagine Joseph would know if he were lying on nails."

The doctor glared at him. "You've put a madman in this ward—with all those other patients?"

"Oh, he's harmless enough, Dr. Rush."

"What concerns me, you fool," Dr. Rush said fiercely, "is the harm that's being done to *him*. He needs peace and quiet, special care. Put him in a decent bed, in a quiet room with sunlight. And make sure he's fed well. The poor fellow looks half-starved."

The doctor's face softened as he looked down at the patient. The man on the cot lay still, his eyes unblinking, the eyes of the living dead. "So your name is Joseph, eh?"

"No use talking to him," Owen said. "He just won't answer, Dr. Rush. No one knows who he is, or where he comes from. I've seen plenty of this kind since the war, and you can't do anything for them."

In the year of 1789 most people would have agreed with Owen. Few agreed with Dr. Rush, even though he was widely respected as a doctor, as a citizen and as one of the revered signers of the Declaration of Independence. But no one would have been annoyed with Rush if only he'd kept his opinions to himself. As a doctor, his job was to cure the ill. It was not his job to write letters to the newspapers, insulting

Benjamin Rush

letters complaining about conditions in Philadelphia hospitals, letters full of nonsense about the proper treatment for madmen and lunatics.

"Dr. Rush, the treatment of these people is none of your business!"

"The mentally ill *are* my business."

"Mentally ill! Rush, you know as well as we do that madness is no disease. Madness is a punishment for sins, and madmen are lost souls. They're bewitched."

"Gentlemen, believe me. Madness is no punishment for sins, nor is it a spell cast by witches. Madness is a disease of the mind. And for every disease there is a cure."

"Proof, Doctor. Where is your scientific proof of this?"

"Unfortunately," Rush admitted, "I have very little."

In matters like these the books were as yet unwritten, the knowledge not yet gained. There could be one way, and one way alone, to gain that knowledge: by study and treatment of people like Mad Joseph. Such treatment would require time and patience and special hospital facilities.

One day Dr. Rush was summoned to a meeting with the hospital trustees. Entering the meeting-room, the doctor was expecting a fight, for he knew that most of the trustees were opposed to his viewpoints and methods.

"Now, sir," said Mr. Coates, the trustees' spokesman, "about this—ah—this Mad Joseph case. We understand you have placed him in a room by himself and have special nurses attending him. This man is mad, Dr. Rush. And there is nothing we can do for him. The hospital is overcrowded as it is. I'm afraid we must let him go."

"Mr. Coates," said Dr. Rush, "once there was a time when it was considered futile to attempt to cure even the simplest of illnesses. Today, we know better. And—"

Mr. Coates said, "You are going to tell me he is mentally ill. But you have been treating this man for weeks, without results. In that time, has he spoken so much as one word?"

"No, but—"

"Mad Joseph. Who is he, Dr. Rush? No one knows. And no one knows where he comes from. Why, Dr. Rush, this madman does not himself know who he is! If a man be lost this way, even to himself, how can you hope to find him, Dr. Rush?"

Dr. Rush stood up. He looked round the table at the trustees. "Gentlemen, we do know who Mad Joseph is. His name is Knight, Joseph Knight."

"But he cannot speak. How do you know—"

"I have found out by chance. He is—or was—a farmer. The farm is just outside of town. And he has a wife, living there in poverty. I asked her, 'Has Joseph always been this way?' 'No,' she said, 'do you think I would have married a madman?'" The doctor paused. "I asked her how long Joseph had been this way. Two years, she told me. Two years, since the end of the war, when Joseph came home from the army."

Dr. Rush looked fiercely round the table. "Mad Joseph—Joseph Knight—was one of the very first to join the Revolutionary Army. He fought under General Washington. And it was the hardships he endured on the battlefields that brought on his illness."

The trustees sat silent.

Dr. Rush said, "We owe a debt of gratitude to this man. We must restore Mad Joseph to himself—and to the nation he fought to make free."

After that meeting, the trustees voted to give Dr. Rush the authority and also the funds to work with Mad Joseph. And his eloquence won him something more. If he proved successful with Joseph and similar cases, funds would be granted to build a special hospital for the mentally ill. Here the insane would be treated as human beings, not as criminals or creatures bewitched.

Mad Joseph. How much depended on

this unfortunate veteran of Washington's army!

"How is he coming along?" Dr. Rush asked, a few weeks later.

"Fine, sir," Owen said. "Took his food himself this morning. But he still won't talk."

"I think it's time for him to leave this hospital."

"What, sir? You're turning him loose?"

"I'm sending him home. And you're going with him, Owen. Stay there with him. See that he remains quiet, at first. And then—well, his wife says he used to be a fine farmer. In his spare time, Joseph used to carve wood. In a few weeks, we'll start him again with his wood-carving. Possibly, Owen, if we busy him with simple things, the things he once enjoyed doing—well, then, just possibly his mind will slowly begin healing itself."

"That's a strange idea, Doctor."

For those days it *was* a strange idea. Yet, two weeks later, Owen was beginning to wonder. Not that Mad Joseph was talking—he wasn't. No, the poor fellow still didn't recognize his wife, or his house, or anything in it. And yet—well, there were times when Joseph's eyes lighted up and he seemed on the verge of speaking.

Busy in the overcrowded Philadelphia Hospital, Dr. Rush was delayed in paying a visit to the farm. Finally arriving there, he found Joseph hacking away at a piece of wood.

"Just sort of hacks at it," Owen said. "Nothing comes of it yet. But he seems to enjoy it, sir."

"We're trying to get him to do some work around the farm," Joseph's wife said.

"Fine, Mrs. Knight. But now we must be careful. I believe we have come to a crucial period. Be sure he gets no shocks. Don't let any strangers frighten him. Keep him in good physical condition. If he comes through this . . . we've won."

A few weeks later, standing in his office, Dr. Rush looked down at a small wooden box. He turned it over in his hand.

"It took him six weeks to carve it," Mrs. Knight said proudly.

"It's lovely," Dr. Rush said.

"It's for you, Dr. Rush," Mad Joseph said. "I made it for you."

"Thank you, Joseph," the doctor said. "You don't know how much this means to me. And, in a matter of a few short months, Joseph, you won't need me any more."

Some time later, Dr. Rush was able to report to the trustees of the hospital: "Joseph is normal and has been so for the past three months. There has been no relapse and no indication that there may be one. I am not claiming that this can be done for all who are mentally ill, but it can be done for many. Gentlemen, I beg you, grant the funds for a mental hospital. This request goes deeper than the well-being of individuals; this request affects the entire future welfare of this country for which all of us fought. It was my privilege to help create this nation with my signature on the Declaration of Independence. Yet I know that my work and Joseph's sacrifice will be wasted, utterly wasted, unless steps are taken to protect and maintain the well-being and the health of all our citizens. No nation is stronger than the people who make up that nation. You, gentlemen, are in a position to serve our people. Serve them by creating this special hospital. Serve them by recognizing madness for the disease it is, and by providing the means to conquer it."

The trustees granted the funds, and the hospital was built. Dr. Rush, the Magnificent Meddler, had won. And when the *First Annual Report of the Philadelphia Hospital for the Mentally Ill* was published, it was an impressive document. "Let us hope," Dr. Rush said, "that we have seen the end of clanking chains and the lash of whips in the madhouse. Our sufferers now taste the blessings of air and light —they have regained their standing as human beings."

THE EPIDEMIC FIGHTER

(BENJAMIN WATERHOUSE)

A prick on a child's arm and a drop of vaccine. Several days of slight fever and a soreness of the flesh—the after-effects of a vaccination. Without such prevention many a child would die of smallpox or be pitted permanently by its scars.

In 1800, an epidemic of smallpox swept through America, leaving thousands dead or disfigured. Whole city populations fled in panic, only to encounter the disease again, in their places of refuge.

But in Cambridge, Massachusetts, which had not yet been affected by the epidemic, a young doctor spoke urgently to the members of the town council. "The experiments of Dr. Jenner in England have shown conclusively that human smallpox *can* be wiped out by administering matter from the animal form of the disease, cowpox. But this must be done *before* the patient has contracted the disease."

The council members jeered, but this did not stop young Dr. Benjamin Waterhouse's efforts to stop the spread of smallpox by inoculation. To know about Dr. Jenner's discoveries was one thing; to persuade the American people that vaccination was safe, quite another. How could you make anyone submit to vaccination while he was healthy? It was asking him to contract an animal disease, cowpox, which—for all he knew—might prove worse than smallpox itself.

Other doctors shrank from the attempt, but Waterhouse persisted. As a result of his one-man crusade against smallpox, he had to endure much abuse and loss of practice.

One day, as he was visiting a sick child he asked the mother, "Is that your little boy I saw in the yard as I came in?"

"Why, yes."

"I noticed the pockmarks on his face. Smallpox?"

"Yes, he had it three years ago."

"And your daughter?"

"Never. Dear God, may she never. Our little boy was so sick, we thought he was going to die."

"He was lucky. But if your daughter got it, she might not be so lucky. Wait, there *is* a way to prevent smallpox. I can vaccinate your daughter right now if you'll permit me."

"With that—cowpox?"

"Hundreds of children have been vaccinated in England already. They—"

The mother was indignant. "No child of mine is going to be stuck with your devilish lancet! I've heard of people turning into animals because of it."

"Animals!"

"Good day, Doctor. You will kindly leave my house." And he was shown the door.

Another time he ran into an old patient in the street. "I haven't seen you since I attended your wife some weeks ago. No doubt my bill was overlooked in the excitement," he added.

"No, I remember it," was the grim reply.

"Good." Waterhouse smiled in relief. "If it wouldn't inconvenience you too much, I need the money rather badly."

"You'll not collect that bill from me, Doctor. This is my way of resisting your attempts to spread cowpox over the city." And he walked on.

Dr. Waterhouse was slandered in the newspapers, denounced by street-corner speakers, avoided by his former friends and patients. Many actually believed those vaccinated with cowpox would turn into oxen. Feeling against Waterhouse ran so high that threats were made against his life. Even his wife was fearful.

One night, as they tiptoed out of their son Daniel's room, Benjamin said tenderly, "At least *he* will not come down with smallpox." With his eyes resting on the scars on his wife's face, he added, "He will not have to suffer what you went through, Eliza."

"You don't mean to vaccinate our *son?*"

He looked down in surprise. "Eliza, you're afraid. You've allowed yourself to be affected by the same groundless prejudices as everyone else. Why shouldn't I vaccinate him?"

Her eyes opened wide in disbelief. "He's your own flesh and blood!"

"That's exactly why I intend to protect him."

Finally Waterhouse decided that the only way to convince the public—and his wife—was by securing the backing of someone whose opinion would be respected. He decided to appeal to Thomas Jefferson, the President of the United States.

Dr. Waterhouse journeyed to Washington. People had told him that the President would never see him; he was far too busy to waste time on foolish ideas. But Jefferson had a scientific mind and he readily granted an interview to Dr. Waterhouse.

"In England," Waterhouse explained to Jefferson, "Dr. Jenner noticed that dairymaids were generally immune to smallpox. Since he knew that those who recovered from smallpox also became immune, Dr. Jenner reasoned that the two diseases were related, that the cowpox was really a milder form of smallpox. Dr. Jenner prepared a vaccine from cowpox and, by infecting some people with it, proved that, after suffering a mild reaction, they then became immune to smallpox."

"I know something of these experiments," said Jefferson. "But what is it you want me to do?"

"Make it publicly known that you endorse vaccination."

"Has the British government given it official sanction?"

"Yes," replied Dr. Waterhouse. "The British Navy has adopted a vaccination policy. It was ordered for the soldiers of the Gibraltar garrison, where the smallpox rate had been high. Now vaccination is being used in private practice throughout England."

"Doctor Waterhouse," said Mr. Jefferson, "as I'm sure you know, I can't order the American people to be vaccinated. But that has nothing to do with my belief in the effectiveness of such a precaution. Do you have any of that precious vaccine with you?"

"Why, yes," the doctor said.

"I want you to leave some of it with me—" Jefferson said.

"But—"

"Together with the necessary directions for its use," he continued.

"What do you intend to do with it, Mr. President?"

Thomas Jefferson smiled. "Try it, of course. On my servants and my neighbors if they'll allow it, on my family and—on myself."

With this gesture of confidence by the President, the tide began to turn in favor of vaccination.

When Benjamin Waterhouse returned to Cambridge, he found that an epidemic of smallpox had preceded him. The church bells kept tolling the deaths of new victims. Red flags fluttered from houses in which the sick lay. He hurried through deserted streets to his own home. Eliza, since she had once had smallpox, was immune, but what about Daniel?

He lost no time in vaccinating Danny. His wife, sick with fear, no longer tried to stop him. When he saw that the vaccination had taken, he told his wife, "Eliza, we have no time to wait. The President has been vaccinated and the people know it. But the President has not been exposed to smallpox since his vaccination. Danny must be. I must prove that he is immune."

So young Daniel Waterhouse, accompanied by his mother, went to live in the hospital at Cambridge. There he was kept for fifteen days among patients dying of smallpox. If, in that time, he did not contract the disease, he was safe. On the fifteenth day, when his father came for him, the little boy asked, "Papa, I wasn't sick like the rest of them, was I?"

"No, Danny, you weren't," said his father, hugging his son to him. And turning to Eliza, he said, "They are beginning to come. People have finally recognized the truth, my dear. Now they are waiting in line to be vaccinated."

The next time Dr. Waterhouse went to Washington, it was at the personal invitation of the President. "I can't thank you enough for what you have done," said Mr. Jefferson. "The whole nation is indebted to you."

"And to you, Mr. President," replied the doctor, "for by your example you made my work possible. As long as such experiments in medicine can take place in our country, it will continue to be as great as the men who conceived it."

Benjamin Waterhouse.

197

THE MASTER NAVIGATOR

(NATHANIEL BOWDITCH)

Nathaniel Bowditch was born in the sea-faring village of Salem, Massachusetts, on March 26, 1773. Since his family was poor, he was forced to leave school at the age of ten and go to work. A queer young lad, that Bowditch boy, Salemites remarked. Arithmetic, numbers, all kinds of mathematical calculations filled his head. While other boys dreamed of ships and faraway lands, Nat Bowditch seemed content to stay on land and dream of numbers.

He worked hard during the day and continued his studies at night. He was only thirteen when he amazed his neighbors by surveying an irregular strip of land over which the local surveyor had thrown up his hands. By the time he was twenty-one, he was known as something of a wizard who could in a twinkling perform calculations in his head which would take most men an hour of figuring with pencil and paper.

In those days just after the Revolution, how could a man best employ such a talent for figures? For the most part, only businessmen and storekeepers were much concerned with arithmetic, and when Nat went to work for a local merchant as clerk and accountant in his store, everyone felt that Bowditch had found his natural place in the world. Everyone, that is, but Nathaniel Bowditch himself.

Nat, too, had the sea in his blood, although most of the people of Salem didn't suspect it. His studies had taken him into the realm of currents and tides, of winds and the stars. He had already compiled an almanac which certain experts said was accurate in tidal and astronomical detail. Quiet and modest though he was, his opinion was beginning to be sought about sea-lanes and proper methods of navigation. It was even rumored that, in his copy of Moore's *Navigator*, the pages were covered with notes and corrections.

"Now there's an upstart for you!" said one of the sea-captains. "Moore's book on navigation! I can't make head nor tail of it myself, and never could, and I've sailed the world these thirty years. It's only the British know the secrets of that book and it was written for them. But here's young Bowditch, now, that land-lubber—never once has he sailed before the mast—yet what does he say to me the other day? 'Mr. Cleek,' he says, as bright as you please, 'Mr. Cleek, perhaps you're lucky you've never tried to use Moore's book, for it's full of mistakes!' " And the captain roared his laughter.

Fortunately for Bowditch, there were other captains more ready to cock an ear to what he had to say. Captain Henry Prince, for one. Prince also could not understand the figures in Moore's book, and he quite often remarked disgustedly, " 'Tis a British book for British seamen, I say, and I'm content to guide my ships by dead reckoning." Yet he always had a sense of uneasiness whenever he said it. The British had bigger ships, but that wasn't enough to account for the way they kept beating the Americans in navigation.

"Dead reckoning," Elias Derby scoffed. "I'm a ship-owner, Captain Prince, but if we go on using these old-fashioned methods of sailing the seas, I'll soon be pushing a pencil in a store, like this lad here." He nodded at Bowditch, who stood behind the counter, packing dry goods into a box for Captain Prince. "No, Captain Prince," Mr. Derby went on, "dead reckoning's good enough for short trips to the West Indies. But now that we're trying to establish regular trade routes to India and China by way of Good Hope, we'll have to do better. Did you know the *Massachusetts* went so far off her course she missed Java Head entirely on her last voyage? The finest ship of Salem's fleet—

and she loses three weeks! And why? Because none of her officers could fix the position of the ship from day to day!"

"The British use chronometers," Captain Prince said. "If we're going to trade with the far corners of the earth, we'll need 'em too."

"Chronometers cost a fortune," Mr. Derby said. I, for one, have little faith in them."

"As you say," Captain Prince agreed reluctantly, "dead reckoning's not enough. And without the chronometers, we'll have to learn how to find longitude by some other methods." He looked across the counter at young Nathaniel Bowditch, and smiled. "What do you say, Nat?"

Elias Derby interrupted him. "We're too busy, my lad, for idle talk."

"It might be wise to listen to him," Captain Prince suggested. "He's the lad who surveyed an irregular piece of property at the age of thirteen, Mr. Derby."

"Yes, I know," Mr. Derby said. "But surveying's one thing, and navigation's another."

Bowditch could contain himself no longer. "I believe, sir, that I can find longitude at sea by making lunar observations."

Elias Derby regarded him with the steady gaze of disbelief. "Even the British officers can't do that, Bowditch. They depend on Moore's calculations."

"Excuse me, sir," Bowditch said. "But I wouldn't advise any seaman to be guided by Moore's book. It's full of mistakes. In fact, I've found five thousand of them so far, and I expect there are many more."

This was too much for Mr. Derby; his mouth opened and then closed, and he looked at Captain Prince.

"I'd listen to the lad, if I were you," said Captain Prince. "I've generally found it mighty instructive. In fact, sir, I want you to allow me to take him along, on my next voyage."

"For what purpose?"

"To navigate the ship by making lunar

observations."

"Yes, sir," Bowditch added. "And I'll find the longitude without a chronometer. I've done the theoretical work on paper. I'm sure I can prove—"

But Derby wasn't listening to him. He was staring at Captain Prince. "Are you serious, Captain?"

"I am, sir."

"But do you realize," Derby said, "one error in the observations he makes can bring a thirty-fold error in the result? That much I know about navigating by the moon and the stars."

"Aye, sir," Captain Prince replied. "I know that, too."

Between the years 1795 and 1800, Nathaniel Bowditch made four long voyages with Captain Prince. The results were almost incredible. And those results soon drew the attention of the British. In 1802, in London, a sea captain named Murray, just returned from a voyage to Manila, was summoned hastily to the office of his shipping line.

His employer greeted him sharply. "Your ship was five weeks overdue from Manila, resulting in heavy losses in trade."

"There was a northeast monsoon, sir. We had to lay over at the Isle de France for two weeks. As you know, we were guided by Moore's *Navigator,* but 'tis apparent there was an error in Moore's calculations—or in ours."

"An error in Moore's calculations?"

"Aye, sir. At Manila, I talked with a Captain Henry Prince of Salem. Do you know, sir, when we docked at Manila, I found that ship from Salem safely there in the harbor. They had reached the port in the face of the very monsoon that threw us off our course."

"And did you learn from this Yankee how to navigate in face of a northeast monsoon?"

"I did, but you won't believe me."

"Perhaps I will," his employer said. "These Yankees have been outstripping our vessels in every foreign port. Somehow, in the past four years, they've learned to navigate ships accurately. But how?"

"Well, sir," Captain Murray replied, "Captain Prince informed me he had a crew of twelve men, all of whom could work a lunar observation."

"Impossible!"

"Why, even the cook aboard can do so," Captain Murray added. "You see, sir, they've got a young man, a clerk of Captain Prince's, who's been doing the teaching. He—"

"The cook?" his employer exploded.

"Aye, sir. Captain Prince called him before us, from the galley, and when I asked him if he could find longitude, he demonstrated perfectly. It was most amazing, sir."

"And this young clerk you mentioned—"

"Bowditch, sir. Nathaniel Bowditch."

"Ridiculous name," his employer said. "You must be making it up."

"No, sir. I've talked with Bowditch himself. Nice young chap. He claims to have discovered eight thousand errors in Moore's book on navigation."

"But our seamen have been guided by the book for years," his British employer interrupted. "The French use it, too."

"I am not a mathematician, sir, but I have suspected there were errors in Moore. Errors which have cost us serious delays. And this young man has just published his own book, with all of Moore's errors corrected. He calls it *The Practical Navigator.*"

There was widespread jubilation in Salem and throughout America when British and French orders in hundreds and thousands poured in for Nathaniel Bowditch's book, *The Practical Navigator.* And in 1802, the young, self-educated mathematician was given an honorary degree from Harvard College. Still, there were skeptics in Salem who maintained that Bowditch's work was all theoretical, for Bowditch had never sailed as skipper and master of a vessel.

On Christmas Eve of that year, a blizzard raged in the port of Salem. Several months before, Bowditch had been given his first command, the *Putnam* out of Salem bound for Sumatra. Half of Captain Prince's capital was invested in this trip, because he believed in Nat and his theories. "I give you my word, Captain Prince," Bowditch had said, "my anchor will drop in Salem before Christmas."

Wearily, the captain turned from his window. Where was Bowditch now? Lost or at the bottom of the sea, with the ship. Any one would be lost in such weather.

Through the flying snow light from a moving lantern flickered and grew stronger.

"Blast it!" the captain shouted. "What's that? Halloo!" he called to the figures approaching along the wharf. "Are you men from the *Putnam?*"

"Aye," a voice called cheerfully against the wind. "The crew of the *Putnam.*"

"And Captain Bowditch?"

"Here!" Bowditch called, hurrying up.

"It's a miracle," Captain Prince said. "Thank God, you're safe."

"No miracle," Bowditch laughed. "Just pure mathematics."

200

THE CONQUEST OF PAIN

(WILLIAM MORTON)

Today, when a patient in need of surgery lies on the operating table, he need have no fear of pain. Behind him stands a trained anesthetist, who holds a special mask to his face, if ether is the anesthetic to be administered. Breathing in its vapor, he sinks slowly into a deep, dreamless sleep. "There now . . . breathe deeply . . . not too fast . . ." He is no longer awake to hear the nurse saying, "Pulse normal, doctor. Respiration normal. The pupils are dilated. He's under." The surgeon can then make the necessary incisions with his instruments. But the sleeping patient feels no pain.

What is this extraordinary substance we take for granted? $(C_2H_5)_2O$, an ethyl oxide, as the chemists call it, produced by the action of sulphuric acid on alcohol. Colorless, quick to evaporate, it is a priceless weapon against needless agony.

Before it was discovered, surgery involved such suffering that several strong men were required to hold a patient down on the table, while the surgeon worked as rapidly as he could. Whiskey might dull the pain for a while, but the doctor's time was limited by many things, particularly the patient's constitution. His ability to bear pain often meant the difference between life or death. Many slipped away to death before the surgeon finished his work.

For long centuries surgery without pain was considered an impractical dream. Yet "impractical" men continued to experiment in the field of medicine in the hope of doing something to alleviate the severity of their patients' suffering. In the thirteenth century, the philosopher Raymond Lully made notes about a white, sweetish fluid which he called sweet vitriol, but he did not know what use might be made of it. For more than two centuries his discovery was forgotten. In the early sixteenth century, Theophrastus Bombastus Paracelsus von Hohenheim, a Swiss physician, mixed some acid of sulphur with alcohol, heated it and condensed the vapor into a white fluid. Paracelsus fed this to chickens and noticed that not only did they take it gladly, but they were instantly put into a deep sleep, from which they awakened without any ill effects. Still, nothing was done with it by men of medicine.

Late in the eighteenth century scientists began to come a little closer to the miracle of anesthesia. In 1772, an English scientist and nonconformist minister, Joseph Priestley, discovered an anesthetic vapor, nitrous oxide, with which he was experimenting on animals when a mob wrecked his laboratory.

Shortly afterward, his discovery was confirmed by the English chemist, Sir Humphry Davy. Because of its effect on himself, Davy called the substance "laughing gas." He announced that it possessed anesthetic properties. Later, it was Michael Faraday who suggested that ether vapors could put people to sleep.

But nitrous oxide and ether remained merely chemical curiosities. They were sometimes used as magic and stage show properties or for parlor amusements. Not until 1841 was there any serious attempt to use them as anesthetics.

In that year an American doctor, Crawford Williamson Long, remembered the "ether parties" of his student days. He dusted off a flask of the stuff and took it with him to liven up a social gathering. During the course of the evening, while under the influence of ether, he tripped over a chair and skinned his knee. To his amazement, the injury caused him no pain! Only as the effects of the ether wore off did his knee begin to sting. Experimenting further, he persuaded a friend who had a tumor on his neck to take ether before he removed it for him.

The operation was successful and painless. But some of the less educated townspeople in Jefferson, Georgia, where Dr. Long practiced, were scandalized. The cries of pain that usually emanated from the patient on the operating table were, to them, a symbol that the devil within was being exorcised. An operation without pain seemed unnatural to them. The clergy led the rest in their outcries against this first use of anesthesia. Dr. Long, an amiable and ambitious young man, responded to public opinion by giving up his demonstrably unpopular ideas.

The next discovery of the virtues of anesthesia was reported in 1844 by Horace Wells, a dentist practicing in Hartford, Connecticut. He had taken his wife to a laughing gas exhibition. There he had talked with a man who had volunteered to undergo the usual experiment. Fascinated, Wells procured some of the gas for himself. On December 11, 1844, he persuaded a colleague to extract his second molar. As he had hoped, Wells felt no pain during the extraction and decided that the amazing properties of laughing gas signified a new era in dental surgery.

Wells went to Boston to see a friend who was then studying medicine under Dr. Charles Jackson. Dr. William Thomas Green Morton, a former dentist, was so sparked by his friend's excitement that his faith in laughing gas soon exceeded that of Wells. Morton took Wells to meet Dr. Jackson.

Although Jackson warned them that the death of a patient might involve them in a manslaughter charge, he did consent to arrange another experiment.

A young student agreed to submit to an extraction before the faculty of the Harvard Medical School. On the appointed day, nitrous oxide was administered to the patient. Dr. Wells grabbed hold of the aching tooth with his forceps—and the patient yelled out in pain.

A riot followed among the spectators. Cries of "Humbug!" "Throw them out!" "Fraud!" sounded through the lecture hall.

The humiliation was too much for Wells, who gave up anesthesia and returned to conventional dentistry. But not his convert, William Morton. Morton believed the experiment had failed because the amount of nitrous oxide had been insufficient. He felt that he must, by further experimentation, correct their error and turn defeat into triumph.

Morton was a dedicated man and, it sometimes seemed, quite an eccentric one. Had he not taken a skeleton along on his honeymoon, so that he could study human bone structure? Now he began experimenting with ether.

At first he used caterpillars and worms for his experiments; then he tried ether on himself. Convinced of the anesthetic properties of ether, all he needed now was a patient. And one day in came a Mr. Frost, writhing in pain from a severe toothache.

Morton studied him. "Well, I think I'll have to extract it, Mr. Frost. How would you like something to take away the pain, so you won't feel the tooth being taken out?"

Mr. Frost looked at him in dismay. "What do you mean to do, hypnotize me?"

"Something far better. Will you try it?"

A fresh jab of pain sent Mr. Frost's hand to his jaw. "Oh, all right," he said warily. "I'll try anything."

On October 1, 1846, the Boston *Daily Journal* informed its readers: "Last evening an ulcerated tooth was extracted from

William Morton had become a man with a mission. His discovery belonged to medicine, to all mankind. He offered it to the physicians of Boston but his offer was rejected. But Morton was not easily discouraged. Finally, he managed to obtain an interview with the eminent Professor John C. Warren, surgeon at the Massachusetts General Hospital.

"What makes you think I should try this method?" asked Professor Warren, who had just come from a difficult operation. "Everyone else has refused."

"Because I know you've just performed an amputation. What wouldn't you give to get those agonized shrieks out of your head?"

Professor Warren looked hard at his visitor. "And why should I trust you?"

"Because," said Morton, "you can't bring yourself to torture a patient unnecessarily."

Professor Warren agreed to allow Morton to administer an anesthetic to one of his patients on October 16, 1846. The patient was wheeled into the crowded amphitheater of the Massachusetts General Hospital amid a deep silence. At Professor Warren's side stood the leading surgeons of Boston. Ranged in tiers before him were scores of students. Professor Warren glanced up at the clock. Then turning, he addressed his audience: "Before beginning this operation, I wish to say a few words. I have been a surgeon in Boston for forty years. On every instance when the knife was applied to live tissue, there was pain. Now a dentist of this city tells us that he has successfully used a substance which will *do away* with pain. Is Dr. Morton here?"

There was a hum of voices in the amphitheater, but no one stepped forward.

"Dr. William Morton?"

Professor Warren was about to begin the operation without using an anesthetic after all when Dr. Morton's arrival was an-

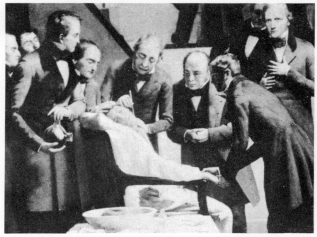

The first operation under ether. Dr. Morton, left, holds the inhaler, while Dr. Warren cuts out the tumor.

nounced. From the doorway, his voice rang out. "Gentlemen, I was delayed because I have worked all night and until this moment to perfect my inhalator for administering the ether."

Dr. Morton approached the patient. "Are you afraid?" he asked.

"No, sir."

"Take this tube in your mouth and breathe in. Breathe deeply. Not too fast. That's better." Dr. Morton looked up. "Will you prick his arm with a needle, Professor Warren?"

"There, did that hurt you?" the surgeon asked, bending over his patient. "Can you hear me? Did the needle hurt?" There was a silence from the patient, whose eyes were closed as if in a deep sleep.

Professor Warren began to excise a vascular tumor from the neck of the patient. The learned surgeons craned forward, the students stood on tiptoe on the benches. Everyone awaited the cry of pain—which did not come. When the patient awoke, he had no memory of what had happened to him. Morton had at last been vindicated for his belief in the value of ether.

From that day, October 16, 1846, the fear of pain no longer hung like a pall over the operating table, no longer stood between the surgeon and his delicate task. After many centuries, the struggle against pain had been won through anesthesia.

203

DOCTOR IN CRINOLINE

(ELIZABETH BLACKWELL)

Elizabeth Blackwell had a unique ambition: she was determined to be a doctor. It was unheard of because at that time—in the 1840's—there was no such thing as a *lady* doctor. She was twenty-three, unmarried and living with an aunt in Cincinnati. Her aunt, of course, was highly indignant that Elizabeth should think of such a thing. It would be quite all right for her to become a schoolteacher, but a doctor! Why, no medical school would admit her.

For a while it looked as though her aunt might be right. Young Elizabeth's application was refused by one school after another. She kept on renewing it for three years before she got an acceptance from the medical school at Geneva, New York. But when the president called her into his office, she realized that her battle was far from won.

The president, Dr. Lee, was obviously embarrassed. He had not expected her to appear, he said. "But I received a letter saying that I'd been admitted," Elizabeth insisted.

"My dear young lady, when your application was received, the faculty turned it over to the student body for action, Geneva being a democratic institution. As a prank the students voted to admit you."

"But—" Elizabeth began.

Dr. Lee interrupted. "To be frank, I would rather you didn't stay. I am sure you would find the studies most repugnant."

"May I ask a question?" she asked.

"Certainly."

"Your letter of acceptance . . . doesn't it constitute some kind of legal contract?"

Dr. Lee's embarrassment changed to annoyance. "Well, if you choose to put it that way—"

Elizabeth persisted. "But I don't want to sue you for damages. I only want to learn to be a doctor."

Angry now, the president warned her, "I can assure you, young lady, the students will make your life intolerable. I mean, there are certain jokes that men play in the dissecting room—"

"I fear, sir," answered Elizabeth, "that those are among the risks I shall have to take. Will you have the goodness, please, to enroll me as a student?"

Not only was Elizabeth made the butt of jokes by the other medical students, but she was ridiculed in the press. The townspeople of Geneva avoided her. The women considered her desire to enter a man's profession a sin. They whispered that she was immoral, that she consorted with the male students. In order to silence these rumors, Elizabeth kept to her room, dressed in black and never accepted invitations to the parties held by her fellow students. Still, the women of the town drew aside their skirts whenever she passed. In the boarding-house where she lived, the other tenants would not speak to her in the hall.

All this she could have borne, but there was one rejection which she had not anticipated and which, after her first term at school, almost caused her to give up medicine entirely.

She had succeeded in persuading the director of Blockley Almshouse to accept her as a volunteer doctor during the summer vacation. Blockley Almshouse was both a poorhouse and a hospital. It was shunned by any citizen who could afford to pay for treatment elsewhere, but for medical students it was considered a laboratory.

Elizabeth was assigned to the women's

ward. There she found indifference, callousness and filth; but worst of all, she found she was shunned as a doctor even by the sick and outcast. An epidemic of typhus filled the wards and there was more work than the staff could handle, but the patients refused her medical help, until one memorable night.

Elizabeth was in the children's ward when she heard a child cry out to a male doctor attending her, "No, no! Please, the *other* doctor. The lady." No sooner had she spoken than Elizabeth was at her side, looking down with gratitude into the child's trusting eyes.

In the fall, Elizabeth returned to Geneva and finished her studies. She was graduated as the first woman doctor in American history. But to hold a diploma was still far from being a practicing physician. If she were to be accepted anywhere, she would need better training than her colleagues. To get this superior training Dr. Elizabeth Blackwell left for Paris.

There she suffered a misfortune. While working on a laboratory experiment, she contracted purulent ophthalmia. She lost the sight of one eye and with it her chance of becoming a surgeon. But it could not prevent her being a doctor. She continued her graduate studies in Paris and London and, after two years, returned to New York.

The experience at Blockley was still vivid in her mind. Treated still as an outcast in her profession, she decided to help the outcasts of society obtain medical treatment. Going through New York's Lower East Side, she inspected the tenements called "fever nests." In them, men, women and children were crowded in unbelievable squalor. Every time another shipload of immigrants docked, the crowding became even worse.

She appealed to a well-to-do Quaker, Stacy Collins, and took him on a tour through her chosen territory. "In this whole district," she told him, "there is not a single clinic of any kind. I want to establish a clinic for women and children, a place where they can come for diagnosis and from which I can go out on visits."

Mr. Collins tried to dissuade her. "Thee will find it hard, certainly, harder than private practice," he cautioned.

Her smile was not without bitterness. "No one will let me practice," she said. "Here, the poor people would come. Like me, they have nowhere else."

Mr. Collins provided her with money to rent a small room on Tompkins Square. There, she opened New York's first Dispensary for Indigent Women and Chil-

Elizabeth Blackwell.

dren. It had a desperate struggle for existence until, with the aid of the Reverend Henry Ward Beecher and the Society of Friends, she succeeded in raising ten thousand dollars. The infirmary she was now able to establish was the first to have women doctors on its staff.

For this very reason the infirmary had difficulty getting even charity cases to avail themselves of its services. Once when a patient died on the operating table, there was a riot on the lawn outside. The rioters smashed windows and might have demolished the hospital facilities had not a dispute arisen among them. An Irish dockworker named Kevin Dwyer who had been brought to the infirmary with pneumonia and had been cured there came gallantly to the defense of the lady doctors. "How can you call them murderers?" wives and children when you hadn't the price of a private doctor. For one dead, look at all as has recovered! Do patients never die in other hospitals?"

Dr. Blackwell appeared in a window to speak to the crowd. "Now you listen to her," Dwyer cried, "her as has gone up and down these streets, entering flats where no other doctor would go because of the cholera."

"Thank you. Please, may I have a word?" called Dr. Blackwell. As the angry tumult of the crowd subsided, she said, "A girl died here tonight. It's true you did not bring her to us soon enough. She had appendicitis and her appendix burst before we could remove it. But it is also true that we doctors cannot cure *every* case

that comes to us. You think it's only because we are women, but that is not true. We have the same training as any other doctors. But the medical profession still has many things to learn. The sooner you stop opposing doctors like myself, simply because we are women, the more we will be able to devote our energy to the job we are here to do: making sick people well."

Later the coroner investigated and the hospital was cleared of all blame. From then on, everything went ahead.

During the Civil War, Dr. Blackwell trained nurses. Then New York State granted her a charter to give medical degrees to women from her hospital. The New York Infirmary and College for Women and Children is still, more than a hundred years later, one of the finest institutions of its kind. Her pioneer work in America ended, Elizabeth's old friend Florence Nightingale asked her to come to England. There she was consulted on medical courses to be offered to women and on the opening of hospitals for women.

When Andrew Carnegie said, "Pioneering does not pay," he uttered only half a truth. It may not pay the pioneer, as in the case of Elizabeth Blackwell, who did not receive the recognition and rewards she deserved until late in life. But society was at once and forever infinitely rich because of the new careers in medicine opened to women and the years of life she gave to many who might have received little or no care otherwise.

FIRST AMERICAN WOMAN SCIENTIST
(MARIA MITCHELL)

To whalers on long sea voyages the stars have always been important. Stars are the only fixed points they can use to chart their course in the open sea. Small wonder, then, that the movements of the stars were a source of constant interest to Nantucket Islanders. In the early nineteenth century, Nantucket was the hub of the whaling industry. Retired sea captains often set up observation platforms on the roofs of their houses to study the stars through telescopes.

To young Maria Mitchell, born on Nantucket in 1818 to Quaker parents, the stars provided a natural focus for her lively intelligence. She was fortunate in having parents who believed that a girl might do more in life than cook and sew. Maria's father, an accomplished amateur astronomer, enjoyed having his daughter join him at his telescope on the roof. Seeing that she had a capacity for learning equal to any man's, he encouraged her studies. By the time Maria was seventeen, her mathematical knowledge had progressed beyond that of her teachers.

Despite the Mitchells' pride in Maria, astronomy was not yet an acceptable career for a woman. She began to look for a position in which she could make use of her abilities and one which would give her opportunity for further study. This she found when, at the age of twenty-one, the Nantucket selectmen placed her in charge of their library, the Athenaeum.

After filing and indexing the books, Maria had time to devote herself to her scientific studies. When her day's work at the library desk was done, she returned home for a night's work—or pleasure—on the roof, recording the changing positions of the stars.

On the evening of October 1, 1847, her family was entertaining guests. Her brothers and sisters were grouped around the piano with their friends, and the elder Mitchells were all comfortably seated on the sofa. Only Maria was missing. There were signs that a storm was brewing and Mrs. Mitchell turned to her husband. "William," she said, with concern, "it is hardly a night for Maria to be outside."

Then they heard Maria's excited voice calling her father from the head of the stairs. The music came to a sudden stop, and one of the young people called out, "Maria, come down, we need your voice."

But Maria said urgently, "I must speak to Father at once!"

When Mr. Mitchell mounted the stairs she said, "There's an observation I want thee to check before the clouds cover the sky. The storm is moving in fast."

There was a roll of thunder along the horizon. Maria beckoned her father to the telescope. "Quick, there's not a minute to lose!"

As he fixed his eye to the telescope, she went on breathlessly, "A comet, a *new comet*, Father! Nearly vertical above Polaris about five degrees. Does thee see it?"

"See it!" he cried. "Maria, when did thee first discover this?"

Clouds now blotted out the sky, and they were spattered with raindrops. Only when they had carried the instruments indoors did Maria have a chance to reply, "Last night, but I wasn't sure what it was."

"Thee must report it immediately. Will thee allow me to write the Harvard Observatory tonight?"

Three months later, Dr. Edward Everett, president of Harvard College, made the journey to Nantucket to visit Maria and her father. With him he brought the latest astronomical journal from Europe. "This journal reached Harvard two days ago, Miss Mitchell," he said. "It states that Italy's most distinguished astronomer, Father Vicio of Rome, saw your comet two nights *after* you did." He paused. "It is indeed *your* comet, Miss Mitchell, the first to have been discovered by telescope since 1831. You know the King of Denmark has offered prizes to any discoverer. Unfortunately, the Danish gold medal will go to Father Vicio."

Maria saw nothing strange in this. Vicio was a famous scientist, whereas she was an obscure young woman. Besides, she was interested in stars, not medals. Her father felt differently, however. "Why should it go to him?" he asked.

"Because of the official regulations," Dr. Everett explained. "They state that the discoverer—by telescope—of a comet must notify the nearest observatory by the very next mail. Now, Miss Mitchell observed the comet on October 1. But your letter did not leave Nantucket until October 3."

Even Maria could not suppress her excitement. "It *did* go by the next mail. Thee are accustomed to Boston, Dr. Everett. But we are Islanders here. When a storm comes up, the boats must stay in harbor until it's over."

"You mean—" began the doctor.

"I mean that on October 2, no ship *sailed* from Nantucket. But my letter *was* sent.'

In 1849 Maria Mitchell received the Danish gold medal, and was hailed as one of the world's leading astronomers. She was the first woman member elected to the American Academy of Arts and Sciences. In 1857 Maria spent a year in Europe at the invitation of leading scientists. At home once again, she devoted herself entirely to astronomy. After her mother's death in 1861, she moved with her father to Lynn, Massachusetts, where she set up a small observatory.

In 1865, she was visited by Mr. Matthew Vassar, founder of Vassar College. He invited her to become its first professor of astronomy.

"I have never taught anything in my life," she insisted. "How can you expect that, by taking a scientist away from her laboratory and standing her up before a class, you can make a teacher out of her?"

But that was not Mr. Vassar's worry. She was, he told her, better known than any other woman scholar in America. If he could announce that she would be on his school's faculty, it would inspire public confidence in Vassar College and assure the support necessary to make a success of the daring venture of a college for women.

Still, Maria Mitchell was reluctant to give up her unique career. At Vassar, of course, she would have the facilities for continuing her research, but hardly the time. Teaching was a full-time job.

She was about to refuse Mr. Vassar's offer when a woman she had never seen before came to see her. The woman was well-dressed and claimed to be prominent socially, but refused to give her name. She had come, she said, because she desper-

ately needed Maria's advice.

"Is it a question about astronomy?" Maria asked.

"Oh, yes," said the woman. "This is my problem. I'm a widow. My poor dear husband died two years ago, and now two men are in love with me. I admire them both, but I don't know which to marry. That is why I've come to you."

Maria's astonishment was obvious. "I've been told you know *everything* about the stars," the visitor continued.

Maria managed to disillusion her guest about her crystal-gazing powers and send her away. Then she sat down at her desk and wrote Mr. Vassar a letter of acceptance. She might not know much about teaching, but at least she could show the young ladies of Vassar the difference between astronomy and astrology.

A pioneer in science, Maria Mitchell soon became a pioneer in the education of women. She taught at Vassar for twenty-two years. At the age of sixty-nine she resigned because of her failing health. Back in Lynn, during the last year of her life, she once more had an unexpected call, this time from a mother and daughter. The mother had been one of Maria's first pupils. Now her child was about to enter Vassar.

"Mother says the college will never be the same without you," the girl said.

"I also want to tell you that the tradition you instilled in me has become part of my life," added the mother.

Puzzled, Maria said, "You have continued the study of astronomy?"

The mother laughed. "No, I'm afraid not. I don't have your talent. I have forgotten my astronomy, but I have not forgotten how to think."

Maria's decision to share her knowledge of astronomy with the young ladies of Vassar College had not been in vain. Her contributions to American education were as much appreciated as her contributions to the science of astronomy.

THE PLANT WIZARD

(LUTHER BURBANK)

Luther Burbank was born in Lancaster, Massachusetts, in 1849. From his early childhood, he showed a particular liking for flowers and plants. He attended public schools and later the Lancaster Academy. In the local library he found books on plant and animal life which fascinated him and he became a student of things that grow in the ground.

His own experiments began with an adventure in the woods when he was seventeen. One winter day he followed some rabbit tracks that led through the snow to a patch of brambles. He was about to turn back when a little patch of green grass growing brightly in the snow caught his eye. He made his way there and found that the grass was springing up beside a small stream. Its waters were quite warm for that time of year, and he knew that its source must be deep in the earth.

This discovery gave Burbank the idea that perhaps other things than grass might grow in winter if they were kept warm. Early in May of the same year he planted kernels of corn in a box of earth indoors. By the time the shoots were too tall to keep in the house, it was warm enough to transplant them in the garden. Young Burbank's corn was ripe a whole month ahead of his father's regular planting, and the life work of the future "plant wizard" had begun.

He continued experimenting with advanced plantings of vegetables for the next four years. In 1870, when he was twenty-one, he bought a farm of his own, a seventeen-acre tract of land near Lunenberg, Massachusetts. It was here that he developed the first proof of his theory that proper selection improves any plant strain.

The object of his first trial was the New England potato, which up to that time had been a scrawny and poor-tasting thing. Burbank was determined to improve this lowly vegetable. His efforts began the day he found a seed ball while touring the potato field with one of his farmhands.

"Did you ever see one of these things?" Burbank asked.

"Sure," said the farmhand. "It's a seed ball—a potato plant gone to seed. They do that, sometimes. And if you plant them there seeds, you get potato plants, same as when you plant the eyes."

"Look!" exclaimed Burbank. "No two of these seeds are exactly alike, and I'll bet that the plants and the potatoes will be as different as the seeds are. Some of the seeds may produce better potatoes."

"And then we can grow a whole patch of bumper ones from these first few!" interrupted the farmhand.

"Yes—and then a big field of even better potatoes from the best ones out of that patch," said Burbank.

Burbank planted the potato seeds, and from two of the plants which resulted he developed a superior potato. There was of course an eager market for them and Burbank might have become a prosperous farmer. He might even have become wealthy by selling the new potatoes as seed. But Luther Burbank was interested in other things than money-making. He was bent on continuing his experiments.

When Walter Gregory, the owner of some large farms near Marblehead, called on Burbank in 1875, it was for the purpose of buying exclusive rights to the "Burbank potato."

"I want to do this thing on a big scale," said Gregory. "I want to make every farmer in the country realize how good this new potato is, so that he'll buy seed potatoes from me. If you just go along as you are, making the Burbank potato general

211

property, it won't spread half so fast. You've got to tell people about a thing to make them want it."

"All right," said Burbank, "I'll sell you exclusive rights to my potato for a hundred and fifty dollars. You see, I want to go to California. I have three brothers there now, and from what they say in their letters, it's just the kind of climate and soil I'm looking for. Plants grow fast in California and I can get quicker results. A hundred and fifty dollars would just about pay my way out there."

Burbank went to California that same year and established a small nursery, where he continued his experiments with vegetables and fruits. In a short time he had built a small but profitable business by the same means he had used in developing the Burbank potato—the process of selection. He became known throughout the country for his invaluable advice to farmers.

One day a fruit-grower named Wells, who had done business with Burbank before, came into the Burbank nursery. Wells wished to take advantage of the growing demand for prunes.

"I've got enough land," he said, "to set out twenty thousand young plum trees next spring. Will you be able to sell them to me?"

Burbank in the field.

"But there aren't that many plum trees in the whole state of California," said Burbank. "However, I'd like to help you if I can. Let me think about this for twenty-four hours, will you, Wells?"

The next day, Luther Burbank agreed to deliver to Mr. Wells, in nine months' time, twenty thousand young plum trees. An idea had come to Burbank out of his knowledge of plant life and his fertile imagination, an idea which helped to gain him the title of "The Plant Wizard."

To solve his problem, Burbank began with the planting from seed of twenty thousand fast-growing almond trees. He then went to see the owner of a neighboring nursery which had more plum trees than any other in the district.

"Next April," said Burbank, "I'll be wanting some plum buds. Will you be able to sell me twenty thousand?"

The nursery owner, surprised at the number of buds Burbank wanted, agreed to sell them to him. "I'll just snip all the buds off about a hundred trees," he said.

"Better snip half the buds off two hundred trees, if you have that many trees," said Burbank. "It'll be better for the trees."

The almond trees came along in fine style, and the following April the twenty thousand plum buds were delivered, according to Burbank's order. Burbank then engaged a staff of experts to graft the plum buds to the young almond trees. Grafting slips of fruit trees to other fruit trees was not a new process. For many years cherry and apple trees, for instance, had been grafted to each other with the result that two varieties of fruit could be grown on the same tree. But in grafting plum buds to young almond trees, Burbank was making an unusual experiment.

It was Burbank's theory that the grafted plum buds would starve out the first sprouts of the almond stocks and transform the tree into a plum tree. This was the case with some of the trees which were grafted, but the majority of the little almond trees were so sturdy that the almond leaves continued to prosper and the plum buds began to wither away.

"We're not going to let these almond trees have their own way," said Burbank. "We're going to break the tops."

"But you can't do that!" exclaimed one of the gardeners. "Without any leaves, the tree will die."

"Haven't you ever seen a tree with its top broken by the wind—but still alive?" asked Burbank.

"Yes," said the gardener, "but there's still some connection between the roots and the leaves."

"And there will be here, too," said Burbank. "We'll snap the tops of these little almond trees and leave them hanging. The leaves will serve their purpose, but there won't be too many sprouts at the top to wolf all the food. Then when the plum buds really start growing, they'll starve the broken almond tops right out of the picture and the almond trees will become plum trees."

Of the twenty thousand almond trees, nineteen thousand, five hundred became fine, healthy plum trees and were delivered to Mr. Wells, who was astounded at the results of the bold experiment.

From experience, aided by an inner sense which must be called genius, Luther Burbank could distinguish good plants from inferior ones. He was able to prove, by large-scale experiments in selection, that it was profitable in the long run to root out inferior plants and give the good plants the fullest advantage of space and nourishment. Burbank cultivated fifty different species of berries and succeeded in originating ten new varieties. He also gave the world many new and useful varieties of vegetables and fruits. Among other creations, he produced a rustless wheat, a spineless cactus, which cattle could eat, and roses without thorns. He once said, "I shall be content if, because of me, there shall be better fruit and fairer flowers."

THE FIGHT AGAINST
YELLOW FEVER

(WALTER REED)

In the fall of the year 1900, when Dr. Walter Reed arrived in Havana, Cuba, a terrible spectacle met his eyes. The dead and the dying lay all around him. Those who had collapsed on the streets lay about on the ground, like limp bundles of rags. Bewildered, they awaited death; and to many of them, death came quickly, pitiless and without reason.

This might have been a battlefield scene. Yet where was the enemy? But it was not a war—it was an epidemic. And the enemy was yellow fever. In the South, the dread fever had also made its presence known. In Texas and Florida, hundreds had felt its silent fury. But here, in Cuba, the fever seemed to have settled like a dark cloud. And it was here that the United States had sent a Medical Commission, led by Dr. Walter Reed, an Army major.

In Dr. William Gorgas' office at the American Army hospital, outside Havana, Reed sat listening to Gorgas' estimate of the emergency. Here, a year or more after the end of the Spanish-American War, said Gorgas, the U.S. Expeditionary Force was facing an enemy far more deadly than the Spaniards. If something were not done immediately, not only might the people of Cuba be wiped out by the fever, the American Army might be decimated. The number of Army cases was mounting daily. "We are enforcing the strictest sanitation—fumigating, burning clothing and bedding, destroying anything and everything that might carry infection. But nothing seems to work."

Dr. Gorgas touched a stack of files on his desk. "These are new cases, reported today. We finish our sanitary work in a district, expecting the epidemic to end there, but it crops out again!"

"What about Dr. Finlay's theory?" Reed asked.

"Finlay?" Dr. Gorgas almost snorted.

214

"Don't tell me you're interested in that foolish mosquito notion of his!"

"Nothing you have done so far has proved effective," Dr. Reed replied quietly. "That's implying no criticism of you, Dr. Gorgas. You've been employing the standard methods used in the States. But those methods seem to be as ineffectual up there as they are down here." He paused. "Dr. Gorgas, my observations indicate that yellow fever is not contagious—that is, not in the ordinary sense. I don't believe it is spread by contamination, or by contact with an infected person."

"Well, you won't get the answer to yellow fever from that Finlay," said Dr. Gorgas. "Don't waste your time on those bottled mosquitoes of his."

"Because I don't want to waste time," said Reed, "I am going to see Dr. Finlay."

For years, Dr. Finlay had been studying the habits of the stegomyia mosquito. He was convinced that in this tiny, buzzing insect lay the answer to the scourge of yellow fever. But who would listen to him?

He sighed. "Dr. Reed, I am afraid my work is still incomplete, and thus unconvincing. There is little I can show you—except this."

He held up a tube. Inside, a mosquito buzzed, trying vainly to get out.

"Infectious?" Reed asked.

"Deadly. The next step in my research," Dr. Finlay said, "would be to let this mosquito sting me. If I were then to contract yellow fever, that would prove my case. But, unfortunately, I have already had yellow fever and, consequently, I am immune to it."

Later, Dr. Reed had a conference with his colleagues on the Medical Commission, Lazear and Carroll, both doctors. They, too, were familiar with the mosquito theory and were convinced it should be tested by an individual as Finlay had advised.

Dr. Reed said to them, "I have here three test tubes containing stegomyia mosquitoes hatched from eggs Dr. Finlay gave me.

Each has bitten a yellow-fever patient. Now, I propose that we—"

"We're all agreed on that," Dr. Lazear broke in, "except for one thing, Reed. Carroll and I don't believe you should be included in this test. You will have to go to Washington, to make your report. And you know further aid to us down here depends on what they do in Washington."

"Lazear's right," said Carroll.

"Then we'll postpone the experiment until I return from Washington. I want to be in on this."

"No," Lazear interposed. "We've got to work fast. When you get back, Carroll and I will give you a full report."

He picked up the test tube, pulled the stopper from it and held the mouth of the tube to his wrist. The mosquito buzzed angrily and darted down the glass toward his flesh.

"Not much to *that*," Lazear said after a moment.

"Now it's my turn," said Carroll, and he picked up another test tube and allowed himself to be stung also.

Some weeks later, when Dr. Reed returned from Washington, he learned that Dr. Lazear was dead.

Carroll reported, "On the second day, I myself developed symptoms—I was pretty sick—but in thirteen days I recovered. Lazear, surprisingly, showed no symptoms whatever."

"Since the mosquitoes bit patients at different times," reasoned Reed, "this must mean that there is a certain period when the stegomyia is *not* infectious. We've got to find out when. But go on about Lazear."

"As I say," Carroll continued, "nothing happened to Lazear at all. Five days after I had recovered, he was bitten again, this time accidentally. He developed yellow fever, and a week later he died."

So their courageous experiment had been successful—but only enough to justify further trial to provide the proof that would convince the most skeptical. The experiment must be undertaken on a larger scale, scientifically controlled from start to finish. They must make a test of a good many cases, which would require a large number of volunteers. Where could these volunteers be found?

Major Reed's answer came in the form of an order from General Leonard Wood, in command of the Expeditionary Force stationed at Quemados. "I hereby authorize Major Walter Reed to call for volunteers for the practice of any medical experiment and the construction of a quarantine camp under his command, to be known as Camp Lazear."

"No man can say with certainty that this experiment will succeed," Dr. Reed told the seventeen men who volunteered. "But all of you know the seriousness of this epidemic. Today, tomorrow, the day after, thousands will continue to die from it. If our work at Camp Lazear is successful, you will win the gratitude of the whole human race for what you have consented to do."

Camp Lazear, a collection of supply tents and makeshift frame buildings, looked more like a construction camp than an experimental laboratory. Located a mile and a half outside Quemados, it was in the center of an area without any previous record of infection. A new building was erected, divided inside by mosquito netting. The seventeen volunteers were split into two groups. The men of Group A would live a normal existence, though under the strictest quarantine, on one side of the netting. On the other side, the members of Group B would submit to bites by the stegomyia mosquitoes.

For several days, the men and the deadly plague lived side by side, the two groups of volunteers, separated only by a flimsy net, breathing the same air under the same roof. Group B, which had submitted to the mosquito bites, fell ill. One by one, the men suffered the familiar fearful symptoms: chills, rising temperatures, a pounding pulse and nausea. On the other side of the netting, the men of Group A watched their suffering with pity—and dread. Would the yellow fever penetrate to them? Would it seep through the netting? Would they, too, begin to collapse?

At the end of ten days, they were still healthy. And while the infected members of Group B were still fighting their way through the last stages of the fever, Reed was able to tell them, "We now know definitely what causes yellow fever."

"A mosquito, yes," Dr. Gorgas now conceded. "However, Major Reed, perhaps the mosquito isn't the sole cause. What about contamination? How do you know that doesn't cause it as well?"

"I'll prove that it doesn't," Reed said.

"How?"

Reed went on to explain, and Dr. Gorgas looked at him in consternation. "But, Reed, if you do that—do you realize the responsibility you're taking upon yourself? You'll be risking your entire future—in the Army —in medicine—"

That final experiment took place in a shack piled high with the filthy bedding and dressings of yellow fever patients. Into this room were led the men of non-infected Group A. Here the volunteers would stay—for three weeks.

"And," Reed stated, "if a single man dies of fever in that shack, I shall resign my post and have myself indicted for manslaughter."

It was a pledge that Dr. Walter Reed did not have to keep. For on New Year's Day, the men emerged from that shack as healthy as the day they entered it.

Their heroism would win them decorations and awards and universal gratitude. For, as Reed had said, what they had done called for more bravery than any battle. To their courage and to the sacrifices of Carroll and Lazear, as well as to the inspiration and perseverance of Dr. Reed and Dr. Finlay, millions who might have succumbed to the dread yellow fever owe their deliverance.

HE MAPPED THE MIND OF MAN

(HARVEY CUSHING)

Back in 1890, when he was a student at Johns Hopkins University Hospital, young Dr. Harvey Cushing had begun his unceasing campaign for perfecting surgical techniques.

"That request of mine has been on your desk for three weeks," said Cushing to the treasurer of the hospital. "When are you going to act on it?"

"But, Cushing," said the treasurer impatiently, "how can I deal with a request that isn't clear? You want money for something or other discovered by—by—who is this Professor Roentgen?"

"Roentgen is a European scientist," answered Cushing. "The one who discovered invisible rays that go right through solid objects. He calls them X-rays—'X' because he doesn't know exactly what they are."

"And you think I should spend the hospital's money on something so vague that it is called 'X'?" asked the treasurer, and dismissed the request.

But Cushing and some friends bought an X-ray machine and proceeded to prove to the hospital how valuable Roentgen's discovery was. It helped surgeons to set broken bones more accurately and to locate internal injuries more precisely.

As Cushing predicted, Roentgen's X-ray machine soon became indispensable equipment in every hospital. In the meantime Cushing went forward with efforts to make surgical techniques, particularly in brain surgery, as infallible as possible. His views in this field amounted to a medical revolution. They were first tested at the Johns Hopkins Hospital on an afternoon in 1904.

William Halstead, the noted professor of surgery at Johns Hopkins University, was making the rounds of the patients. One, a young woman, was under the care of both Cushing and another surgeon of his own age named Crews. They had agreed in their diagnosis: a tumor of the brain.

"What have you decided should be done, Dr. Crews?" asked Halstead.

"Surgery, sir. The tumor must be removed."

Cushing concurred.

"Quite a responsibility," said Halstead, "when you consider that nine out of ten brain-tumor patients die on the operating table. And, so, which one of you will operate?"

"I should like to, sir," said Crews. "I plan to make my incisions, scoop out the tumor and be finished in less than a half-hour."

"I disagree," said Cushing. "Surgeons *had* to hurry when we had no anesthesia. Now we should take our time to make sure that every step is precise and perfect."

"Why take all that time?" asked Crews. "It takes only a moment to stick in your hand—"

"Why your hand?" interrupted Cushing. "Why not sterile rubber gloves? We talk about the connection between microbes and disease, but in the operating room too many surgeons still use their bare hands."

"But rubber gloves are so clumsy," said Crews, "and in an operation of this nature one cannot afford to lose that delicate touch."

"You're wrong, Crews," said Halstead. "If you dissect slowly and carefully, if you use fine instruments and a dry, sterile field, you can reduce the damage to sensitive human tissues. Dr. Cushing, I want you to perform this operation."

In 1912 Cushing went to Harvard as professor of surgery. He remained there for three years, performing such marvels in the operating theater and giving such brilliant lectures that his name became known

Dr. Harvey Cushing.

throughout the world.

Then, in the spring of 1915, Harvey Cushing went off to the battlefront. "It is there that I am most needed," he told his friends as he sailed for Europe.

Throughout the war Harvey Cushing remained in field hospitals directly behind the front lines, performing many delicate life-saving operations. Most were operations on the brain, but these were not to emove tumors but fragments of shrapnel.

In 1918 Dr. Cushing was called before an American general in a command post just off a shell-pocked road. The general looked annoyed.

"Will you tell me, Dr. Cushing," he asked, "why you can't make out your medical reports on our regular printed forms?"

"But those printed forms are little more than postal cards, General," said Cushing. "There's barely room for the patient's name and number, and no space to describe what's wrong with him."

"Those exact and thorough reports of our cases take too long to write up—and to read—Dr. Cushing. We have to save time."

"But we save lives, sir," said Cushing. "I've been a surgeon more than twenty years and I am glad to say that 90 per cent of my brain operations have been successful. Complete case histories, sir, helped make that possible."

"I appreciate that, Dr. Cushing, but—"

Cushing interrupted the general, and there was a touch of anger in his voice. "I'm sure, sir, you wouldn't order an attack without giving your men maps. Well, the human brain is still pretty much unmapped territory. These long case histories of mine are an attempt to create a map for this precious and delicate area. Now do you understand, General?"

"You have put a new light on the question," said the general. "Carry on, Dr. Cushing."

Toward the end of 1918, after overworking himself for months, Cushing was stricken with a painful nerve disease. His hands became gnarled and stiff. It seemed that he would never be able to perform another operation. When he returned to the United States, however, he painstakingly retrained his hands until he was able to operate as skillfully as before.

A great deal of his vitality had been drained away and now, after a single operation, the sweat of exhaustion would stand out on his forehead.

Despite the painful limitations to his activity, Cushing continued his demonstrations in the operating theater, as well as his classroom lectures. Doctors from all over the world came to observe his work and to listen to his lectures. From Russia, in 1929, came Ivan Pavlov, the great physiologist and physician.

Pavlov watched Cushing remove a brain tumor. Only local anesthesia was used, so the patient, a Mr. Cauldwell, was able to speak to Cushing throughout the operation. The tumor, in the left temporal lobe of the brain, had paralyzed the right side of the patient.

Cushing proceeded step by step in his precise and delicate manner. As he began to cut away the tumor, the patient spoke out in amazement. "Look, Doctor! The fingers of my right hand—I can begin to move them!"

A few moments later, Cushing lifted the entire tumor away.

"Dr. Cushing!" exclaimed Cauldwell. "Look at this! I can move my whole right arm! Will you let me shake your hand as the very first thing that I do?"

Joyfully Cushing shook his patient's hand, gave instructions to his assistants as to the closing up of the incision, and then turned away wearily.

"I would shake hands with you, too, sir," said Pavlov as he and Cushing left the operating room. "In operations on the brain, during which nine out of ten patients once died, nine out of ten now walk out of the hospital very much alive. And we owe it all to you, Dr. Cushing—to your skill and your ability to transmit your knowledge to other surgeons."

THE BUILDERS

American foresight, ingenuity, and accomplishment have been subjects of wonder and admiration since the days of Benjamin Franklin. The argument that a project was impossible to achieve has acted only as a spur to the overcoming of obstacles by our men of ideas. President Washington was one of the first to realize that a canal joining the Great Lakes to a south-flowing eastern river would bring the rich treasures of the middle-west to an Atlantic coast city whence they might be distributed not only to the nation but throughout the world. President Thomas Jefferson's many practical inventions have contributed so much to our civilization that he has become one of our country's most popular heroes.

The construction of the Erie Canal required invention—and invention was forthcoming. This is the American story from the earliest days of the Republic through such triumphs of yesterday as the Holland Tunnel and such awaited completions as tomorrow's St. Lawrence Seaway. Further victories of those scientists who, in air-borne ships, explore the outer boundaries of our world and bring back contributions to our knowledge of atmosphere and space, will, before these words are published, make reports in this morning's papers seem unremarkable and long-accepted truths.

Possibly because our citizens have given patiently of their brain and brawn to the measureless labors that have created this nation, they have felt trained by experience to carry on the tasks that ever lie ahead. They believe that the freedom of thought and action they enjoy is responsible for the virtues they like to think as typical of Americans—the inventive mind, the "know-how" that comes through experiments in large-scale production, the humility of men who unite their separate powers in the common interest.

THE INVENTORS

"A tool is but the extension of a man's hand, and a machine is but a complex tool. And he that invents a machine augments the power of a man and the well-being of mankind."

HENRY WARD BEECHER.

THE INVENTOR OF INTERCHANGEABLE PARTS

(ELI WHITNEY)

What did Napoleon Bonaparte mean to the American inventor, Eli Whitney? In the year 1798 the man who was to master most of Europe was only a name to a mechanic in Hamden, Connecticut. Eli Whitney had other things on his mind. A few years before, he had invented the cotton gin. It should have made his fortune, yet here he was, almost penniless. He could sue the planters who had stolen his invention, but legal proceedings were too expensive. With his business failing, he could not pay his workmen; and, as for himself, he was lucky to get three meals a day.

When he received an invitation to dinner from Pierrepont Edwards, a merchant of New Haven, Whitney decided to use the opportunity to ask for a loan. After all, he had a federal patent on the gin. With sufficient time and money he would make those Southern planters honor it.

At dinner, however, Edwards startled him by discussing Napoleon. "Here's this mad Frenchman out to conquer the world, and what are we doing about it?" He stared accusingly at his guest. "No guns, no ships, no army, no navy—nothing."

"That all takes time," said Whitney.

"Time!" Edwards brought his hand down heavily on the arm of the chair. "Tell me, isn't your cotton-gin business pretty much on the decline?"

"Oh, I wouldn't say that," answered Whitney hurriedly. "Especially not if I can secure a loan to tide me over until—"

"Until it's too late?"

Whitney looked up in surprise. "Too late for what?"

"This man Bonaparte—don't you understand that he means to conquer the world? His privateers are already blockading England. What good are the new gins if we can't carry on our cotton trade with England?" He paused. "And the French landing in Louisiana. Colonists, they call themselves. Visitors. Tourists. But precious few land without muskets in their hands. No, Eli, what we need now are *guns*, by the thousands."

Whitney shook his head stubbornly. "I am not a gunsmith, sir. I am a maker of cotton gins." Mr. Edwards apparently didn't understand the problems involved. A musket was a complicated machine, not easy to manufacture in quantity. "I'm afraid I'm committed to cotton gins at the moment, Mr. Edwards. I wanted to approach you about a loan."

"Not for that," said Edwards sharply.

Eli Whitney rose to go.

"Please sit down, Mr. Whitney. The proposal that you undertake to manufacture the muskets we need is not mine alone. It originated with the Secretary of State and the Secretary of the Treasury—Mr. Jefferson and Mr. Wolcott."

"Why me?"

A smile played at the corner of Edwards' mouth. "I think perhaps it is because you are on their conscience. They issued a patent to you which was openly flouted." Then, growing more serious, he added, "Besides, Mr. Jefferson may be wrong, but he believes you are the best mechanic in America. He invites you to Philadelphia. Will you go?"

In Philadelphia, Whitney conferred with a committee. The Federal Government wanted flintlock muskets 59½ inches long of .69 caliber, for which it would pay $13.40 apiece. That seemed fair enough—until Whitney heard the rest of the contract. Ten thousand muskets in ten months. The inventor smiled indulgently. What the committee asked was clearly an impossibility. Why, it would take the best gunsmiths in America ten years to produce that many muskets. He agreed to try to do it in two years.

"Try?" chided a member of the committee. "Come now, Whitney, that's not good enough."

"Very well, I promise to deliver ten thousand muskets in two years' time. If I fail, I will deliver my apologies to this committee."

Apologies? If he failed, Congress would demand forthwith the forfeiture of a $30,000 bond!

Whitney burst out laughing. "Then I have come to Philadelphia just for the air. Gentlemen, I do not have thirty dollars."

Wolcott, who headed the committee, produced a paper which he handed to Whitney to read. It was an agreement by the merchants of Hamden and New Haven that Eli Whitney would fulfill his contract. If he did not, they would lose the bond they were posting for $30,000. Among the names of the contributors were Whitney's creditors, and also that of the man who had sent him to Philadelphia—Pierrepont Edwards.

When months passed and not a single musket was produced, people began to gossip. They said Whitney was planning to use the government funds for making his cotton gins. Certainly the materials being shipped to him were not those used in making muskets. When he was questioned by the indignant merchants, he explained, "With those materials I am making machines."

"But we understand you are under contract to make muskets, not machines."

"I must build machines and train men to use them before production can begin," the inventor insisted.

The two years had almost elapsed when one of Whitney's workmen stamped into a tavern in Hamden. He had just quit his job.

"It's too much for me!" he told his companions. "I never saw a machine shop like that in my life. Worm gears, ratchets, cycles—a mechanic's got to learn geometry to work there!"

"What is Whitney up to?"

"I'm sure I don't know," said the mechanic. "He thinks he's going to turn out muskets, all exactly alike."

When the length of the contract expired, Whitney had hardly begun to meet his quota. He had spent all the money advanced to him by the government. But he could not secure an extension of time. Since he could not pay them, his workmen were leaving. Then the merchants who had posted bond descended on him, demanding an explanation.

"Gentlemen," he told them, "all I need is a little more time, a little more money. My machines are all built."

"You spent all this time just getting ready to begin production?" demanded an irate businessman.

Whitney got up from his desk and led the merchants into the shop. "I have had to design new machines. Do you understand? Each one is an invention. Here, look at this box. I place a piece of iron in it, then file, like this. And it's no longer a piece of iron, but a firing pin. Or here. With this I bore a diameter. I don't have to use my eye, my hand. No need for compass or calipers, no time lost. And the moment the diameter is reached, the tool

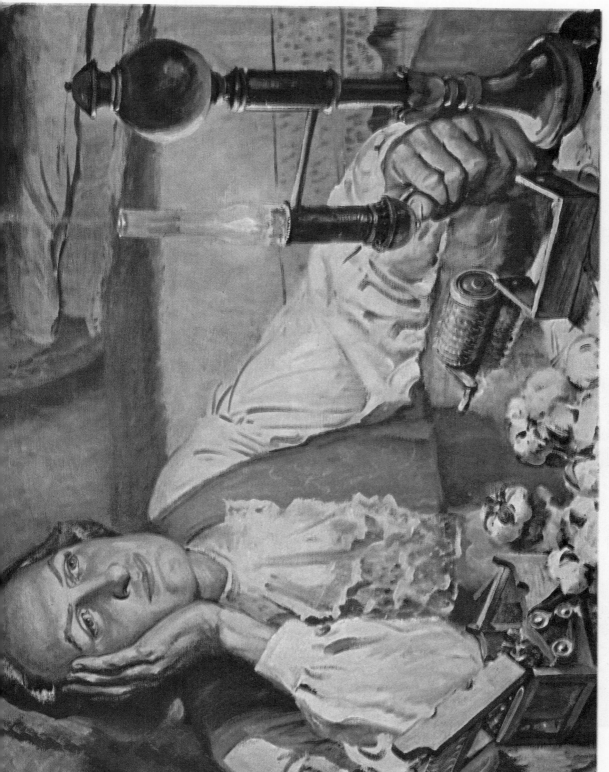

Eli Whitney and his cotton gin.

Whitney demonstrates his interchangeable-parts rifle.

stops. It is exact." As the businessmen examined his equipment, Whitney went on, "I have constructed machines that make guns with interchangeable parts. Nobody has ever done it before. Nobody even dreamed of doing it. Now it's an accomplished fact."

In Washington, Eli Whitney faced the committee. Mr. Adams, President of the United States, was there; and Mr. Jefferson, now Vice-President. There, too, were Oliver Wolcott and General Simeon North and other prominent persons.

"You contracted to deliver ten thousand stand of arms, Mr. Whitney," said General North, "and the government has received only five hundred."

"I know," answered Whitney.

"Were those five hundred good pieces?" asked Jefferson.

General North bridled. "Yes, sir, they were. Could have been made by a watchmaker. They should be, after two years!" Turning to Whitney, he demanded, "How much money have you received from the government to this date?"

"A little more than $20,000."

"Then your muskets have cost us not $13.40 apiece, but $40.00."

Whitney looked from one member of the committee to another. "Only if you cancel the contract now, gentlemen. General North, perhaps you would not mind describing very briefly to these gentlemen just how guns are made?"

"Why, the gunsmith," said the general, "bores the barrel on a lathe. Trues it by grinding, a little here, a little there. Then he carves the stock and fits the barrel to it. He forges the lockplates—very delicate, skilled work. He files the lock parts, trying them all the time until they fit. Then he assembles the parts of the lock plate, screws the plate into the stock, puts the musket on the shelf and starts the next one."

"And the muskets?" asked Whitney. "Because the parts are individually made

by hand, aren't they different, one from another?"

"Of course."

Whitney began to uncover some boxes which he had put on the floor. "You see here," he explained, "the parts for ten muskets. Now, General North, if you will select the parts for me, I will assemble a musket for you while you watch."

"But I don't know which part is for which gun."

Whitney smiled. "You may select any one of each part. Since they are all standardized, one will do as well as another."

There were cries of "Charlatan" and "Magic" as Eli Whitney quickly and effortlessly began to slip the different pieces of the gun into place. When it was assembled, he loaded it and fired a shot at a target through the open window.

Mr. Jefferson rose and, taking the gun from Whitney, extended it to the awed committee members. "Gentlemen, I give you Mr. Eli Whitney's musket."

"With the machines I have," said Whitney, "I can produce not just ten thousand muskets, but a *hundred thousand.*"

The committee unanimously agreed to return the bond and supply Mr. Whitney with whatever he needed to complete his work. But before the committee dispersed, the inventor asked to be heard on one last point.

"We are threatened by Bonaparte now, gentlemen, and so I have built machines to make muskets. But if we can produce instruments of war, we can also learn to make cheaply articles of peace—clocks, machines for tilling, for planting, printing presses."

"Yes," said Mr. Jefferson, "you have taken the first steps in an industrial system in which machines will be standardized. Let us hope that these machines may be used not to standardize the individuals who use them, but to give them a liberty which has never been possible before."

THE FARMER WHO HATED HARVEST TIME

(CYRUS McCORMICK)

It stood behind the barn—a useless, neglected machine. Now and then, when the day's farming was done, Robert McCormick would stroll out and have a look at it. He would stare at the contraption, and then, hearing the clang of the dinner bell, would turn away, trudging wearily back to the house, his mouth grim, his heart aching.

Year by year, season by season, the machine rotted away on its wheels. Rust gathered on its iron parts, and soon the wheels wouldn't run at all. Wind, rain and snow wore the wooden parts away. Fungus spread over it. Grass and weeds grew up about it. And to Robert McCormick, it was as if those weeds were smothering his dreams.

Then, one day, hearing the clatter and screech of metal, he ran out behind the barn. His son Cyrus was playing with the rusty machine. "Get off that thing!" he shouted, grabbing Cyrus and yanking him away. "You leave that machine alone, or I'll give you a whippin'!"

"But, Pa!" young Cyrus cried, bewildered. "It's nothin' but a heap of old junk."

"You leave it be," his father warned. His voice was bitter, "Like you say, son, it's a heap of old junk. But I spent years workin' at it, Cyrus. And if I'd made it run the way it should . . ." He sighed. "Well, it would have been a great day for us farmers."

"But what is it, Pa?"

"A reaper," his father said. "Leastways, that's what it *would* have been, if I'd made it work. A mechanical reaper for cuttin' down grain. You could have hitched a horse to it, and the horse would have pulled it."

"Gosh, Pa, that's wonderful."

The father spoke again. "As long as man has lived, sowin' and reapin' the fields,

Cyrus H. McCormick

he's never been able to build such a machine. And I reckon I wasn't picked out to be the one to do it, son." He sighed. "A pile of old junk. Just a lazy man's dream. Come away and forget it, Cyrus."

But Cyrus couldn't forget it. In those days, the early part of the nineteenth century, a farmer's life was a hard one. He would rise before dawn to begin his work. All day, in all kinds of weather, he would toil with his hands and a few simple tools. When the sun went down, he would walk in slowly from the fields, back aching and legs weary, bone tired. That was the way it was for Robert McCormick on his farm in Rockbridge County, Virginia, in the 1820's. And that was the way it was for Cyrus, his son, who toiled beside him.

The worst of all, it seemed to Cyrus, was harvest time. The grain had to be cut when it was ripe; a delay of a day or two might mean the loss of the entire crop. Harvest was a race with time, a race with the weather, sweltering heat or drenching rain, a back-breaking fight with Nature. What tools, what equipment did a man have to help him in this battle? A scythe—and his agonized muscles.

Cyrus hated harvest time, with its round-the-clock toil, as most farmers did. And, as he grew up, he remembered his father's dream, that rusting contraption behind the barn. One day he walked out there, pulled it clear of the weeds and began to study it. Where had his father gone wrong? Where had he made his mistakes?

In a small blacksmith shed set up on the farm heavy hammers began to ring out. There was the gasp and the wheeze of bellows, the angry hiss of white-hot iron being plunged into water. Mr. McCormick would come to the shed and look in on his son. "Cyrus," he'd say, "now don't you go

N. C. Wyeth's painting of the public test of the world's first successful reaper. On page 231 a contemporary print of the event is shown.

wastin' *your* time trying to make that thing work. No family can afford to have more than one darn fool in it."

"You didn't waste your time, Pa," Cyrus would say. "And I'm not wasting mine. This reaper is gonna *work!*"

So the dream of the father became the dream of the son. Months of work, and the reaper seemed finished. Mr. McCormick looked at it, astonished. It sure looked as if Cyrus had done it!

Harvest time had come and a nearby farmer, John Ruff, agreed to allow one of his wheatfields to be used for a demonstration. From many miles around, farmers arrived on horseback, or afoot, excited by the talk of this new machine. They gathered round it, fingering the reel, examining the frame, the cutting knife. "Strange-lookin' animal." Someone laughed. "I calculate it should do a real quick job of ruining your wheat, Mr. Ruff."

There was a general chorus of laughter. But when Ruff called out, "Cyrus, get go-in'!" everyone fell silent. And as the horse walked off, pulling the machine, and began to circle the field, there was no laughter at all. For all these farmers felt that a great event might be happening. If this machine worked, it would mean a revolution in wheat farming.

But as Cyrus said later, "I reckon I ruined just about the most beautiful field of wheat in all Virginia." For the machine broke down, and then broke down again and again, smashing against the stones, powerless on hilly ground, the cutter failing. He'd never forget Ruff's shrill shouting—"Stop that infernal machine! You're trampling that grain, you're matting it, you're cutting the heads off the wheat! The whole field's ruined! Cyrus, get that contraption out of here before I smash it!"

"I reckon you were right, Pa," Cyrus said later. "There's two of us fools in this family. But I'm going to make it one less. I'm going away."

Humiliated, he did leave the farm to set-tle in the back country. Here he tried to forget the failure, his dream. Finally, after months of this bitter seclusion, he returned home.

"Cyrus," his mother said, "folks have been talking about your reaper."

"And laughin', I'll bet."

"Not everybody," his mother said. "Lots of 'em want to know when you're going to finish it."

"I wouldn't touch that machine," Cyrus said, "if it was the last thing between me and starvation. I'm twenty-seven now; time to be doing something with my life. Pa, you've saved some money. Let's go into the iron business. Look at the important families around here—the Weavers, the Mayberrys, the Jordans—they're all iron-masters." His face was grim. "You don't see anybody laughing at *them*, Pa."

He went on to explain. If they could find an iron ore bank, with wood and water-power nearby, they could become ironmasters. For from six to eight thousand dollars they could set up a smelter and a foundry. Another six thousand would be needed for operating expenses. "Iron ore is selling for fifty dollars a ton at Richmond. We could clear four thousand dollars' profit a year."

Some time later, a letter arrived at the McCormick farm from another part of the state, where father and son had set up their iron foundry. When Mrs. McCormick opened it, she read the dismaying news: "Dear Ma—I haven't written you since Pa and I left because I didn't want to say what I had to say. Things are bad. We been struggling and sweating and slipping. We got creditors and sheriffs crawling all over us. You can figure to see us back home soon. We lost the ore bank. We lost the furnace and foundry. Pa wants you to tell Mr. Mc-Chesney we're coming to see him for a loan. Looks like the only thing is to mort-gage the farm we tried to leave. . . ."

So father and son returned, this time to a farm they could no longer rightly call their own. With a two-thousand-dollar

Trial of McCormick's Reaper.

mortgage on it, they had little to look forward to except another defeat. For how could they produce enough wheat on five hundred acres to pay off a debt like that?

"Everything I do," Cyrus said, "everything I touch is a failure." He followed his father into the fields. What did life hold for him? Sweating, back-breaking toil, as in his earlier years, life with a scythe in his hands? Bitterness burned in him again.

Now and then, just as his father had done long ago, his steps would lead him to the ground at the rear of the barn. Here lay the abandoned reaper. The weeds were growing over it, rust was discoloring the metal. If only it had worked! If only—well, for one thing, he thought, I should have made the main wheel heavier. The blades should be wider. And—

No, Cyrus McCormick, he told himself, you leave that machine alone! Let it rot. Do you want to be laughed at again?

Yet, after a hard day's work in the fields, he would return to it. Now, if I changed the cutting angle . . . If I added another reel here . . .

He hated that machine and he loved it. Finally the love grew greater than the hate. "Well, Pa," he said, "I reckon your fool son is about to make a laughingstock of himself again. Will you give me a hand and pull that heap of junk over to the blacksmith shed?"

A few months later, at a county fair, Cyrus McCormick drove his darn-fool machine around and around a field of golden grain. With the other thousands assembled there, the governor of Virginia stood up to cheer. "Friends, the victory has been complete. The field has fallen before the reaper. Thanks to this young inventor, we can look forward to seeing our tillers of the soil begin to straighten their backs and walk upright."

So the dream of the mechanical reaper had passed from the father to the son. And, triumphing over defeat and bitterness, the son had realized their hopes.

231

Self-portrait of Samuel F. B. Morse.

INVENTOR OF THE TELEGRAPH

(SAMUEL F. B. MORSE)

In 1811, Samuel Finley Breese Morse was twenty years old and a homesick art student in London. Not that things had gone badly with him. In fact, everything had gone just as his father, the Reverend Jedediah Morse, of Charlestown, Massachusetts, had hoped. He had early become aware of his son's artistic talent and had put him in the hands of Washington Allston, one of the most celebrated painters of the day. Allston, in turn, after observing the young man's quickly developing talent, decided that Morse should go to London for more study.

There Morse had met the famous painter Benjamin West, who, though an American, was President of the Royal Academy. West, with a kindly interest in all American art, agreed to look over a painting that young Morse intended to offer to the Royal Academy. West exclaimed, "How talented you are, Mr. Morse! However, this painting is not finished. It needs more work, much more work. Here, for instance, this line of the jaw—and here—and here."

After Morse had worked on the painting for another week, he again showed it to West.

"Your coloring is excellent, Mr. Morse," remarked West, "and I like your composition. But the painting is still not finished. See that muscle in the arm? And those finger joints? The modeling could be improved. And if anything in a painting can obviously be improved, then the painting is not finished. Is that not so, Mr. Morse?"

Morse took the painting back to his studio and chafed over the fact that he could not get to work on it immediately. But that afternoon had been set aside for a letter to his mother. If the letter were not written it would miss the packet boat. He thought how wonderful it would be—as he had of-ten thought before, when he was lonely and homesick—if one could send and receive messages from loved ones the moment they were written!

But three thousand miles were not to be passed over in an instant—yet. People who lived far apart had to wait long weeks before hearing from each other.

Portrait of Lafayette by Samuel F. B. Morse.

The miraculous achievement for which young Morse yearned in 1811 remained no more than a wish for many years. The word "telegraph" had already been used to describe an instrument that could instantly transmit messages, but such an instrument was yet to be invented.

Before he was forty years old, Morse had become one of the most popular portrait-painters in the United States. In 1829, at the peak of his artistic career, Morse again went abroad. It was on his return voyage to America, three years later, that he became engaged in the conversation that was to shape the rest of his life.

He was in the dining saloon, talking with some shipboard acquaintances, when one of them, Dr. Charles Jackson of Boston, drew from his pocket an object which he called an electromagnet.

"I bought it in Paris," said Dr. Jackson. "Just a piece of iron shaped like a horse-shoe and some copper wire twisted around it, as you see. But when an electric current is passed through the wire, the iron becomes a magnet."

"Must there be a certain length of wire for the magnet to function?" asked Morse.

"No," answered Dr. Jackson. "It has been demonstrated that electricity passes instantaneously over any length of wire."

"The velocity isn't retarded at all by the length?" asked Morse.

"Faraday has lately proved that it is not retarded, Mr. Morse," said Dr. Jackson.

"Wonderful!" exclaimed Morse. "Gentlemen, why couldn't an electromagnetic machine be used to transmit messages? By breaking the circuit, signals could be sent. The spark would be one sign, its absence another and the time of its absence still another. A code could be worked out which would correspond with words, and we would achieve instantaneous communication."

"If it's possible," said Dr. Jackson. "But isn't it strange that you, an artist, should be so much interested in science?"

"Are science and art really so far apart?" asked Morse. "I've always been interested in science. I even specialized for a time in physics when I was at Yale."

Immediately upon his return to the United States, Morse began experiments on the telegraph. The need of money became his chief obstacle. During his stay in Europe other portrait-painters had become fashionable. He could get no commissions. He tried teaching art, but his pupils were few. Then, in 1835, when he was forty-four, he received an appointment as professor of the literature of the arts of design in the newly formed New York University in Washington Square.

This position gave him a small income and rooms in the main building of the University, which was still being constructed. In these rooms Morse contrived such a maze of wires that his friends regarded a visit to him as a perilous trip into a labyrinth.

Financial aid and practical assistance from Alfred Vail at last enabled Morse to demonstrate his invention before a Congressional committee in Washington in 1838. Encouraged by a favorable reception, Morse hurried to Europe to obtain foreign patents. He failed in his European mission and returned to America to find that interest in his invention had dwindled.

These were the darkest years of Morse's life. His friends had fallen away from him. No wealthy people wished to have him paint their portraits; no students sought him out except those who could pay only the smallest of fees. Grief struck in his family life as well. His wife died and he was now alone, with four small children to support.

Somehow Morse managed to finance one more desperate effort to arouse public interest in his invention. During all of one night, Morse himself had laid a mile of copper wire insulated with pitch, tar and rubber between Castle Garden on the Battery and Governor's Island. The previous ay he had published an announcement in he New York newspapers that his invention—a submarine telegraph—was to be demonstrated to the public. On the morning of October 19, 1842, a crowd gathered outside Castle Garden and waited skeptically for Morse to exchange messages with his friend, Professor Gale.

Morse tapped out his message and waited impatiently for Gale's response from Governor's Island. It did not come, and the crowd began to move away with cries of "Fraud! Fraud!"

Looking out across the water, Morse realized why he had failed. A ship between him and the island had just raised anchor, and there, caught up into the air, plain as day, was one of the severed ends of his cable.

Morse refused to accept defeat. Deciding that his best chance lay in a Congressional appropriation, he went to Washington, D.C. There, in the Capitol, he set up his invention and stood beside it day after day trying to explain it to indifferent Congressmen. Finally, an appropriation bill for a Washington-to-Baltimore telegraph line passed the House of Representatives and went to the Senate. The session, however, drew toward a close without any action on the bill having been taken.

On the closing day of Congress, March 3, 1843, Morse left the Congressional gallery, believing that he had heard the last piece of business on the floor and that he had been once again, and this time completely, defeated. The Senate, however, remained in session and at midnight, just before adjourning, the appropriation for the first telegraph line in the world was passed.

The good news was brought to Morse by Annie Ellsworth, daughter of an old friend, the commissioner of patents.

"And so, Annie, when the line is built, it is you who must select the first message," declared Morse.

On May 24, 1844, a throng of govern-ment officials assembled in the Supreme Court Chamber and watched Samuel Morse communicate by telegraph with his friend Alfred Vail in Baltimore. Annie Ellsworth had selected the message from the Book of Numbers. It was simply the phrase "What hath God wrought!" When Morse received the message back from Vail, and without error, the crowd broke into applause.

The world owes much to the genius and perseverance of Samuel F. B. Morse. Through his contribution of instantaneous communication, he stands as one of the makers of the modern world, and his artistic contributions also entitle him to be honored. His paintings hang as art treasures in the world's leading museums.

Samuel F. B. Morse.

Photograph by Mathew Brady.

235

FROM FLYING KITES TO FLYING MACHINES

(WILBUR AND ORVILLE WRIGHT)

Kites and bicycles may seem like "kid stuff" to many people, yet in two important incidents in American history they played a major part: that of Benjamin Franklin and his experiment with electricity and that of the Wright brothers and their flying machine.

It was just about sixty-five years ago that Wilbur Wright and his younger brother Orville started a bicycle repair shop in Dayton, Ohio. Like many other youngsters, they liked to "fool around" with machinery and were always reading reports, magazines and books on science and mechanics. Their special hobby was kites—flying them, building bigger and better ones, observing air currents and factors of balance, weight and strain. Their

Dayton neighbors were amused to see th serious Wright boys playing with kites s much of the time, but they weren't play ing, they were studying. When they rea of the gliding machines tried out by for eign engineers, their own imagination were fired. They determined to build a improved glider that would be free o mechanical faults.

Balance was the big problem. They dis covered that lack of even balance made glider come down. As a result of a chang in air current or a slight shift in weight the glider would tilt, perhaps sidewise perhaps backward or forward. To contro this, the boys perfected two devices: the added an extra little plane in the front o the glider to be used as an elevator. Whe

Wilbur Wright.

Orville Wright.

The Wright brothers at Kitty Hawk.

e driver wanted to send the glider up down, he adjusted the angle of this evator accordingly. That took care of the rward and backward problem. To hieve sidewise balance they made the ngs flexible and connected the ends of e wings with the driver's seat. If one e went down, all the driver had to do s to pull the wire to raise the wing on that side. These two balancing and controlling devices seemed to make a great difference. If perfected, they could pave the way for a flying machine.

For further improvement and development the Wright brothers moved their scene of operations and research to Kitty Hawk, North Carolina. There they worked unremittingly—gliding, studying, fixing,

The Wright brothers' Type B Flying Machine.

changing—until they were confident their machine was right.

The next problem was to add power to this controlled glider. Of course, any engine would be heavier than air, but if it weren't too much heavier, then its power, supplemented by natural buoyancy, could keep a properly constructed and balanced machine in the air.

Steam engines were, of course, out o the question, but a new, light, internal com bustion engine had recently been deve oped. Engines of this type were used i automobiles but were still too heavy fo their purposes. The Wright brothers wer sure, however, that a lighter kind coul be made, and they promptly set abou making it.

They decided that a 15-horsepower engine could drive the two propellers of their machine fast enough to keep it in the air. They proceeded to make such an engine, with four cylinders, in their bicycle shop in Dayton. It was late in 1903 that they took the engine down to their base at Kitty Hawk and attached it to their improved glider-flying machine.

One thing more was needed, and provided for, in their calculations: initial momentum. That was elementary to a kite-flyer who knew enough to run a bit with his kite to get it well started in the air. The Wright brothers built a little road of wooden rail—the first airstrip—and then on December 17, 1903, they were ready.

The brothers tossed a coin to see who should pilot the machine on its first attempt at flight, and Orville won.

Once all was set, the brothers started the engine. Its propellers whirled, and Wilbur, with a running start, pushed the machine to the end of the rail and it was off and up! It came down in twelve seconds. Not much, but something had been accomplished.

Wilbur had his chance now. Orville pushed and once again the machine went up. This time it stayed up fifty-nine seconds and covered a distance of more than eight hundred feet. Unquestionably, this was traveling through space in a heavier-than-air machine. The Wright brothers had flown . . . man's conquest of the air had begun.

The 1903 Wright motor. Weight, with magneto: 178½ pounds.

JEAN PIERRE   BLANCHARD.

London, Pub.? July 1.1785 by I.Sewel, Cornhill.

THE FIRST FLIGHT

(JEAN PIERRE BLANCHARD)

It had been attempted once before. An American named Wilcox had invented a contraption which, with the aid of a cluster of forty-seven balloons, would lift him into the air. Once clear of the earth, he thought, the contraption would fly. Thus, with the backing of the American Philosophical Society, he arranged for an experiment on the banks of the Schuylkill River. The balloons lifted him high into the air. But when he came down to earth with astonishing speed, the spectators left the demonstration convinced the idea of flight by man was poppycock. Man can't fly, they said, and anyone who thinks he can ought to be restrained behind bars, like any other lunatic.

So when the French balloonist Jean Pierre Blanchard and his strange "aerostat" arrived in Philadelphia in 1792, people thought him mad, too. Right from the beginning he met with trouble. At Oeller's Hotel the members of the staff examined his aerostat suspiciously. It looked like a huge wicker basket, painted blue and studded with spangles. It was too heavy for one man to carry, for it was full to the brim with varnished silk.

"What do you use this stuff for?" asked the innkeeper, running a finger over the material.

"It is a balloon, my friend," explained Blanchard. "Folded up, of course."

"A balloon?"

The Frenchman shook his head at such ignorance. "You have not heard what is a balloon? But, my friend, you shall see. You shall see it carry me from the earth into the clouds."

The innkeeper decided it would be best to detain this deluded stranger until he could notify the magistrate. He read the entry in the hotel register: "Jean Pierre Blanchard, aeronaut, citizen of France."

"And the balloon," said the innkeeper to his clerk, "take it to the stable."

"To the stable! You mean to soil my beautiful machine by putting it in among the horses? This beautiful machine that has flown like a bird across the English Channel?"

When the magistrate arrived, Blanchard realized his difficulty. "I was fortunate enough," he explained, "to meet your good Dr. Franklin in Paris. It was he who encouraged my ambition and invited me to come to America." Only then did he learn that Benjamin Franklin had been dead for two years. "I had hoped," he said, "that the one who drew lightning from the clouds might live long enough to witness my first ascent to them in America!"

The disappointed Frenchman was taken before the Philadelphia City Council. Once they had decided it was safe to have him walk the streets, he collected his balloon and began the mission which had brought him to these new United States.

First of all, he hired a sailmaker to repair the damage his balloon had suffered in Oeller's stable. Then he had a printer make up five hundred subscription blanks pledging five dollars each to cover the expenses of the proposed ascent.

On hearing that Blanchard intended to go through with his project the councilmen sent a protest to Governor Thomas Mifflin. Blanchard's experiment, they said, was in defiance of all laws—scientific, philosophic and divine. It was also, they said, an outrage against public morals—a crime because it amounted to suicide, and a sin because God meant the birds to inhabit the air and men, the ground.

Some time later Thomas Jefferson, then

Secretary of State, received the following message:

> Excellency: As minister of the Republic of France to the United States of America, allow me to intercede in behalf of my countryman, M. Blanchard. Being at present in sanctuary at the legation of France because of danger to his very life and limb, M. Blanchard craves audience with his Excellency, George Washington, President of the United States.

In the interview with Washington which Jefferson arranged, Blanchard attempted to explain his aerostat. He filled the balloon with a gas called hydrogen. Hydrogen being lighter than air, the balloon bag, when filled with it, could lift the basket and whatever was in it, into the sky. By making use of the air currents at different altitudes, the machine could be steered. The balloonist could throw out sandbags, used as ballast, when he wanted to rise and he could release gas when he wanted to descend.

"Well," said Washington, "no doubt it will all seem perfectly clear when we see this remarkable ascent."

"You mean that I have Your Excellency's support? I may proceed with my plans?"

President Washington smiled. "Of course, Monsieur Blanchard. Go on with your arrangements. If you encounter any more difficulties, refer your critics to me. I'll see that they are denied the privilege of witnessing this marvel of the age."

Once it was known that the balloonist had the President's backing, elders of various towns wrote to Blanchard, promising him a royal welcome if he would land in their vicinity. With some amusement, the Frenchman was obliged to turn down all offers. When and where his balloon landed depended on the gods and the winds. All he knew for certain was that on Wednesday, January 9, 1793, at ten o'clock in the morning, weather permitting, he was scheduled to take off from the prison courtyard.

At the last minute he was approached by the eminent American scientist, Dr. Benjamin Rush. He asked Blanchard if he could read his pulse and was granted permission by him. "Your pulse is 84 on the ground," Dr. Rush told him. "Read it at the climax of your ascent. The difference will be of considerable interest to science." Blanchard also accepted a barometer, and bottles for sampling the upper air, supplied by other American scientists. He saw to it that the ballast was in place and that he had a supply of food.

Then there was a loud cheer to announce the arrival of the President of the United States. Blanchard busied himself disconnecting the hydrogen apparatus. The enormous balloon strained at its moorings. Its inventor climbed into the basket. He was about to order the balloon freed when the President approached him. "Wait, Monsieur Blanchard!" Washington ducked among the ropes. "You are creating quite a sensation. Every roof and tree is jammed with spectators. Here, at least, the people have accepted you. But who knows what reception is in store for you when you land? Against possible danger, I have prepared this document. The situation being without precedent, a passport was the best thing I could think of. Good-by and good luck."

As soon as the balloon was free of the ropes, it soared into the sky. Up and up it went, floating away to the north, still gaining in altitude until it disappeared from sight.

Blanchard, from his basket, watched Philadelphia recede in the distance. He looked down on the Delaware River, a thread winding through a snow-covered countryside. The winds were carrying him faster now. With the last of his ballast gone, he attained an altitude of 5,812 feet. He checked his pulse—84 on the ground, 92 at the climax of his experiment.

He reached up and carefully opened a valve, releasing hydrogen from the bal-on so that it began a gradual and uniform descent. To the east and south, his view was impeded by mist. Then the round seemed to rise to meet him.

A few miles east of Woodbury, New Jersey, just before eleven o'clock, a farmer reined in his rearing horse. Then he caught sight of the apparition which had frightened the animal. A monster was gliding down out of the clouds and seemed to be making straight for him. In terror he ran toward the house. His wife stood on the back porch, wringing her hands. "The Lord's judgment is upon us, Everard! It's the devil himself come to take us away."

Old Taggart, from down the lane, came running. "If you'd seen what I've seen! It was *that* big! Oh, *look!*"

"Shall we shoot it?" asked Everard.

"No, let's surround it and take it alive." The contraption had touched the ground in the cornfield, its swollen bladder collapsed, leaving a tangle of ropes. Only then did the farmers notice a figure climbing out of what looked like a huge wicker basket. The figure came toward them. "Good day, my friends," it called out.

"Who and what be ye?" demanded Everard.

"Ssh, don't talk to the demon," cautioned his wife.

"I am Jean Pierre Blanchard, aeronaut. I have just flown from Philadelphia in forty-five minutes."

Other neighbors began slowly to close in on the stranger. "Looky here, mister," called Everard in a loud voice, "it's fifteen miles to Philadelphia. Surround him, lads."

There was a short scuffle and Blanchard lay with his shoulders pinned back in the snow. "I have a paper from the President," he cried out. "Just let me get it and you can see for yourselves who I am."

When they had read the document, the people's incredulity turned to awe. Four men carried the basket on their shoulders to the nearest inn. There Blanchard got the witnesses to sign a deposition to the effect that they saw the bearer settle in his balloon in Deptford Township, County of Gloucester, in the state of New Jersey about 10:56 A.M. on the ninth day of January, 1793.

Back in Philadelphia, Blanchard met with Washington once more, and the two men fell into a conversation about their mutual friend Benjamin Franklin and the possible future uses of the balloon.

"I am no prophet, Mr. President," said Blanchard. "Who knows to what uses the balloon may be put in generations to come? Should you ask me what good it is, I would answer you as Dr. Franklin once answered such a question. I would say to you, sir, 'What good is a newborn baby?'"

Blanchard's Balloon.

FIRST AIRMAN
OF THE
ARMY

(THADDEUS LOWE)

Early in the Civil War, Professor Joseph Henry of the Smithsonian Institution invented a small electromagnetic coil to replace the cumbersome batteries formerly required to operate the telegraph. He was eager to demonstrate his invention to President Lincoln—why not have the President receive a message from a captive balloon flying over the White House? It would be the first message ever transmitted from the air to the earth by telegraph.

Finding a balloonist to make the ascent was no problem for Professor Henry, for among his friends was the young balloon enthusiast, Thaddeus Lowe.

"Of course I'll make the ascent for you," said Thaddeus. "But let me ask a favor in return. I know that you are acquainted with General Winfield Scott at the War Department. Will you accompany me to his office and introduce me to him?"

"Why not?" said Professor Henry. "But why do you want to meet General Scott?"

"You may recall," said Thaddeus, "tha on my last ascent, I maneuvered my bal loon into southerly air currents and wa carried all the way from New Hampshir down to North Carolina—and then on northerly current I maneuvered my wa back to Baltimore. Well, Professor Henry on that flight I looked down and saw Con federate troops—thousands of them marching toward Richmond. I haven' been able to get the idea out of my hea since then. Balloons can be valuable fo observation and military reconnaissance Surely, as an experimental scientist, yo must grant that my idea deserves a test."

"Yes, I do," said Henry. "But you ma not find General Scott as enthusiastic. Yo know how he feels about new ideas. Nev ertheless, come along. We'll walk over t Scott's office right now."

Their call on General Scott was brief He was pleasant enough at first; he aske

Professor Henry and Thaddeus to sit down and even offered them a cigar. However, as soon as Thaddeus had explained the purpose of their visit, the general reddened and rose from his desk.

"I'm amazed, Professor Henry, that you would assume I might be interested in such a harebrained scheme. And as for you, young man, I should think you could serve your country far better than by playing with balloons. Toys—that's all they are. Only a madman would go aloft in one!"

"What did I tell you?" said Professor Henry to Thaddeus when they were again standing in the street.

"I shall knock at some other great man's door," said Thaddeus with determination.

A few days later, Thaddeus, accompanied by a telegraph operator named Fogarty, took his balloon aloft near the White House for the demonstration of Professor Henry's electromagnetic coil. The balloon was held captive at a height of two thousand feet, that being the total length of the telegraph wire to be used in the demonstration.

From a window in the White House, President Lincoln and Professor Henry observed the ascent of the balloon.

"I wonder how they like it up there, swinging and swaying in that little basket," said the President. "If I were in it, I expect I'd be hanging on for dear life, wondering how soon the rope to the ground was going to break."

"Here comes the message, Mr. President," said Professor Henry.

"Why, your invention seems to work quite well, Professor," said the President. "Congratulations! What is Mr. Lowe saying to me?"

Slowly, out loud, as he received the message from the balloon, Professor Henry repeated it to the President.

To President Abraham Lincoln.

Sir: I am honored to send you the first message ever telegraphed from an aerial station. Forty miles to the north, great clouds of dust indicate the approach of marching troops. They are, of course, Federal troops. But may I point out, Mr. President, how valuable this message would be were they Confederate forces, marching from the south? It is my belief, sir, that observation balloons can contribute materially to the winning of battles and I earnestly wish to demonstrate this in the field..

Respectfully,
Thaddeus Lowe.

Professor Henry smiled as the import of the message became clear. Thaddeus had indeed knocked at the door of another great man.

"Do you wish me to transmit a few words to Mr. Lowe, sir?" he asked the President.

"I am inclined," said the President, "to grant this young man his wish. Do you vouch for his ability, Professor Henry?"

"When it comes to getting off the ground in a balloon and moving around up there in all those crisscross currents of air, Thaddeus Lowe knows more about it than anyone else in the country," declared Professor Henry.

"Then send him this message," said the President. "'Professor Henry agrees with me that you should have an opportunity to demonstrate your belief. You will report to General McClellan with the Army of the Potomac immediately. A. Lincoln.'"

General McClellan proved to be as impatient with the idea of an observation balloon as General Scott had been, but this time Thaddeus Lowe came armed with orders from the President himself and he was therefore permitted to put his plan into operation.

"I'll need about twenty men, sir," said Thaddeus as the interview came to an end.

"And what do you need twenty men for?" exclaimed the general.

"My assistant aloft will be Mr. Fogarty, the telegraph operator," said Thaddeus. "But I'll need twenty men on the ground to help get the balloon aloft, and to man

245

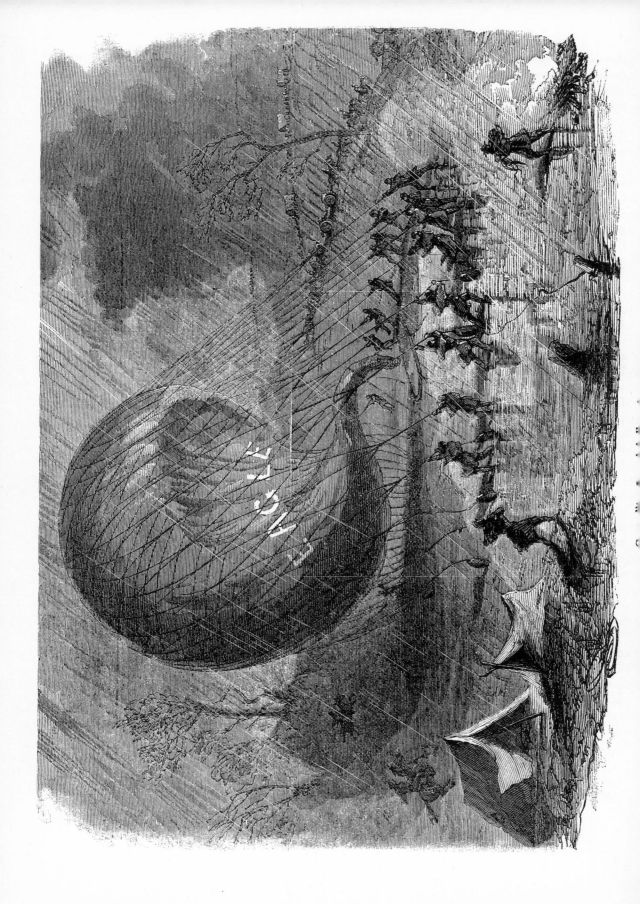

the portable gas-generators. The President mentions them in his letter, sir."

"Yes, so he does," said the general, scrutinizing the orders with impatience. "You shall have them. But hereafter, Mr. Lowe, speak to my lieutenant. Everything will be arranged."

Determined to prove the military value of observation balloons to General McClellan, Lowe made numerous ascensions in the first few days after his arrival at the general's camp. Fog and rain, however, hindered observation, and Lowe could report nothing of significance to the general's headquarters. Then, suddenly, the air cleared as the storm shifted south, and Lowe looked down on the Chickahominy River, swollen with the rains.

"Hey, Fogarty!" he exclaimed. "Look down at the bridge. The river's smashing it to pieces. That means that half our army across the river to the south is isolated from all supplies and right in the path of the Confederates. Quick! Send this message down to McClellan: 'Just observed that bridge across Chickahominy River has been washed out completely.'"

In a few moments, Lowe received the following answer from McClellan: "Thank you for the information, but look carefully and you will see my headquarters in trees fifty feet from washed-out bridge. Do you think I'm blind? Do not answer, as I want telegraph lines clear. Also, get that infernal gasbag out of the sky and stop revealing our position. Also, prepare to return to Washington immediately."

"I refuse to give up," said Lowe to Fogarty. "See those trees down there? They're bending with the wind toward the north. But up here, at this level, the wind is southerly. I propose that we take a little trip, Fogarty. Now listen carefully. If we drop our rope and telegraph wires, the wind will take us south—over the Confederate lines. And, then, when we've seen everything the enemy's up to, we can merely drop down to a lower level and catch the northerly wind. That'll bring us back here somewhere, and we can tap a telegraph line and report what we've seen to McClellan."

"Off we go!" cried Fogarty as he dropped the last of the telegraph line and the anchoring rope to the earth.

Within a few minutes, the balloon was directly over the Confederate lines and it was easy for Lowe to perceive the strategy that was being planned. A long line of infantry was moving up from the southeast to attack McClellan on the left, while the cavalry and artillery were being deployed to a position from which they could attack on the right.

"If McClellan isn't warned in the next half-hour, he'll be trapped," said Lowe. "Stand back, Fogarty, while I open the hydrogen valve. We'll drop down to that northerly wind and see how fast we can get back to our own army. Then we'll try to land near a telegraph line and report to McClellan."

Lowe's plan worked perfectly and enabled McClellan to save the Union Army from disaster. The value of the observation balloon in warfare had indeed been proved. A few days later Thaddeus Lowe received the following communication from the Secretary of War: "At the suggestion of President Lincoln, you have just been appointed to the newly created post of Chief of Aeronautics, United States Army. You will proceed immediately to organize a United States Army Balloon Corps, consisting, at first, of five balloons and the personnel necessary to operate them in the field."

In thousands of balloon ascensions, many of them under heavy enemy fire, Thaddeus Lowe continued to revolutionize the theory and practice of military observation from the air.

"I think of the air as a great new empire," he told Professor Henry, "and I foresee a time when men will be as much at home in it as they are on the earth."

INVENTOR OF THE TELEPHONE

(ALEXANDER GRAHAM BELL)

Can a dog talk?

The boy Alex Bell claimed that it wasn't at all impossible. In fact, he said, he had taught his own dog, Rags, to speak. And if you wanted proof—"Well, let me show you. Here, Rags! Come here!"

Tail wagging, Rags came and jumped into the boy's lap. Alex gently took the dog's head between his hands. "Now, see— if I move his mouth this way, then that way —Rags, say, 'How are you, Grandmama?'"

The dog began whining while the boy's hands were busy at its mouth. "OW . . . AH . . . OO . . . G . . . MA . . . MA."

It did, in fact, sound very much as if Rags might be asking after Grandmama's health.

A trick? Yes. But then again, an experiment. An experiment which was to help Alexander Graham Bell considerably when he taught the deaf to speak.

From his father, Alexander Bell had inherited an intense interest in sound and speech. Melville Bell, as a professor of elocution in Edinburgh, had developed a visible speech chart showing how sounds looked, for use in teaching pronunciation. And he gave his son an understanding of the mechanics of the human throat. It was this knowledge that made possible Alex's experiment with the dog.

Having reached manhood, Alexander Bell continued his father's work, conducting classes, lecturing, and giving private lessons in the elder Bell's system of "Visible Speech." The intensity and volume of his work dangerously affected his health, however, and in 1870, the Bell family came to America for a change of climate, settling in Brantford, Ontario. Eventually, Bell found his way to Boston, where he began teaching the deaf to speak, particularly deaf children.

Important and rewarding work though it was, Bell's scientific interests soon carried him into other fields. He became interested in experiments involving electricity. With a young man named Thomas Watson, he invented a multiple telegraph. Another invention, or rather the possibility of one, fascinated him even more. "If I can get a mechanism," he told Watson, "that will make a current of electricity vary in its intensity when a sound is passing through it, I can then telegraph any sound—even the sound of speech. That's right—we'd be able to talk by telegraph."

"A wonderful idea," Watson said, "but—"

"Yes, I know," Bell said. "Do I have the electrical knowledge to work it out? No. Well, then I'll get that knowledge."

But there was another objection, in some ways more serious. The research, the experiments that would go into such a project might take years. What's more, they would be expensive. Backers would be needed, people willing to invest money in what, at that time, seemed a fantasy.

"A telephone!" exclaimed a skeptical businessman. "I could speak over a wire? Somebody else could hear me and I could hear him? Do I look crazy, Mr. Bell?"

"I'm a banker, Mr. Bell, not a fool."

"A preposterous scheme! Black magic!"

These were the answers Bell received to his pleas for financial aid. It was a discouraging search, but then he finally secured a backer, the wealthy father of Mabel Hubbard, a deaf girl whom he was teaching to speak.

Bell and Thomas Watson began their experiments, and during those following months the deaf girl and her teacher fell in love. Then, one evening after dinner at the Hubbard home, Gardiner Greene Hubbard spoke impatiently. "Mr. Bell, I have

been thinking about your invention."

"It takes a little time, Mr. Hubbard," Bell explained. "You see, the telephone—"

"I'm talking about your multiple telegraph. *That* could be a financial success. You could sell it to the Western Union people. You need the money."

"But the telephone comes first."

"I am afraid," Mr. Hubbard said, "that I cannot keep pouring my money down a drain. And another thing—I understand that you and Mabel—well, I'm afraid I cannot give my consent until your financial position improves." Mr. Hubbard walked from the room, leaving Bell alone with his daughter.

The girl was deaf, but, by reading their lips, she had understood everything. Now her mouth moved. "Alex," she said. "You—work—on—the—tele—phone. I—will—wait."

He had taught her the words, but the feeling behind them was her own.

In 1877, Bell and Mabel Hubbard were married and sailed for a honeymoon abroad. In the meantime, the telephone became the sensation of the day. Some skeptics dubbed it "the shoebox on the wall." As it grew from the shoebox on the wall to its present form, it became an institution of American life and the life of the entire world!

Bell turned next to the development of the photophone, which would carry sound by a light beam. While working on it, he was called to the White House. President Garfield had been shot. The bullet had lodged in Garfield's abdomen, and the surgeons were unable to locate it. By using the photophone, which would give a signal when passing over the area where the metal lay, it was hoped the bullet could be located and then removed.

Unfortunately, the photophone had not as yet been perfected. Years after Garfield's death, however, Bell's sound detector, now known as the "Telephone Probe," did become an important contribution to medical science.

For this and other discoveries, honors poured upon Alexander Graham Bell. The Volta Prize, the Legion of Honor, an honory degree from Heidelberg, the freedom of the city of Edinburgh—recognition enough to overwhelm an ordinary man. But Alexander Bell was never content to bask in glory. From Beinn Bhreagh, his estate at Cape Breton, his activities ranged far—farming, stock-raising, photography, aviation.

For the comforts and conveniences of modern life, we owe much to this man who thought far more of service than he did of honors. "There is much to do in the world—" he said, "so many more things to find out about!"

Disheartened, Bell abandoned his research, resolving to earn enough money by teaching to marry the girl he loved. But the idea burned within him: vocal transmission by electricity! It would not let him rest. So, though he had to continue teaching by day, he worked on the telephone at night with Watson. Months passed and their long tiring work in an attic laboratory resulted in only one failure after another.

"Mr. Bell," Watson said one night, "you look tired. You need sleep. Why don't you stop and—"

"Let's try the thing once more, Watson."

"But you'll collapse if you go on this way."

"Just once more," Bell said, rubbing his eyes.

"All right," Watson said. "Be careful of those batteries, though. You were so tired last night you knocked one over and burned your clothes, remember?"

Following a trail of wire, Watson walked into another room. Closing the door behind him, he sat down at a bench. Yawning, he stared at the receiving apparatus. What could they expect tonight but another disheartening failure?

Awaiting the signal from Bell which would inform him that the experiment was under way, he had the receiver pressed to his ear when he heard a crash from the other room. Poor Bell! Had he knocked over a battery again? Well, let's hope he hadn't spilled a bottle of acid.

But what was that coming out of the receiver? It couldn't be—and yet . . . Those batteries! The mechanism crackled, "Mr. Watson, come here—I want you. Mr. Watson, come here." The mechanism was saying, "I want you!"

These were the first words ever spoken over a telephone. The beginning of an era in which electric communication was to bring the words and ideas of men across plains, forests, lakes and mountains, under seas, over the world—an era in which men would communicate with each other, unseen, through the mysterious impulse of electricity.

THE GREAT INVENTOR

(THOMAS ALVA EDISON)

As a practical scientist, as a genius in applying mechanically principles of pure science, Thomas Alva Edison has had no peer. He had some 1,300 patents to his credit and his inventions—electric light, the phonograph, moving pictures—are among the most important in modern life. He devised improvements in many fields and industrial processes, from gadgets to major machines.

How did he find the time? Well, he had the habit of getting along with very little sleep, but that doesn't explain it. More important was a habit of mind. He thought quickly and his reasoning progressed rapidly from a fixed point. Almost automatically he could achieve a new point of view, a fresh approach.

A little story told by Walter S. Mallory, who worked closely with Edison for many years, provides a fine demonstration of the way the "Wizard of Menlo Park" operated.

In 1898 Edison was fifty-one. He was engaged in perfecting a process to smelt low-grade iron ore on a scale never before attempted. He had invested his entire fortune, some three million dollars, in a new type of ore-reduction plant in the Sparta Mountains of New Jersey. The plant was barely beginning to operate at full capacity when the vast deposits of high-grade iron ore in the Mesabi Range in Minnesota were discovered. The Mesabi ore was not only high-grade, but it was lying near the surface. It could be dug up and loaded for the smelter very cheaply.

Walter Mallory, manager of the ore-reduction plant in New Jersey, went to Edison to tell him the bad news. He knew how large Edison's investment was and expected him to be depressed.

"We'll shut down at once!" exclaimed Edison, almost gaily.

"But what about all our equipment—the giant rollers, the machinery?" asked Mallory.

"We'll have to find some other use for them," said Edison, "something that needs crushing and milling. Something like—let me think a moment. Yes, cement!"

"But we don't know anything about cement," said Mallory.

"Get me every book you can find on it," ordered Edison. "I'll study the subject while you wind up the affairs of the ore-reduction plant."

"I don't see why you're so cheerful," ventured Mallory.

"Why shouldn't I be cheerful?" asked Edison. "I'm out of the manufacturing business and back to inventing again!"

Edison's study of the Portland cement business convinced him that the methods then used were inefficient and wasteful. Too much of the heat used to cook the lime went up the chimney. Edison announced that he would use a kiln nearly twice as long as the one in general use. "Impossible," cried all the experts. But Edison set up an experimental plant, put Mallory in charge and proved to the experts that they were wrong.

It was on a broiling-hot summer day during these experiments that Mallory received a telephone call from his home.

Mallory turned to Edison. "My little girl, Charlotte, is worse!"

"But you didn't even tell me she was ill," protested Edison.

"It didn't seem like anything at first," said Mallory. "She injured her kneecap a few days ago, and then yesterday necrosis set in. The doctor says this terrific heat is making it worse. The temperature in her room is 97 degrees. I'm afraid there's nothing we can do but pray that she lives through these intolerable days."

"We must end the heat wave," declared Edison.

"The weather reports say it will last several more days," said Mallory.

"Hang the weather reports!" said Edison. "We don't have to worry about the weather in the whole state of New Jersey. All we care about is the weather in your daughter's room."

And he set out to do something about it.

Fond as Mrs. Mallory was of Thomas

Edison, she did not approve of his invasion of her daughter's sick-room and the rumpus caused by hammer and nails.

"I'm sorry to have to disturb you and little Charlotte," explained Edison. "But it won't take long. I just want to fit this box into the window."

"Please do it quietly, Mr. Edison. Quietly, quietly," said Mrs. Mallory as she hovered over Charlotte. The little girl had not spoken for several hours; her fever was mounting and she moaned as she shifted from side to side.

"And now I shall have to move this electric fan," said Edison.

"But it's where Charlotte can get the most benefit from it!" said Mrs. Mallory.

"Please trust me for just a few minutes,"

Young Tom Edison ready to demonstrate his phonograph.

253

Edison and his son Charles in an electric auto car.

said Edison as he put the fan near the box in the window. "Quick, now," he said, turning to Mallory. "Take that chunk of ice your wife has been using for ice-packs and put it in the box in the window. And then open that window across the hall just a few inches—from the top."

In a moment, Edison's plan was in operation. "You see, Mrs. Mallory?" he asked "Now the only air that can enter the room is coming through this box. The air, blown by the fan, passes into the box over the ice. That cools it. With the window open across the hall, there is a continuous circulation of cool air through the room. It ought to keep the room at least ten degrees cooler than outside."

"Why, it's much cooler in here already," said Mallory, and at that moment, Charlotte called out for her mother.

Charlotte Mallory was saved from immediate danger by Edison's air-cooling device; but it was another matter to make her well again. Her convalescence was discouragingly slow, and the doctor said there was no medical tonic that would do her any good.

"What she needs is a change of scene," he said one day to Edison and Mallory. "But I don't dare risk moving her. It's no longer a matter of medicine—it's a matter of cooperation from her own tired little body. She needs normal acceleration of the glands and impulses, a natural quickening of the nervous system which would be more likely to come from the stimulus she would get from new surroundings."

Edison took the doctor's remarks very much to heart. He returned to Charlotte's sick-room the following day to conduct another experiment. At first the nurse had tried to keep Edison from proceeding with whatever it was he was going to do. He had startled her by asking the sick child, "How would you like to go on a trip with me, Charlotte? Just a little trip, a sort of picnic?"

Of course Charlotte had exclaimed, "Oh, I'd love to!"

Knowing that Charlotte could not leave her room, the nurse feared that Edison's invitation would end in a crushing disappointment.

"But perhaps she won't be disappointed," whispered Edison to the nurse and Mr. and Mrs. Mallory. "Besides, the doctor said that she needed natural stimulation."

With the permission of Charlotte's parents, Edison continued with his experiment.

"Because we can't go outdoors to the picnic, we'll bring the picnic in here," said Edison to Charlotte. "You can pick your favorite picnic spot. Where will it be? Under some trees at the edge of a field with a brook? On a sandy beach down by the seashore? Or on the side of a mountain, with a fine view and tall pines all around?"

"The mountains!" said Charlotte excitedly.

Edison took a small bottle from his pocket, went over to the air-cooling box in the window and poured out some fluid in front of the fan. Soon the air was filled with the bracing odor of evergreens and the smoky pungence of a wood-fire.

"Oh, you make it all seem so real!" said Charlotte, laughing with pleasure.

"I have several other bottles with me," said Edison, "and each has a different kind of picnic in it. It isn't magic, my dear Charlotte—it's just plain chemistry. But it's great fun, don't you think?"

Aided by Mr. Edison's air-cooling contrivance and by his "chemical' picnics, Charlotte Mallory soon recovered from her illness.

Edison had solved a problem not only because he had the knowledge—and he had a great deal of that—but chiefly because he knew how to apply his knowledge, in a fresh new way if an old way wouldn't do.

THE MEN OF ENTERPRISE

"O America because you build for mankind I build for you."
WALT WHITMAN, *By Blue Ontario's Shore.*

FIRST AMERICAN WORLD-TRADER

(STEPHEN GIRARD)

At the wharf, a small sailing vessel was loading and a small boy watched, as boys watch such things the world over. This was Bordeaux; the year, 1764. Everyone in the French port knew that the ship was bound for the West Indies.

The boy took a deep breath, walked up the dock and spoke to the captain.

"I'd like to ship aboard as your cabin boy," he said.

The captain grinned. "How do you know I need one?"

"I keep my ears open, sir."

"Well, if I *do* need a cabin boy, I need a good 'un. You're only a half-pint lad. You don't look strong to me and you seem to be blind in the right eye. How old are you? What's your name?"

"My name is Stephen Girard. I'm fourteen years old and I *am* strong. Feel my arm. I can see more with my one eye, sir, than most men can with two."

"Well—I'm not going to get into trouble helping you run away to sea. Got your mother's permission?"

"My mother's dead."

"An orphan boy, eh?"

"Not exactly. My father's alive. He's a merchant, an officer in the naval reserve. But mostly I'm on my own. I've even got a little money to buy a share in the cargo."

He got the job, and in the next few years young Stephen sailed the Atlantic from France to the West Indies and up the coast of the British colonies in America. He lost no opportunity to improve himself, and in the next twelve years became a licensed pilot, a ship's officer and finally, at twenty-six, master of his own ship. In 1776, he took another crucial step. In command of a vessel bound for New York, he changed course and sailed up Delaware Bay toward Philadelphia.

"The British have blockaded New York," he explained to his mate, "and I think we are close to war."

"Do you suppose the colonies will try to become independent of Great Britain?"

"Yes, and they have a chance of succeeding as long as the British are outsailed."

"You really believe that, sir?"

"So much so, mate, that I'm planning to settle in this new country and throw my lot in with hers. That ship we outpointed to windward, rounding the Cape, was a British blockader. Passing her like that was an omen. You didn't know it, my friend, but I was saving my own property. I'm no longer working for the shippers. This is my own vessel; the cargo is mine. And when we land in Philadelphia, you and the rest of the crew can return to France at my expense, but I'm going to settle there till the blockade is over."

For a time, Girard settled at Mount Holly, New Jersey; then he opened a store in Philadelphia. Gradually his business grew, and he yearned for peace so he could again send cargoes to sea in his own stout vessels.

He married the daughter of a shipbuilder, and in 1778 became a citizen of the

Commonwealth of Pennsylvania. After American independence had been recognized abroad, he bought and built several fine brigs and sent his cargoes to every port in the world. And through good judgment and skillful organization he amassed a fortune. He built new ships, bought real estate, extended his banking connections. His agents were in many European cities, sending him detailed reports of conditions abroad. His fortune grew to tremendous size for those days, for he was, in effect, a banker as well as a merchant.

When, in 1810, he learned that Napoleon had annexed Holland and that all Europe was closed to American commerce, he revised the sailings of his vessels and established new trading routes—to South America and to China—and he developed a tremendous business in the Pacific area. He introduced the American flag to many ports around the world, and in the banking centers of the world the name "Stephen Girard" was as good as gold.

That same year Congress refused to renew the charter of the government's bank —the United States Bank. The merchants were worried. There would be no way for them to get the huge credits they needed in doing business with foreign countries. But Girard provided a way. He started the Bank of Stephen Girard, which achieved immediate prestige. Since it had practically unlimited credit in every corner of the globe, it was a great help in the development of American commerce.

Then in 1812 Girard and his bank came to the rescue of the U.S. Treasury. A new $16,000,000 government loan was a dismal failure. Only $6,000,000 was raised and the Treasury was desperate. Girard, his friend David Parish, and John Jacob Astor formed a syndicate, subscribed the whole ten million and financed the bond issue through the Girard Bank. The syndicate knew that Stephen Girard's endorsement would go a long way toward selling the loan to the public. "And," said Girard, "what is not disposed of, I'm perfectly willing to hold."

In many other ways the former cabin boy from Bordeaux won not only great wealth but in addition the esteem and gratitude of his countrymen. But he always regretted that he did not have a formal education, and he never forgot what it meant to be a motherless boy. At the time of his death in 1831, he left the great bulk of his vast fortune, some $6,000,000, in trust for the education of "orphan boys." Today Girard College in the city of Philadelphia stands as a lasting, living monument to its founder, who blazed trails across the high seas and showed the way for American business.

Office of Stephen Girard, Water Street above Race, Philadelphia.

Edwin Drake, left; his first oil well; William Smith who drilled the well.

THE TREMENDOUS TRIFLE

(EDWIN DRAKE)

The directors of the Pennsylvania Rock Oil Company sat around a long table, waiting anxiously for Edwin Drake's report on their critical situation.

What did Drake know about oil? Precious little. Yet Bissell, the president of the company, had hired him to inspect certain properties at Oil Creek, Pennsylvania. If Drake's report were bad, the company might as well go out of business. Even if it were good, the company might go bankrupt anyway. It had come upon hard times. As an illuminant, oil had been losing out to kerosene derived from coal and other substances by a process discovered in 1852. Now, kerosene was outselling oil, 20 to 1. One thing could save the Pennsylvania Rock Oil Company —greater production. By flooding the market they could hope to compete.

But there lay the rub. To get oil, deep trenches were dug. The oil seeped up from the ground and collected in pools. Then, it was siphoned off and taken to the distillers. All attempts to improve upon this crude and slow process had failed. Unless a speedier way to extract the oil were found, there was little point in acquiring more oil-bearing land.

For some reason Bissell had faith in young Drake. "He believes in the future of the petroleum industry," was the only way he could explain it to his associates. He acknowledged that Drake had never been in the oil business before. When Bissell hired him, he had been a conductor of the New York, New Haven & Hartford Railroad.

When Drake arrived, his face was beaming. "There's oil at Oil Creek, Mr.

Bissell," he reported. "Lots of it."

"But can we get it out in quantities?" Bissell asked. "In the quantities we need to compete with coal-oil?"

"Not if we use the old methods," Drake said. "But we can if we dig for it—sink wells, instead of digging trenches."

"*Dig* for it?" exclaimed Bissell. "Don't you know what happens when we try to drill a well?"

Drake nodded. "Yes. As soon as the shaft is pulled out, the hole caves in. But I think we'll find a way to do it. I stopped off at Syracuse and Pittsburgh, before coming back here. They drill a lot of salt wells around there, you know. I spent a few days studying their operations—"

"*Salt* wells? What in the name of Jehosaphat have salt wells to do with oil?"

As Drake explained it, the connection became less bizarre. Deep below the earth were lakes of oil. Above this oil were beds of salt, sometimes wells of salt water. Digging salt wells was a far older craft than oil production. "And I've learned a great deal from their drilling methods," Drake said. "Bissell, I want you to send me back to Oil Creek, to oversee the operations."

"All right," Bissell said. "But just remember, Drake, we're in oil, not salt. And you'd better work fast. If you don't, the company's done for."

Once more, this time accompanied by his wife, Drake set out for Oil Creek. There he called on Uncle Billy Smith, famous for locating salt wells.

Smith was seventy years old. For fifty of those years he had been a digger of salt wells. His boast was that he'd never brought in a tainted salt well. So when Drake approached him and said, "I want you to help me find oil," Uncle Billy looked amazed.

"There ain't nothin' worse for taintin' a salt well than oil," he said. "I've always avoided oil-producin' ground like the plague."

"If you avoided it," Drake said, "then you know where it is. That's why I want to hire you, Uncle Billy."

"Mr. Drake," Uncle Billy said, "you're no fool."

"I want you to dig for me," Drake said. "To dig in a place you'd avoid when you dig a salt well."

A few weeks later, Uncle Billy said as they walked near what is now Titusville, "Well, Colonel, this is it. Look down at your feet, son."

"Are you sure?"

"For fifty years," Uncle Billy said, spitting on the ground, "this here's been the kind of land I've shied away from—because it would've fouled my salt wells."

"We'll start digging then," Drake said. When he looked at the ground, however, his heart sank. Beneath his feet there might be an ocean of oil—but the ground was loose and spongy, just like all the other possibly rich oil lands he had dug in hopefully, only to have the wells cave in.

Three days' work, and Uncle Billy and his crew had drilled twenty feet down. Then, the shaft was drawn up—and, as Drake had feared, the hole caved in.

"Isn't there some way to stop it from doing that?" Drake asked.

"Don't know of any," Uncle Billy said. "Colonel, it looks like we're finished. It'll act that way every time."

But Drake declared fiercely, "We'll punch holes in that sawdust until we get one that stays. I came here to hit oil. And I'm gonna hit it if it kills me."

The months passed. Drake began coughing a great deal—a doctor advised him to rest; otherwise—

"No," Drake said. "I'm too close to what I came here for. I'm not going to let this thing lick me."

One day, Uncle Billy shouted, "Boys! Stop that engine!" He turned to Drake, his face telling bad news. "We hit bedrock, Colonel."

Drake said wearily, coughing a little,

"Have you got a shaft that'll punch through?"

Uncle Billy nodded. "But you know what'll happen, Colonel, when we pull that shaft out—"

Drake's illness had weakened him. He had been on the job for days with very little rest, and now he could barely stand. He looked around for a place to sit down, and then lowered himself to the ground. Leaning back, he supported himself against a stack of cast iron pipes. They would be used to siphon off salt water, if the shaft encountered any.

"How much of this have we got?" Drake said suddenly. "I mean these pipes, Uncle Billy."

"A hundred feet or more."

"Then we've got a chance," Drake said, leaping to his feet. "We'll sink that pipe in the ground, down to bedrock—and then we can drill through it."

"Huh?"

"We'll drill through the pipes. Don't you see? The pipe will act as a casing—to keep the walls of the hole from caving in when we withdraw the shaft." He passed a hand across his brow. "All these months it took me to think of a trifle like that!"

And that trifle created a new petroleum industry. That day of August 27, 1859, at sixty-nine feet, the first oil well in history gushed forth. Little knowing it, Drake had ushered in a new era.

But his story does not end here. A curious and pathetic aftermath must be recorded. Years later, a newspaper reporter paid a visit to Uncle Billy Smith. "I'm looking for Colonel Drake," he said. "Do you know where he is?"

"Son," Uncle Billy said, "I'd like to know where he is myself. So would a lotta other people that's mighty grateful to him, includin' those in the oil industry. After we hit that oil, he stayed on here at Titusville for four years. Then he took sick and went off with his family. Took all his savin's—close to sixteen thousand dollars—

and just disappeared."

"One thing I don't understand," the reporter said. "Why didn't he patent that casing idea? It's revolutionized the oil industry. He could have made a fortune."

"Now that's the funny thing," Uncle Billy said. "He was a fine man, Colonel Drake was, but he never had much head for business. All he wanted was to bring in that oil. Thought that casing idea was just a trifle."

Later, Edwin Drake was found. Ill and poverty-stricken, he was living with his family in New Jersey. Backed by the grateful oil industry, the Pennsylvania State Legislature granted him a substantial annuity for the rest of his life. And, at Titusville, a statue was erected in his honor.

The Drake oil well.

THE GREATEST SHOW ON EARTH

(P. T. BARNUM)

The art of selling, the outsize campaign, the "Come one, Come all," now has a more dignified vocabulary: promotion, salesmanship, advertising, public relations. But whether the more genteel approach is the same as the old ballyhoo, spiel, pitch or flimflam is no great matter. It has played a big part in the bigness of America.

Professors may call it an imaginative, yet practical, use of psychology, an application of the basic laws of human behavior to business schemes. This adroit playing on the responsive chords of human weakness has been attacked as an evil, but others have praised it. They say that if America has the highest standard of living, it is partly because of the promoters, the advertisers, the showmen—who knew how to spur our curiosity, sharpen our appetites, stimulate our dreams.

So let us look at Americans' readiness to be astounded, through the story of the greatest American showman of them all.

In 1835 a Connecticut Yankee named Phineas T. Barnum came to New York to seek his fame and fortune. He started modestly enough by opening a grocery store, which brought him and his family a fair living. Others might have been satisfied with that, but not Barnum. Storekeeping was forgotten when he took a trip to Philadelphia to buy sugar and other supplies. He returned with a Negro slave woman so old and dried-up that she looked like a mummy. Instead of being able to serve others, this slave had to be waited on. She was blind and too feeble to walk.

To Mrs. Barnum's horror, she learned that her husband had paid a thousand dollars for her. And he had sold the store and gone into debt besides!

But Barnum had something in mind for the slave woman, Joice Heth, who said

she was 160 years old. With her came a bill of sale in the handwriting of George Washington's father. It said she had raised George Washington from a baby. Barnum's quick imagination saw a way to gain a fortune from her.

He printed handbills describing his animated mummy. Crowds flocked to see the blind and shriveled Negress who prattled about dear little Georgie Washington. Over many months Barnum's profits exceeded fifteen hundred dollars a week, an amount which today would be equivalent to five times that sum.

Inevitably, the novelty wore off and attendance began to drop. Another man might have contentedly pocketed his profits. But not P. T. Barnum. He wrote anonymous letters to the newspapers denouncing Joice Heth as a fraud. She was made of India rubber, the letters said, and her voice was projected by a ventriloquist.

Again, crowds of people came, eager to see if Joice Heth was real. Papers all over the country printed controversial letters about the India-rubber woman. Barnum took her on tour, and by the time she died he had made a fortune from his shrewd purchase.

It was Barnum who coined the phrase, "There's one [a sucker] born every minute." By that he meant everybody. For everybody has a streak of gullibility, and even the great P. T. Barnum was swindled out of the fortune he had made on Joice Heth.

And so he was penniless when he approached Francis W. Olmstead, a wealthy New York realtor, with a strange proposition. Without a cent to contribute as his share, with nothing to offer by way of security, Barnum proposed to go into business with the rich Mr. Olmstead.

Fortunately for both of them, Olmstead had the imagination to see that Barnum's cleverness and enterprise were the best kind of capital. Olmstead took up the offer, and it proved to be the most profitable deal of his business career.

Olmstead owned a building in which a man named Scudder was exhibiting a collection of curiosities gathered from all over the world. It was called the American Museum, but few knew of its existence. It was losing money steadily and for some time it had been up for sale. Nobody wanted it. Yet Barnum took it over.

In a few months the museum was one of the sights of New York. Barnum placed floodlights on the roof, anticipating the bright lights of Broadway. The visitors swarmed to his "lecture room," where he originated the idea of the continuous performance. And—another Barnum "first"— he was the first businessman to spend the whole of his first year's profits on advertising. And how it paid off!

At his American Museum his most sensational exhibit was a midget twenty-eight inches high, General Tom Thumb. To promote the midget general, Barnum arranged to have Queen Victoria give him a private audience. As he explained to the American ambassador, Everett, his procedure was simple. He knew that one could play on the vanity of kings and queens, just as one played on the vanity of John or Jane Doe. He merely sent a note to Queen Victoria that he would be coming to England on his way to France to present General Tom Thumb to King Louis Philippe. That had been enough. To make sure that Great Britain would have precedence over France, Queen Victoria had issued the coveted invitation for a command performance.

It would take many pages to describe all his notable publicity feats and innovations. There is room for only two more here. Though he had never heard her sing, he made the soprano Jenny Lind a top-drawer attraction to the American public. Through his phenomenal success with his "Swedish nightingale," as he billed her, Barnum helped to establish concert-going in this country, then considered a hopeless musical wasteland.

Barnum also showed he could recognize the genius and enterprise of a rival—and make use of them to his own advantage. Barnum had organized the first two-ring circus and menagerie, "The Greatest Show on Earth." Its publicity had been built largely on stunts with elephants. Then a rival circus-owner, James A. Bailey, managed to breed a baby elephant, said to be the first one born in captivity. The newspapers were full of it.

To get hold of that attraction Barnum offered a hundred thousand dollars for the mother and baby. Today that sum would be equivalent of a half-million dollars or more. Barnum did not doubt for a moment that Bailey would accept the offer. It was more money than he was likely to make from a lifetime in the circus business.

But Bailey had not been studying Barnum, whom he had taken as his model, in vain. He outsmarted the master himself. He used Barnum's telegram in his own advertising. The newspapers carried the offer, and the streets were flooded with throwaways displaying copies of Barnum's telegram with the heading, "This is what P. T. Barnum thinks of our baby elephant!"

But, instead of giving way to resentment, Barnum decided to take advantage of this turn of events. Recognizing that in Bailey he had met another great showman, he decided that it would be wiser to have Bailey as his partner than as his competitor.

With Bailey's circus amalgamated with Barnum's, a stupendous entertainment evolved, truly "The Greatest Show on Earth." Three rings and four stages . . . trapeze and slack-wire acts going on all the time . . . the world's best acrobats . . . its most fantastic clowns . . . its strangest animals. The traveling circus became a beloved American tradition. Its inheritors, the Ringling Brothers, have, until recently, carried on its stupendous tradition.

In Hollywood and Broadway and on radio and TV, the Yankee enterprise and daring imagination of P. T. Barnum have filtered into every kind of entertainment. In merchandising, advertising and public-relations, his techniques have been applied, with new twists, tricks and teasers to bring the exotic and the unexpected into American life. He told them what they wanted to see—and he knew how to make them come—"Come one, Come all."

Barnum's Museum (left) in the 1840's.

THE INDIA-RUBBER MAN

(CHARLES GOODYEAR)

SHIPWRECK AT SEA;
200 PASSENGERS DROWN

Reading this newspaper headline one day, Charles Goodyear felt a chill of horror. Then, reading on, he came to a statement that seemed the most shocking of all. The ship had been equipped with life-preservers made of India rubber. Wearing them, the passengers had leaped into the sea, but not one of the "life-preservers" had floated.

In 1834, crude rubber was an interesting new material. A few companies already had begun to use it, manufacturing various articles from it, including shoes. But the material could not be depended on. In hot weather the shoes melted; in winter they turned as hard as rocks.

Rubber meant little to Charles Goodyear the day he read that newspaper account. A partner in his father's hardware business, he had concerns and troubles of his own. Yet the story of the shipwreck haunted him.

Then, one morning while doing some business in New York, he happened to pass a store above which a sign read: "Roxbury India Rubber Company." Behind the plate-glass display window he saw an object that caught his attention. It was a round circle of rubber.

After a while, the door opened and a man stepped out. "You've been staring at that for the last half-hour," he commented. "Why?"

"It's one of the new India-rubber life-preservers, isn't it?" Charles Goodyear asked. "I've been wondering about that shipwreck the other day. The passengers were all wearing these—"

The man interrupted him gruffly. "These preservers are still in the experimental stage. They're not quite perfected yet."

"What's wrong with them?"

The man scowled, but the young man seemed genuinely interested rather than idly curious. "The inflating apparatus isn't quite right; a good many of them develop air-leaks," he explained.

Goodyear studied the life-preserver for a moment. "The air-stem is set too loosely in the rubber. If you'd just put a screw thread on it and fasten it with a clamp, then it would fit tight and air couldn't leak around the stem."

"I'm the manager of this company. How much do you want for that idea?"

"If it will help save lives," Goodyear answered, "then I don't want anything." And he started to walk away.

The man caught his arm and drew Goodyear into the store. "What do you know about India rubber, young man?"

"Not much."

"Just this week, we've had more than 20,000 rubber shoes returned. All of them smelled so bad we had to bury them. We can't seem to find out how to keep the stuff from melting. Look here, you seem to be clever enough. Think you could find out the right way to treat India rubber?"

"I can try."

That evening, when Goodyear returned to his Philadelphia home, he amazed his wife by rushing into the kitchen and demanding a kettle. Filling it with water, he threw into it a lump of crude India rubber. Then he brought the water to a boil on the stove. "I'll heat it," he explained to his wife, "until the rubber melts. You see, nobody knows how to cure rubber properly, but there *must* be a way. Now, when the heat makes this rubber soft and pliable I'm going to knead it the way you knead dough. Then I'm going to roll it as thin as I can with a rolling pin, and—"

Thus Goodyear's experiments began—

Charles Goodyear.

experiments that were to fill ten years of his life. His methods of research were crude, but that was not unusual in the early years of the nineteenth century. At that time, in America, there was no such thing as organized chemical research. There were a few pioneers who believed in the commercial possibilities of certain materials, but these men had to carry through their experiments in makeshift laboratories, usually in their homes.

No sooner had Goodyear begun his ex-periments than another difficulty faced him. His father's hardware concern failed. Creditors were hammering on the door, demanding their money. Goodyear was only a junior partner, but he was held accountable. And the law in those days was firm: if he didn't pay off the debts, he would have to go to prison.

For the next few years, Charles Goodyear was seldom out of prison for long. But even this hardship did not discourage him. The little money he possessed went into purchasing crude-rubber gum for his endless experiments. When he had no more money, he borrowed from his friends.

Before he came near success, all the rubber-manufacturing companies failed. Still, he kept on with his search. Finally, in 1836, he began to treat rubber with sulphur. Then, obtaining modest financial backing, he began manufacturing rubber articles of various kinds in Roxbury, Massachusetts.

Success seemed at hand. The Post Office became interested in his work. Could he make waterproof rubber mailbags?

"The Post Office man will be here any minute," he said to his assistant one day. "Are the rubber mailbags still in the storeroom?"

"Aye, that they are, Mr. Goodyear," his assistant said. "All one hundred and fifty of them hanging on hooks, as you ordered."

"This is a great day for us, Nathaniel," Goodyear said.

Once more, however, Goodyear suffered disappointment. When the Post Office inspector arrived and was taken into the storeroom, a sickening sight met their eyes.

"Look, sir!" Nathaniel cried. "The bags have fallen off the hooks!"

"Yes," Goodyear said sadly. "But I just can't understand it."

The Post Office inspector picked up one of the bags from the floor. "They've melted. Melted the way India rubber always does."

"But my new process—" Goodyear said. "It worked on raincoats, and carriage covers—"

"I'm canceling the order here and now," the inspector said. "You're a fraud, Goodyear, a fraud!"

Goodyear went back to his weary labors. This time it was almost impossible to get financial aid of any kind. His failure on the government order convinced people that it was impossible to make use of rubber in any practical form.

He became an object of ridicule. "If you see a man in a rubber coat with rubber shoes and a rubber cap and a rubber purse

without a penny in it, that's Goodyear." Wherever he went to attempt to borrow money, the door was slammed in his face. He sold all his possessions to buy more rubber for his experiments. Again and again he went back, starting the experiments all over along many different lines. And every process he developed that promised success failed him.

By the spring of 1839, he was almost ready to give up. Then, returning home late one winter night, he found his wife waiting for him in the kitchen.

"Charles, you look half-frozen. Come over here by the stove."

"Couldn't raise a cent," he said wearily. "Everyone laughs at me. They think I'm insane." He was holding a wad of gum rubber mixed with sulphur, tossing the wad from one hand to the other.

"Why should you care?" Goodyear said. "I've taken everything from you, given you nothing. We're living in poverty—" He raised his hand and angrily hurled the rubber wad from him. It landed atop the stove, making a sharp hiss. Goodyear stared at it, astounded. The rubber should have melted, but—"Look, Clarissa!" he cried. "Look! It's charred, like leather! And the rim around the charred part is—is even *more* elastic than natural rubber!"

It was true; he had found the way. At last he was on the track of the vulcanizing of rubber. It took five more years of experiments to learn the correct proportions of sulphur and gum, the right amount of heat to apply, and how best to apply it. Before his death, Charles Goodyear lived to see rubber used in five hundred different ways. Today more than thirty thousand different ways have been found to utilize it.

For his courage, his devotion to an idea, and his faith in himself and his work, the world owes him a lasting debt of gratitude. And it may be said that the history of the rubber industry for its first twenty-five years is also Charles Goodyear's personal history.

HE DREW THE NATION TOGETHER

(HIRAM SIBLEY)

Hiram Sibley, a prosperous Rochester merchant, had just concluded his business in Washington, D.C. He went into a telegraph office to wire his wife that he would be home the following Tuesday.

No one was in the dingy outer office when he entered. On the fly-spotted wall hung a clock, but it was not running. The whole atmosphere was disagreeable.

Becoming impatient, Sibley knocked on the floor with his cane and called out, "Hello! Hello, there! Is anyone in?"

From an inner room came a sleepy voice, "I heard you. Coming right away."

Then a carelessly dressed man shambled in.

"I want to send a telegram to Rochester," said Sibley.

"Rochester, eh? That's all the way up in New York State, ain't it?"

"Yes."

"Got it writ out, mister?"

"Yes," said Sibley, and handed the message to the man.

The telegrapher began reading it aloud with the slow caution of one who had only recently achieved literacy: "October 4, 1849. Mrs. Elizabeth Sibley . . . That's your wife, I reckon?"

"Yes, but what—"

"No offense, Mr. Sibley, just curious."

The telegrapher continued to read slowly: "Business concluded satis-fact-orily. Leave Washington today. Arrive home Tuesday. Kiss the children. Hiram. . . . That right?"

Sibley nodded.

Then the telegrapher began counting aloud, "One, two, three, four, five, six . . . Look here, mister, 'kissin' the children' is gonna cost you some. The charge is $1.75 for ten words and twenty-five cents for every word over. Still want 'em kissed?"

"Yes," said Sibley, fuming.

"Up to you," said the telegrapher, shrugging. "Now all that's gonna set you back $2.50, Mr. Sibley."

The telegrapher peered into Sibley's face, expecting him to wince. In 1849, $2.50 had the value of about $25 today.

But Sibley showed nothing but irritation over the telegrapher's familiarity. He took out two silver dollars and a silver half-dollar, and the coins rang on the counter.

"Can you tell me when this will arrive?" he asked.

"Waal," drawled the telegrapher, "that's a question. Ain't easy to answer that one. Takes time to figure out."

He pulled down several books from a shelf, blew off the surface dust, and began turning pages.

"From Washington to New York, that will go quick enough. It's our own line. Let's say it gets to New York tonight, about eight o'clock. Then it'll start upstate tomorrow morning."

"But why not immediately—tonight?" asked Sibley.

"Because we ain't got no lines out of New York. We got to transfer to another company's lines."

"Then why can't the transfer be made tonight?"

"Because the messenger boy has to deliver the message to the office of the other company, and the messengers quit at seven o'clock. Stands to reason it can't go at eight when they quit at seven. It'll have to wait over till the morning."

"What happens tomorrow then?"

The telegrapher searched another book. "From Albany it'll have to switch to Buffalo on another line. That's going to mean another messenger boy, and you know

268

Hiram Sibley.

how they are. I'd say it might get to Buffalo tomorrow night. Can't be sure though."

"Good Lord! Why can't it go direct to Rochester from New York?"

"Because the New York-Rochester company don't do no business with us, and we don't do no business with them, that's why. The nearest place we have a connection is Buffalo. From there it might go to Rochester by mail."

"When on earth *will* this message reach my wife?"

"Reckon she might git it Wednesday mornin'."

"But I'll be there myself on Tuesday."

The telegrapher grinned. "So you will, so you will. Give your wife a surprise, eh? Better than her waitin' around for you."

Such scenes were not uncommon in the early days of the telegraph. Sibley himself had had other occasions to fume over the delays and the inefficiency of the telegraph when important business decisions waited on messages that never came through, or arrived so garbled as to be incomprehensible.

When he invented the telegraph, Morse had given the world the possibility of instant communication across great distances. But it required an organizing genius and a strong will to turn that possibility into practical reality.

In 1849 there were more than fifty separate telegraph companies. Some of them were absurdly short-distance lines. Few of them were financially sound. Most of them lacked the means to train their operators, to pay wages that would attract educated employees, to put in first-rate equipment or to obtain office space in other than mean and shabby stores.

The industry was expanding, it was true, but each new company intensified the disorder. The Eastern seaboard had a confused network of lines, and some were groping westward to the Mississippi. It was progress, but progress in chaos.

Because of the shortage of skilled workers, the inadequate equipment, the slovenly conditions and the general confusion, the service was naturally inferior. It was, moreover, so expensive that most people resorted to telegraphing only in emergencies. That was why, for a long time, a telegram was received with dread. As often as not, it carried a message of the death of a loved one.

Almost daily, and without warning, rates were raised or lowered, connections with other companies were changed. Not only the public but the companies themselves suffered from this disorder. Most of the small companies were on the verge of bankruptcy and their stocks were almost worthless.

Unless an orderly system could be established, the young telegraph industry appeared doomed never to realize its possibilities of service to the public and profit to the investors. Among the businessmen who understood this was Hiram Sibley.

He interested a group of businessmen in Rochester in organizing a company to merge the existing telegraph lines and thus make unified operation and direct communication possible. This would realize at last the full possibilities of Morse's invention, and by reducing the costs, bring telegraph service within the reach of everyone's purse.

In promoting this idea, Sibley often quoted from the *Federalist Papers*. In these, Madison and Hamilton and other great statesmen of our founding period had argued for a complete union of the states and a central government. It seems unbelievable now that heated argument about so obvious a need should have been necessary. But it had taken not only Federalist pleas but bitter experience to convince the states of the value of unity.

In the field of telegraphy the same lesson had to be learned. On September 6, 1850, Hiram Sibley and his associates formed the New York and Mississippi Valley Printing Telegraph Company. Then, valise in hand, Sibley went through the country, slowly weaving the separate but tangled strands of the existing telegraph system into an orderly network.

Where it was possible, he enlisted the companies at once by sound arguments or hard cash. Where this was not possible, he tracked down individual stockholders, and bought up their shares until he had assembled a controlling interest. Then, acting as majority stockholder, he merged the line. In some cases these stocks had not paid dividends for years and the stock certificates had been thrown away or used to patch up leaking pipes! Finally, only one company remained outside the network—the last obstacle to a unified system.

That obstacle was a formidable one. It was the Erie and Michigan Telegraph Company. Its owner was Ezra Cornell, founder of Cornell University. There was no hope of buying him out; he was too wealthy already to rise to the bait of a money offer. And it was not likely that even the persuasive Sibley, using the best Federalist arguments, could talk him into a merger. He was proud of his independence. Indeed, it did not appear likely that Cornell would listen to *any* argument, since he had become infuriated by Sibley's purchase of outside holdings of his company's stock.

Nevertheless, Sibley wangled a meeting with Cornell. He brought to Cornell, who was an imaginative businessman, an idea that fired his imagination. How would Cornell like to join him in stretching the

legraph lines all the way across the con-
ment to link the Atlantic Coast with the
cific?

Cornell's eyes glowed.

"That would be possible," Sibley ob-
rved, "only with the establishment of a
ified telegraph system."

Ezra Cornell held out his hand. And
us a new and larger network came into
ing: the Western Union Telegraph
ompany.

But though Sibley had converted Cor-
ll with that inspired idea, he found it
rder to sell his scheme to his former
sociates. "String another line, thousands
miles of wire, through impassable forts, over desert and mountains? A wild
eam! It would take an impossible sum
money and probably twenty years. . . .
hat investors would wait that long?"

"We can get the backing of the govern-
ent," said Sibley.

"Oh, those politicians!" was the scorn-
l reply.

Sibley went to Washington. "Those poli-
cians" were fired by his reasoned en-
usiasm. On June 16, 1860, Congress
ssed an act to "facilitate communication
tween the Atlantic and Pacific states by
ectric telegraph." It was stipulated that
e work be completed in two years.

Construction began from two ends—
stward from Placerville, California, and
estward from Kearney, Nebraska, until
en the western outpost of the nation's
legraph system. Though the Civil War
d begun, it did not deter the enterprise.
ncoln gave it priority, declaring that the
tablishment of such communications was
ilitarily desirable. The first pole of the
w line was driven in on July 4, 1861.

Under Sibley's direction the work was
rried on unceasingly. There were
ushes with Indians. New terrain brought
w engineering problems. An unexpected
fficulty developed when unscrupulous
ntractors would not carry out their obli-

gations unless they were "greased" with
extra sums.

In one such case the defaulter happened to be a relative of Brigham Young,
leader of the Mormons in Utah. This man
had extorted a new contract on higher
terms for telegraph poles and then had
failed to deliver them, alleging that transportation rates had gone up. But after
Sibley visited Brigham Young, however,
the poles materialized as if by magic, and,
at the Mormon leader's command, the second contract was torn up.

One hundred and thirty-two days after
construction had started—not the two
years set by Congress, nor the twenty
years predicted by Sibley's detractors—the
telegraph spanned the continent. The Atlantic and the Pacific could now communicate quickly with each other.

The first message raced across the singing wires—"To Abraham Lincoln, President of the United States: The people of
California desire to congratulate you upon
the completion of this great work. They
believe that it will be the means of
strengthening the attachment which binds
both the East and West to the Union, and
they desire in this, the first message across
the continent, to express their loyalty to
the Union and their determination to
stand by its government on this, its day of
trial. They regard the government with
affection and will adhere to it under all
fortunes. Stephen J. Field, Chief Justice
of California."

And so, at a moment of crisis, while the
first battles of the Civil War were being
fought, a thin wire helped to draw the nation closer together.

Nearly a century later, the telegraph industry has bound the nation together
more thoroughly than even Sibley
dreamed possible. News and business data
are instantly available to even the farthest
states. The vast network of cables is a
monument to his vision, enterprise and
faith.

POWDER FOR PROGRESS

(IRÉNÉE DU PONT)

Éleuthère Irénée du Pont would often think back to that day in September, 1784, when his father invested him with the full rank of Esquire. Barely fourteen years old, Irénée was led by his older brother Victor into the presence of their father. The Sieur du Pont, Inspector General of Commerce in the cabinet of His Majesty, Louis XVI of France, then intoned the words of investiture: "No privilege exists, Irénée, that is not inseparably bound to a duty. This privilege involves a special obligation to protect innocence and weakness, to oppose injustice, to maintain peace, to devote yourself to the service of mankind. These are the pledges that you are to make, and it is because I believe you are capable of fulfilling them that I am arming you with your sword."

Irénée never forgot those words. During the following years, Irénée spent much of his time at his father's apartment in Paris. Here he listened to the conversation of many famous men who visited his father. Among them were the Americans Thomas Jefferson and Benjamin Franklin, the English philosopher James Hutton, as well as Lafayette, Talleyrand and Antoine Laurent Lavoisier, the great chemist.

One evening, Lavoisier lingered after the other guests to speak with the Sieur du Pont. "Do you realize the extent of your son Irénée's interest in chemistry?" he asked.

"I know that you gave him some saltpeter for his window-sill garden and that he has watched the plants grow and thrive with great fascination," replied the Sieur du Pont.

"More than that," said Lavoisier. "Irénée showed me a paper he wrote describing how saltpeter is mixed with charcoal and sulphur to make gunpowder. I was amazed by his accuracy and discernment. And I say these things to you because I am thinking of training a successor. I must have someone to carry on my experimental work at the government gunpowder plant at Essonne. Who knows, Monsieur du Pont? Perhaps Irénée will become my successor."

At sixteen, Irénée was taken into the gunpowder plant at Essonne to work under Lavoisier. At twenty, he was Lavoisier's chief assistant and felt secure enough of his future to marry Sophie Madeleine Dalmas. But their plans were disrupted by the fury of the French Revolution. The "Terror" sent Irénée's teacher, Lavoisier, to the guillotine and his father to prison.

Giving up his chemical studies, Irénée joined the National Guard. To support his family, he managed a printing shop that his father had started in the old Capuchin monastery in Paris. These were the dark days of the Reign of Terror. At one time it seemed that the Sieur du Pont was doomed to follow Lavoisier to the guillotine, but the tide turned and it was Robespierre's head that rolled from the swift-dropping blade.

Upon the Sieur du Pont's release from prison, he decided to seek a life of freedom in the new republic of the United States. He organized a colonization plan for French refugees. With his second wife, his two sons Victor and Irénée, their wives Josephine and Sophie, and their children, the Sieur du Pont sailed for America. New Year's Day, 1800, marked their arrival, and their first home in this country, at Bergen Point, New Jersey, was called "Goodstay."

It was a disappointing hunting expedition by Irénée in the woods near "Goodstay" that started the du Pont family on its notable career. "What a miserable time I had today!" Irénée complained to his fa-

Eleuthère Irénée DuPont. Painting by Rembrandt Peale.

Jefferson urges DuPont to go into the powder business (1804). Paul Revere is second from the left.

ther. "Three times this American gunpowder failed and my game got away. Everywhere in this country I see the need for a good powder—for food, for furs, for clearing the land, for defense against the Indians. I think I shall build a powder mill where I can put to use the experience I gained under Lavoisier."

Irénée's plan went forward quickly. The Sieur du Pont corresponded about the matter with his old friend Thomas Jefferson, now Vice-President of the United States. Jefferson agreed that nothing was so much needed as a dependable supply of good gunpowder. He urged du Pont to build the mill and expressed the desire that the site selected be near Philadelphia, then the nation's capital.

There was no doubt in Irénée's mind about where he wanted his mill to be. He had already selected a site on the banks of the Brandywine River near Wilmington. "I don't speak English very well," he said, "and there is a large colony of French people in Wilmington. I think that will be useful to me."

In January of 1801, Irénée sailed for France with Victor to form a stock company and raise funds with which to build the mill. They returned in July with full financial support pledged, and with Irénée named as director. On July 19, 1802, Irénée moved his family to a crude log house on the Brandywine River, and the construction of the mill began.

Several months later, with the walls of the buildings rising slowly, Irénée was visited by Peter Bauduy, one of the stockholders. "Do you know what you are doing, Irénée?" asked Bauduy impatiently. "Why are you making those walls three times as thick as the walls of other mills? And all those small buildings are quite unnecessary. The stockholders clamor for results, and all you do is use up more and more time and more and more money!"

"I know what I am doing, Peter," said Irénée firmly. "You live in Wilmington, but my workmen and my family live here on the Brandywine, and I must be mindful of their safety. That means that the walls must be thick, and it also means that I must have all those small buildings. It is dangerous to burn charcoal and to dry powder under the same roof. Lavoisier taught me that."

At last the mill began to produce gunpowder. Its high quality was at once recognized. But it was sold, as was customary, on a long-term credit, and Irénée constantly had to borrow from banks to finance his operations. He was faced by

An early DuPont poster.

debts and insufficient capital throughout his life, but he knew that with their mill the du Ponts had finally gained a firm economic foothold in this new country of their choice. Not only had they become American citizens, but wagon-trains were moving everywhere into the virgin wilderness of the West, carrying precious kegs of du Pont gunpowder to settlers and frontiersmen.

In 1817, a fire wiped out most of the mill buildings, and the banks would not lend the necessary money for reconstruction except on Irénée's personal notes. For years, he rode on horseback to Philadelphia every five or six days, thirty miles each way, to renew them.

"Here it is, 1824, and you are making a triumphal tour of the United States, while I must show myself to the bankers each week so they may be sure I am still alive," said Irénée laughingly to his dinner guest, the Marquis de Lafayette.

"You see, Monsieur," put in Sophie proudly, "Irénée borrowed enough money not only to rebuild the mill but also the homes of the workmen, as well as to provide pensions for them."

"That was but just," said Irénée modestly.

"And I understand you have satisfied all your father's and brother's creditors also," said Lafayette.

"Why not?" asked Irénée. "They would have done the same for me."

"Never has a country gone so far in so short a time," said Lafayette, "and you have had a most honorable part in it, Irénée. I was pleased to hear that President Monroe had appointed you a director of the Bank of America and that your opinion is being sought on new legislation to help manufacturing and farming. Oh, yes, I am also very interested in what your son Alfred has just told me about the new uses you are finding for the products you manufacture."

"Alfred is devoting his time to chemistry," said his father, "and he shall be my assistant here, just as I was assistant to Lavoisier, so many, many years ago. Do you remember, Monsieur, those wonderful evenings of conversation in my father's apartment in Paris?"

"Yes, Irénée, I remember them," said Lafayette softly, "with Jefferson, Franklin, Lavoisier and all the others. Some of our dreams are coming true!"

When Éleuthère Irénée du Pont died on October 31, 1834, the Delaware *State Journal* wrote of him: "We have lost a friend whom we loved and venerated, this community a benefactor, our State its most useful and valuable citizen."

PURE AND SURE

(DR. EDWARD ROBINSON SQUIBB)

Dr. Squibb had just come home after a long day at the Brooklyn Navy Yard, where he served as assistant director of the Naval Medical Supply Depot. An impressive-sounding title—but behind it lay the unimpressive weekly salary of $22.11. This was the fall of 1857, and while in those days such a sum might have supported a bachelor, it wasn't enough for a family man like Squibb.

For all his ten years' service in the Naval Hospital and the laboratory, whose output of drugs under his direction now supplied some ten thousand men of the United States Navy with first-class pharmaceuticals, Squibb's rating was only that of Passed Assistant Surgeon. His request for a promotion had been at headquarters for six months now. When would the answer come through? The application was not the only thing, however, that was on his mind.

"What's the matter, dear?" Caroline Squibb asked, noticing his worried face.

"Eh?" Squibb said. "Oh, I was just thinking of Connors—the drug-supply man." He could no longer contain his rage. "The nerve of that fellow! Came in today, bold as brass, *demanding* to know why I'd rejected his shipment of eight hundred pounds of quinine bark. Quinine bark! Our analysis had turned up, I told him, eight hundred pounds of sticks, stones, earth, goatskin, bits of iron and lead! And do you know what Connors said to that? 'Squibb,' he says to me, 'I've been delivering drugs to the Navy for ten years, and I'll be delivering them here long after you're gone. Now, Squibb, there's no need to put on your Sunday-go-to-meeting attitude with me!'"

"What did he mean by that?" Caroline asked.

"He wanted to bribe me, of course—so I had him thrown out."

At that moment, there was a knock at the door and Squibb went to answer it. "Dr. Tully!" he said to the man on the steps. "Come in, come in. Paying us a social call?"

"I wish I could say so," Dr. Tully answered, in an agitated tone. "But I'm afraid—Squibb, I know you've closed your laboratory for the day, but can you open it again tonight?"

"Of course," Squibb answered. "But why—"

"I seem to have made a ghastly error. Some medicine I'd prepared for some of my patients—I can't imagine what happened. I've made up this particular preparation a thousand times. Never before have there been toxic reactions. But all day I've had calls from my patients. Some are desperately ill. And they all show signs of acute poisoning."

As he spoke, he snapped open his medical bag and withdrew a small bottle. Hands trembling, he passed it to Squibb, who uncorked the vial and smelled it.

"Wintergreen?" Squibb asked.

Dr. Tully nodded. "Yes, it's a cough medicine." And then, seeing Squibb bring the bottle to his lips, "Here! Don't do that, Squibb!"

But Squibb disregarded him. He poured a drop of the fluid on his tongue, then tasted it. After a moment, he said, "Arsenic. We'd better get to the laboratory at once."

The tests confirmed Squibb's opinion. "In this two-ounce bottle is almost a full grain of arsenic!"

Dr. Edward Robinson Squibb as Assistant Surgeon in the United States Navy.

"But where could the arsenic have come from?"

"Probably the oil of wintergreen. Where did you get it?"

"From the same drug supplier I've used for years. Why would they put arsenic into oil of wintergreen?"

"As a preservative," Squibb explained. "Probably they had an old batch lying around the warehouse and added the arsenic to keep it looking and smelling fresh. It's an old trick."

All that night, Squibb and Dr. Tully rode from house to house, from patient to patient. At dawn, Squibb returned home. Of the patients who had received the poisoned bottles, some were well, others would recover—but one had died.

It was this death that depressed Edward Squibb most. The patient had been a baby boy, and the mother's grief affected Squibb profoundly.

It was not Dr. Tully's fault. How could any doctor, in 1857, be absolutely sure of the quality of the drugs he used? Every time he mixed a prescription he was gambling. That, in fact, was why the Navy had set up its own laboratory.

When Squibb's wife gave birth to a son, he couldn't help wondering: will our child be next? Clearly, it was not only the Navy that must be protected from adulterated drugs. Was there any sane reason why a private drug concern couldn't maintain absolute standards of purity in its products?

"In regard to your appeal for a raise in rating, Squibb," his superior officer at the Navy Yard said one day. "If ever a man deserved it, you do, but—"

"They've turned me down?"

"The Secretary of the Navy claims it can't be done without an Act of Congress, Squibb."

"Well, I'm afraid I can't wait that long." Squibb smiled. "Not with a family to support. I'm sending in my resignation today."

After ten years, it was not easy for him to give up his Naval appointment, but he had already decided what he must do. And in Brooklyn, on a spot where, but a few short years later, the Brooklyn Bridge would cast its shadow, Squibb hung up his sign: "E. R. Squibb & Co., Reliable Pharmaceuticals."

And *reliable* was not a word he included lightly. He meant to manufacture products that doctors could at last use without fear, drugs they would give their patients with the certainty that each ingredient was precisely what it was supposed to be . . . and nothing else.

This was Squibb's vow and he lived up

to it. Then, two years later, on the eve of the Civil War, his factory burned down. Trapped behind a work-bench, he received burns on his face and hands that scarred him for life. His business, moreover, had been destroyed in those same flames.

At home, waiting for his burns to heal, Squibb wondered what he could look forward to. Tension between the North and South was mounting. The Navy was willing to give him back his commission, but he refused. "If there's going to be real trouble," he said, "the government will never be able to produce enough medical supplies for a wartime Navy. And who will supply the Army? Are they going into the pharmaceutical business, too? I hate to think what will happen if war does come. Alone, the government laboratories will never be able to do the whole job."

But what could he do? His business lay in ruins, nor could he borrow the money needed to re-establish it. All his assets were gone, save one—his reputation.

One day Squibb's home was filled with visitors. The parlor seemed bursting with doctors—Dr. Minor, Dr. Crane, Dr. Dudley, Dr. McClellan, Dr. Delafield—and Mr. George Sampson, President of the Brooklyn Savings Bank.

What were they here for? "For a twofold purpose," their spokesman explained. "First, of course, as old friends, to tell you how happy we are to see you up and around again. And, Dr. Squibb, we think your fight to produce good drugs deserves our support. We represent a large group of the doctors of New York City, and we want to subscribe to a fund to rebuild your factory."

Squibb was deeply moved. What finer testimonial could there be to the success of his efforts? He rebuilt his factory, and not a moment too soon. For in 1861, the Civil War began. Through the four years that followed, Squibb's plant functioned day and night, supplying the Navy with top-quality drugs. Nor was he surprised when, in February of 1865, he received a visit from a high Army officer.

"The situation is critical, Dr. Squibb," the general said. "The Army medical laboratories have not been able to fill their production quotas. This is a matter of grave concern to General Grant. He is preparing a final assault upon Lee's armies and he won't move until his Surgeon-General tells him that the Medical Department can handle every casualty. The Surgeon-General is in no position to give him such assurance."

"When will the campaign begin?" Squibb inquired.

"I can give you only a general idea. Early spring."

"That gives us a few months," Squibb said.

"For you to produce the drugs, yes," the general said. "But then it will take months to get the supplies to the front and allocated to the field stations."

"How soon can you start moving the supplies?"

"What?" asked the general.

Squibb stood up from his desk. He walked to the door. "Would you come with me, please, General?" Puzzled, the general followed him out of the office toward the factory.

"Right this way, sir," Squibb said, leading the general into a warehouse. "There are your supplies, General."

"My supplies?"

"I have been stock-piling these drugs for three years now, just for such an emergency. I felt your laboratories couldn't do the whole job alone. I earmarked a certain percentage of our production for reserve, just held it back. Here it is . . . all yours." He paused. "I hope it will mean less suffering and many more lives saved." And the Army doctors could depend on these drugs—thanks to Squibb's concern for purity and his endless vigilance.

PIONEER AMERICAN ENGINEER

(JAMES B. EADS)

The steamboat sat in the water, ready to sail. Along one side, the paint still fresh and glistening in the sunlight, her name had been lettered: *The City of St. Louis.* This was to be her maiden voyage, and Jim Eads was excited. He stood on the bank, his bare toes digging into the earth, and studied the vessel. Then his hand reached out to make an adjustment of the paddle-wheel and the *St. Louis* tilted, swinging away from his touch. Grabbing a deck-rail, Eads pulled the boat back to him.

While truly a paddle-wheel steamboat, authentic from stem to stern, the *St. Louis* was only a six-foot model floating in a pond. Unaided, Eads had built her with his own hands, using cheap timber and metal scraps. Since he worked as a clerk six days a week, with only his Sundays free, the job had taken him months. But now—

The Eads Bridge over the Mississippi at St. Louis.
Painting by Louis Bouché.

well, there she was, steam up, ready to go. He stepped aboard, or rather straddled, the *St. Louis,* pulled a switch, and took off across the pond.

From a nearby hill, a local farmer smiled as he watched the paddle-wheel turn. A queer one, this young Jim Eads. He was only seventeen, but folks said he stayed up all night studying those books on engineering; then he came out here on Sundays.

But you had to give the boy a lot of credit! That little steamboat was making its way across the pond, its paddle-wheel churning and its whistle tooting.

Building machines and engines was more than a spare-time hobby with Eads. In 1838, at the age of eighteen, working as a purser on a real Mississippi steamboat, he used his free time to study the boat's machinery. But machinery wasn't his only interest. For countless hours he stood by the rail, staring down at the waters, studying the currents, the rapids. In later years, James Buchanan Eads' writings on currents and the control of waters would be recognized as masterpieces of their kind. But, meanwhile, a man had to make a living, and in 1842, along with a few associates, he went into the salvage business. The little company purchased materials and began building a bell-diving boat, necessary for salvage operations in the river.

"Boat finished yet?" he asked one day.

"You can't build a bell-diving boat in a month," his partner Campbell protested. "And what's this I hear about your accepting a contract with that St. Louis firm? Man, that's a load of pig iron they lost. How are we going to raise it?"

"We'll get it up."

"But without a bell-diving boat, or even a diving bell?"

"I hired a diver," Eads said. "He brought his equipment with him from the Great Lakes."

"Oh," Campbell said hopefully. "Then we have a chance—"

"Trouble is," Eads went on, "the river is too fast. His bell is good only in calmer waters. Says he won't go down."

Campbell was dismayed. "In that case—"

"But let me show you." Eads led Campbell to the deck and pointed to the derrick set up at one end of the barge. A large round whiskey hogshead had been attached to the derrick.

Campbell said, "What's that barrel doing there?"

"I've knocked one end out of it," Eads explained, "and set up a slat inside to sit on. 'The James B. Eads Impromptu Diving Bell.'" He grinned.

"You expect the diver to go down in that?"

The diver strolled over to where they stood. "I'd be crazy to do it."

"Don't blame you for feeling that way," Eads agreed. "But this is the only chance we've got to get that iron off the bottom. And I'm afraid that by accepting that contract, I've risked too much. Campbell, if we don't get that stuff up, our company will be finished. Joe," he called to the derrick operator, "I'm ready to go down."

"Ready here, Mr. Eads."

"But it's suicide to go down in that thing!" Campbell protested.

A few minutes later, sitting inside the hogshead, Eads was well below the surface of the Mississippi. Inside the barrel, the air had grown dense and he could sense the pressure of the rushing waters against the flimsy wooden sides. Below him, he could see the wrecked vessel. On the next descent he would have to begin hoisting out the metal. He gave the signal to have himself raised. Nothing happened. He gave the signal again, alarmed. Something had gone wrong. Was Campbell right—was this suicide?

Then he felt the barrel rise.

The machinery of the derrick had jammed, the operator explained. But when Eads went below a second time, all went smoothly. As he said, "Any new ideas I get, I'll test them first. I wouldn't ask any man to do what I wouldn't do myself."

That statement became Eads' byword. People knew him by it, just as they came to expect him to do the impossible. For instance, there was the bridge.

In 1865, Congress passed a bill authorizing a bridge across the Mississippi at St. Louis. Enemies of the project succeeded in amending the bill so that it called for a 500-foot center span and 50 feet of clearance. No one could build such a bridge, it was said. For one thing, the foundation would have to be based on sand. In no time at all, the river would eat that sand away. Why, before you knew it that bridge would be sailing to New Orleans!

Eads, working as head engineer for the construction company to which the contract had been granted, said, "The usual river bottom is three feet of constantly shifting sand. In my experience, one hundred feet of sand are sometimes swept away, clear to bedrock. The job is impossible, yes—if we build it on sand. But we're not going to build it on sand. We're digging down to the bedrock."

Since his plan called for the foundations to be built beneath the water—at one place the high-water mark was 136 feet—with an unknown depth of sand and gravel below the water, how could the foundation piers be sunk to bedrock? Impossible.

Eads agreed. Impossible—that is, if the old bridge-building methods were used. New methods, he said, would have to be invented, new techniques. . . .

And in the following seven years, he was to demonstrate that such new techniques could be devised—if the engineer was as determined and resourceful as James Buchanan Eads!

Down through the water the shafts were sunk and then seamed off from the surge of the surrounding river. Then, on the river bottom, the task of pumping out began. Little by little, over the many months, to the constant beat of the pumps sucking up water and sand, the shaft cut down below the river level. And the deeper the shaft sank, the more difficult and hazardous the work became. The air became denser and denser. In the treacherous darkness, lit only by candles, the men sweated and dug their way down. Lungs labored for breath, tools slipped from sweaty fingers. There were accidents, but Eads kept the casualty list low by his insistence on safety measures, by the creation of underwater air-chambers. Each time he met an apparently insuperable obstacle, he invented a method or a new appliance to overcome it.

It took three years to reach the foundation rock and four more years to complete

Jas. B. Eads

the bridge. And in 1874, thousands of people, some of them having traveled hundreds of miles, flocked to see this modern marvel. Missouri and Illinois were joined, and James B. Eads, who had united them, stood among the first rank of bridge engineers. Foreign governments sought his advice, and many cities in the United States retained him as an expert on the flow of water and on river improvements. His perseverance, his daring, his determination to find new and better ways inspired and served as a model for the men who were to build many roadways of steel and concrete over American waters.

HIS MONUMENT IS UNDER WATER

(CLIFFORD HOLLAND)

In lower Manhattan about the time of World War I, a small crowd of Battery Place bystanders collected around a man lying on the pavement.

"Stand back, everybody!" a policeman ordered. "Stand back! Haven't you ever seen a drunk before?"

The man on the ground protested. "Li'l dizzy, tha's all," he wheezed. "The bends . . . I got . . . the bends . . ."

Not just drunk, the policeman decided, but raving drunk. Then he turned around irritably; someone had broken through the crowd and was bending over the man on the pavement.

"What's wrong, O'Rourke?" the man asked. "Has it got you?"

"Thass ri'," O'Rourke said. "It's—the bends—Mr. Holland. Ge' me back—the chamber—"

"Who are you?" the policeman asked. "You know this drunk?"

Clifford Holland said, "I'm one of the engineers on the subway tunnel, over there." He pointed toward a fence set up around a construction site. "This man is not drunk. He has what doctors call 'caisson disease.' Sandhogs call it 'the bends.' He's one of the tunnel-diggers on this job. Give me a hand, please—we've got to get him back to the tunnel, into the compression chamber."

Inside the compression chamber, Holland slammed the metal door shut and turned a valve. The valve hissed and soon the air in the metal chamber became dense.

"How do you feel, now, O'Rourke?"

From the wooden bench where he lay, O'Rourke tried to smile. "Better, Mr. Holland."

The air continued to hiss. On the steel wall, a meter registered the pressure, its needle moving upward slowly: 34—35—37 . . .

"My head's clearing up fine now," O'Rourke said.

Holland turned off the pressure. He turned another valve, and, little by little the air escaped from the chamber, the needle on the meter moving in reverse.

This was the only cure for "the bends." O'Rourke had been laboring deep in the tunnel, in an atmosphere three times as heavy as above ground. He had put in a hard day, without enough rest. When he emerged into the street he had been suddenly overcome. The change in atmospheric pressure had been too much for him. This was not unusual. Sometimes the bends did not hit a man for some hours, or even days, after he had left the tunnel. As Holland watched O'Rourke recovering, he determined that this sort of thing should not happen again.

But Holland was only an engineer on the subway tunnel being dug under the East River between Manhattan and Brooklyn. He had discussed the problem with the contractor. His arguments were good, Mc Martin said, but not practical. "Look at it this way. Your plan is to have four shifts a day. Rest periods every three hours. Why the men would spend half their working time going on and off the job and just sitting in those decompression chambers. Holland, if I'd made a bid including costs like that, I wouldn't have won the contract. Somebody else would have grabbed it."

Holland said, "Remember that last East River tunnel? More than three thousand cases of the bends and twenty-four dead. And God knows how many crippled or incapacitated for life."

"These men know what they're doing when they take a tunnel job. What are you

Holland, an engineer or a social reformer?"

"As a human being," Clifford Holland replied, "I hate any kind of suffering. As an engineer, I hate waste, whether it be materials, time or men. The methods will have to change, McMartin."

A few days later, the tunneling shield was flooded and the men had to flee. The shield was a huge metal cylinder of the same diameter as the tunnel it was boring. Powered by hydraulic jacks, it pushed forward through the muck, which poured out through large openings, to be scooped up and carried away. As the shield was driven forward, steel walls were built behind it,

the shell of the future tunnel.

Now, with the flooding of the shield, work had to be halted.

"What should we do now?" McMartin asked his engineer.

"Increase the air pressure to forty-eight pounds," Holland said.

McMartin looked at him in amazement. "Forty-eight pounds! You'll kill the whole crew! They can't work under pressures as high as that, Holland."

"They can," Holland said, "*if* you adopt my plan. Accustom them to the pressure slowly. Work them in thirty-minute shifts.

No longer than that."

"But that will increase our labor cost six times!"

A few days later, however, workers were lined up for medical examinations in the construction office. The doctor checked each one. This man: "Yes, he'll do." That man: "No, his heart couldn't take it." Another man: "Yes." A fourth worker: "Too stout. Sorry. A fat man is more prone to the bends—it's a matter of nitrogen in the bloodstream."

"Nitrogen?"

"It's a gas," said one of the other workers. "Get too much of it in your blood, it blows you up."

Clifford Holland led the first shift of selected workers through the doors of the air-lock. Inside, the men—some of them old-timers, some of them new—seated themselves on wooden benches. Holland turned the valve, and the air-pressure in the chamber began to rise. The men held their noses, as instructed, forcing the air back to their eardrums. This relieved the pressure in the sinuses. "Otherwise,'" Holland explained, "your passages may become blocked. And that's very painful."

He watched the men carefully. Pressure 32—33—35— A new worker seemed a bit groggy. "Sure you want to go through with it?"

"I'm all right," the man said after a moment. "It's better now."

"Now we're getting up to really high pressure," Holland said. "All of you must watch your reactions carefully."

35—37—39—the men began to cough and splutter. Holland turned the valve and the hissing stopped. When it seemed safe to proceed, he turned the valve again. 42—43—44—45—6—7—FORTY-EIGHT!

Holland cut the air.

"Say, I feel terrific," said one worker. "Like I'd had a straight shot of brandy."

Holland said, "That's what we've got to watch. Our bodies are getting several times the normal amount of oxygen. Makes you feel peppy, but your energy burns out faster. The minute you feel the slightest fatigue, let me know."

Pushing open the door, he led the men into the high pressure area of the tunnel. In the dim lighting, the shield loomed ahead of them. The pumps had got rid of the water.

"These are the hydraulic jacks," explained Holland. "They push the shield forward and the muck from the other side comes through these openings like toothpaste out of a tube. I want it cleaned away, then loaded on these cars. And be sure to keep clear of that crane, when they start sliding the new steel sections into place."

A half-hour later and the workers filed back into the decompression chamber. They were fatigued, but as the air-pressure was lowered toward normal, everything appeared to have gone well. Holland's plan seemed a success.

As the men walked toward the mouth of the tunnel and reached the sunlight, however, one of them screamed in pain and collapsed. That was dismaying to Holland, but such failures became rare. Day by day, Holland worked out further improvements and the number of cases of caisson disease steadily decreased.

When that tunnel was completed, a problem which engineers had been attempting to solve since Ralph Dodd planned the world's first tunnel under the Thames River in 1798, was finally licked. In all, six great tunnels were built under Clifford Holland's guidance, including the one between New York and New Jersey below the Hudson River, which bears his name.

The Holland Tunnel is a monument to this great engineer. It is likely, however, that Clifford Holland himself would regard as his greatest achievement the medical report on the workers who built the Holland Tunnel. Of 2,500 sandhogs not one died from the subterranean enemy, caisson disease.

PURSUERS OF THE AMERICAN DREAM

Born to the service of mankind and welcoming to her shores immigrants from many lands, America has never wanted for idealistic citizens who looked beyond geographic and political boundaries. The arts speak a universal language and foreign countries have not been slow to recognize the values of our contributions to them. The poetry of Edgar Allan Poe, the prose of James Fenimore Cooper, the painting of James Whistler, the music of Stephen Foster, are all representative examples of the fact that American artists have found wide responses in many countries other than the land of their birth.

The contributions of creative artists are only a part, however, of America's participation in the world's advancement toward better living for all men. Through the influences of such dedicated campaigners for general public education as Horace Mann, Mary Lyon and Booker T. Washington important steps have been taken toward a goal that, because of their example, will eventually be attained throughout the world.

Quite as valuable, too, have been the efforts of those who have fought with persistence and courage toward enlightened reforms in the fields of mental health, rehabilitation in prisons, the abolishment of slums, rights for the under-privileged.

In all of the nation's history American artists, educators, and reformers have been workers in the same vineyard—seeking the realization of the ideals and principles set down by the Founding Fathers in the Declaration of Independence and in the Constitution of the United States—that all men may have equal opportunities in a land of freedom and justice.

THE EDUCATORS

"I desire to see the time when education, and by its means, morality, sobriety, enterprise and industry, shall become much more general than at present."

ABRAHAM LINCOLN, 1832.

THE NATION'S SCHOOLMASTER

(NOAH WEBSTER)

The Continental Army led by George Washington won independence from England in the Revolutionary War, but the United States was still dependent on England in many ways and there were other battles still to be won. One of the most important of these was education, and the story of the fight for *American* rather than British education, for an *American* rather than a British language, is the story of Noah Webster, a poor schoolmaster from Connecticut.

One day in 1782 when he was twenty-four he called on Dr. Ezra Stiles, president of the college of which he was an alumnus —Yale.

"Dr. Stiles, here is the manuscript I told you about, the spelling book which I've shown to Thomas Jefferson, James Madison and the people at Princeton and the University of Pennsylvania."

"I'll be glad to look it over. But I'm very much interested in your ideas on education. This speller is to be the first of a series?"

"Yes, a series of textbooks designed to revolutionize the whole system of American education. The one we have now scarcely can be called American. Our textbooks originate in England. Our history, our geography, our public sentiments, are all too greatly influenced by the British. I

expect to follow this speller with a grammar and then a reader, Dr. Stiles. My hope is to accomplish three things: to simplify and unify our language and lay down a common rule for spelling and pronunciation; to offer moral instruction to youth without the awesome atmosphere which now surrounds it; and to promote a spirit of patriotism. America must be as independent in literature as she is in politics."

Dr. Stiles walked over and put his hand on Webster's shoulder. "I am very much interested in this," he said. "Indeed, I see in this book of yours a far-reaching force. But I fear you've approached it much too timidly. *The American Instructor* is too modest a title for such a book. I suggest that you call it *A Grammatical Institute of the English Language.* Assuredly you will be considered presumptuous. You will be attacked from all sides. But your purpose is worthy of the battle."

"You are proposing, Dr. Stiles, that I set myself up as an absolute authority."

"I am proposing more than that," said the great educator. "I am proposing that you become the *law-giver* in language here in America."

Noah Webster's *Grammatical Institute,* in spite of attack and ridicule, gained immediate popularity. But Webster had sold his royalty rights for a few hundred dollars

Noah Webster

292

and was as poor as ever. He traveled through the country, preaching his doctrine of nationalism, edited a profound but not too successful publication called the *American Magazine,* then later published a series of popular essays of simple philosophy under the title *The Prompter* and became active in public affairs. In 1793 he moved his family to New York and became editor of the *American Minerva.* His editorial views met with violent opposition and in May, 1800, he gave up that work.

"What are you going to do now?" asked Samuel Bayard, his associate.

"Finish the work which I have been dreaming of for years. I am about to compile a complete dictionary, Bayard. I'm about to record the American language."

He set aside a period of five years in which to complete his dictionary. But he soon realized that it was an undertaking to which he might well dedicate the remainder of his life. He was determined to include all words in what he called the "living" English language. By 1813 he had mastered twenty languages. Slowly, painstakingly, hour after hour, year after year, he collected his material. The task seemed endless, the work often frustrating. But Noah Webster was a dedicated man. He was a scholar who would not compromise. He kept on with his job, until he felt sure it was right. It was not until 1828, when Webster was seventy, that his dictionary was completed.

Now in the United States the name "Webster" is almost synonomous with "dictionary," and the Connecticut schoolmaster has his proper place in America's golden Hall of Fame.

The Noah Webster Home.

THE GREAT EDUCATOR

(HORACE MANN)

The year was 1837; the place was the hall of the Massachusetts Legislature. Just the day before, the State Senate had passed a law establishing a Board of Education. It was to advance considerably the cause of public education in America.

Horace Mann, who had been the chief driving force in getting the bill passed, was leaving the Senate. For the sake of his growing family he was retiring from political life to return to his law practice. He had an important case coming up, for which he expected to receive a high fee.

Walking down the wide stone stairway, he was greeted by James C. Carter, who had initiated the Board of Education Bill.

"Well, you must be pleased that your bill was passed," Mann remarked.

"Yes, thanks to you," replied Carter. "But the job isn't finished by a long shot."

"I'm sure Governor Everett will sign the bill today," said Mann. "There will be no delay there."

"We're not concerned about that," said Carter. "But it will take more than his signature to put the bill into effect."

"Just what do you mean, Carter?" asked Mann.

"Everything depends on the man we get for Secretary of the Board," said Carter. "He will have to inspect every school in the state. That will mean constant traveling. The improvements he will want to make will cost money. That will mean new taxes, and you know how people resent that. He will have a constant fight on his hands to obtain the necessary funds. He will have to be so devoted to the cause of public education that he will be ready to fight constantly and to travel all the time. It will call for endless personal sacrifices."

Mann nodded. "But the bill had so many devoted supporters," he said, "it shouldn't be hard to find such a man among them."

Carter smiled. "I've just seen Governor Everett and we've agreed on the right man for the job."

"Splendid!" said Mann. "Who is he?"

"His name," said Carter, "is Horace Mann."

Mann was speechless. "Impossible!" he said. "My family needs me now. I must provide for them. That's why I'm not seeking re-election. As you know, I'm returning to my law practice. The yearly salary for the Secretary of the Board, as I recall, was set at a thousand dollars. I mean to do better than that for my family."

Carter held up his hand. "Of course, we can't pass an ordinance compelling you to accept the appointment. But Governor Everett and many others besides myself feel that the one man who can make this new Board work is *you*. Our hope of genuine educational reform rests with you."

Mann thought of the many private legal fees he would have to forego. He would have to put in twenty years of strenuous work as Secretary of the Board to earn what three or four months' close attention to the pending railroad merger negotiations would pay him.

Then he remembered the sharpness of his own hunger for learning. The opportunity had been granted him at long last to acquire an education. Now, here was the opportunity to help satisfy the hunger of thousands of poor boys. They could become lawmakers like himself, writers, statesmen, engineers, and, in any case, better citizens if they had a chance to get a good education—if there were enough good schools for them.

He held out his hand to Carter. "I think it is my duty to accept the appointment," he said.

Horace Mann's decision did not surprise

Horace Mann.

Carter. He knew how devoted Mann was to the cause of public education; he knew that personal experience had shaped Mann's resolve. It was not until Mann was twenty that he had been able to get any proper schooling. He had seized upon the opportunity like one to whom it meant a new life. He applied himself with such con-

centration that in six months he was able to pass the entrance examinations to Brown University, from which he was graduated with honors. Then he had gone on through law school to make a brilliant reputation for himself as an attorney. He had just closed a brilliant political career.

And now? Many of Mann's friends

thought his acceptance of the Board of Education appointment would mean that he would have to bury himself in administrative work. Yet, as it turned out, it was in his work as the Secretary of the Massachusetts Board of Education that Mann found his true career. He was to win undying fame as America's greatest educator.

Horace Mann served as Secretary of the first Board of Education for twelve years. He traveled incessantly throughout the state. He also traveled abroad to keep abreast of the latest European advances in education. At the end of each year Mann wrote a detailed report, recommending changes and outlining new projects through which the educational system might be improved. These reports made educational history. They were studied not only in Massachusetts but in other states and in Europe as well. They became the framework for modern education in America.

But to carry out his recommendations proved to be no simple matter. Conservative teachers who objected to new methods, taxpayers who resented any increase in school taxes, farmers who were inconvenienced by longer school terms which took their sons away from the fields, employers who were deprived of cheap child labor by the new public school attendance regulations, and also those who thought that Mann was wrong in insisting on spare-the-rod teaching methods—all were ranged against him.

Once, when Mann was inspecting the schools of a certain city, a delegation of angry citizens tried to run him out of town.

Some shouted, "We won't pay our taxes till they throw you off the Board!"

Others said, "We don't want your immoral new ideas!"

"Imagine," said another, "Mann wants to coddle our children so they'll *like* going to school! How can education be any good if they like it? That's not discipline; that's wicked!"

"And keeping them in school till they're fourteen!" said still another. "Preventing them from earning their bread and butter!"

But, later, a grateful mother stopped him one day and whispered, "God bless you, Mr. Mann, for what you're doing for our children." And Mann knew that his labors had been truly fruitful. In time, the good new schools Mann built and their better-educated graduates silenced Mann's enemies and critics. All over the United States, school systems were reorganized according to Mann's suggestions.

After twelve years as the head of the Massachusetts Board of Education, Mann felt that his work in the state was done. Later he helped to found Antioch College in Yellow Springs, Ohio, where he sought to apply his educational principles to the field of higher education. Antioch College was co-educational, and its students combined periods of work, which Mann regarded as an important part of their education, with classroom study. Through the "Antioch experiment," as it was called, Mann's influence on education was further extended.

If the excellent American schools of today draw students from all over the world, it is due in large part to the vision, the leadership, the devotion and self-sacrifice so freely given by Horace Mann.

PIONEER WOMAN EDUCATOR

(MARY LYON)

Mary Lyon was born near Buckland, Massachusetts, in 1797. As a child, she received only that small amount of education that was customary for girls in those days. But Mary was not at all satisfied with this minimum of knowledge, this smattering of needlework, music, painting and French. She determined to go on with her education.

At the age of sixteen, she began teaching in the Buckland School for seventy-five cents a week, plus board. After four years of this she was able to afford a year's study at Sanderson Academy in Ashfield. But now, that wonderful year was over and Mary had to leave the Academy.

Squire White, however, came to her with extraordinary news.

"As a member of the school board," he said, "I have been asked to tell you that, in recognition of your brilliant scholastic record, the board has voted you free tuition for another year!"

"Another year at Sanderson!" exclaimed Mary. 'I scarcely know how to express my gratitude!"

"If you'll maintain the same standard of excellence you did this year, the Academy will be fully repaid," said the squire. "One of your teachers said that even though you're only a girl, you are fully capable of college work."

"Squire White," said Mary in her firm but quiet way, "I shouldn't be surprised if someday girls are admitted to colleges, too."

"To colleges, Mary? Never!" he declared.

"I should not presume to argue with you, sir," said Mary, "but—well—I must say that I disagree with you. And someday, Squire White, I shall try to convince the people of America that women, as well as men, are entitled to a higher education!"

Mary left Sanderson Academy the following year but continued to educate herself while she worked as a teacher. Within ten years, girls from every state in the Union were being sent to her classroom, for it had become evident not only to the girls whom she taught, but also to the parents of these girls, that Mary Lyon was an inspired teacher.

In 1834, when she was thirty-seven, Mary was directing a seminary at Ipswich, Massachusetts. One day, she appeared in the sitting-room of Mr. Abbott, president of the board of trustees, and submitted her resignation.

"But surely you're not retiring?" asked Mr. Abbott.

"No, I expect to work harder than I've ever worked in my life!" said Mary. "You see, Mr. Abbott, for seventeen years—ever since I left Sanderson Academy—I've been pursued by one dream. And I must resign from Ipswich Seminary to make it come true! My dream, Mr. Abbott, concerns the thousands of intelligent girls who are poor as I was and who are starved for knowledge. I am going to devote the rest of my life to helping them obtain an education."

"Just what is it you intend to do, Miss Lyon?" asked Mr. Abbott.

"I am going to conduct a personal campaign throughout New England to raise fifty thousand dollars to start a girls' seminary, a school where tuition will be so low that almost any girl can attend!"

"You are the most brilliant woman I have ever known," said Mr. Abbott, "but I think you have given yourself an impossible task."

"Difficult, but not impossible. Women are the mothers and the teachers of men. Therefore, they must be well educated. The men of America, in their own interest, should help women to obtain a fair education. This is what I shall go out and tell the people."

Mary Lyon found her personal campaign for funds very hard going. She had to contend with the irrational notion that the minds of women lacked the capacity to learn and that, therefore, higher education for women would be a waste of time and money. She also had to combat the prejudice that it was immodest and even immoral for a woman to lecture from a platform. It was a spectacle and a scandal!

But Mary Lyon's dignity and earnestness gradually won allies to her cause. Money for the building of the seminary began to accumulate. On October 3, 1836, the cornerstone of the new school was laid. It was to be called the Mt. Holyoke Seminary. Mary had received helpful advice in planning its program from Dr. Hitchcock of Amherst, a neighboring school for young men.

Mary's old friend Squire White and the Reverend Dr. Hawkes were among her most loyal supporters. Shortly after the laying of the Mt. Holyoke cornerstone, however, these two men called upon Mary with sober faces.

"You know that Dr. Hawkes and I, and many other public-spirited citizens, believe in your endowed seminary for girls. Above all, we believe in you," said Squire White. "But today we must urge you to give up your dream of such a school—at least for the present."

"But we have raised more than half the necessary money—the foundation has been dug—the walls are going up!" exclaimed Mary.

"For three months, Mary," said Dr. Hawkes, "I have gone about trying to raise money for your school—and I have not been able to raise a penny. I fear, Mary, that you have not realized the seriousness of the financial depression which has overtaken the country."

"And there are other problems, too, Mary," his friend put in. "For instance, Mr. Benton, the Boston merchant who had half-promised five thousand dollars, now refuses to contribute anything because he disapproves of your plan to have the students share in the housework."

"But no girl will have to spend more than an hour a day at housework!" said Mary angrily. "Oh, if he could only read the letters I've received from prospective students—letters expressing their gratitude for a tuition fee as low as sixty-four dollars a year. Helping with the housework here is one of the things that make it possible! Did you know, Squire, and you, Dr. Hawkes, that I have received applications from two hundred more girls than our school can accommodate the first year? Gentlemen, I have a little more than a thousand dollars left of my own. I shall contribute that right now to Mt. Holyoke so that the building can go forward, and tomorrow I shall set out on another tour of New England to raise the rest of the money!"

Mary Lyon's persistence in the face of all obstacles triumphed. Mt. Holyoke, America's first permanently endowed institution for the higher education of women, opened—as Mary had planned—on November 8, 1837.

At the close of its first year, Mt. Holyoke received a critical test as the public gathered to hear the oral examinations of the students. Not only were a number of distinguished educators from the United States in attendance, but a speech was to be made after the examinations by Dr. Harris, a famous English educator.

Mary Lyon was so nervous about the impression her students would make on the visitors that she was unable to remain in the examination room. It was not long before Dr. Harris appeared in the office to which she had retired.

"I have an apology to make to you, Miss Lyon," he said. "I had expected to find Mt. Holyoke the usual girls' school, to find

Mary Lyon.

the usual sweet young ladies. And I had written a flowery, meaningless speech which should not be too far above the heads of such young ladies. But now that I have listened to their replies in the examinations, I find your students better informed than many college men! I must rewrite my speech, I'm afraid. I mean to praise your students to the skies!"

Mr. Benton, the Boston merchant, was the next to step into Mary's office. "I want to say that I was terribly mistaken," he said, bowing to her. "I see now that the housework of the students *is* a part of the training, not drudgery. I shall tell everyone in Boston that you have the finest school for young ladies in Massachusetts. A remarkable accomplishment, Miss Lyon!

You may count on my support."

"I do believe this particular battle is won," said Mary Lyon later to Squire White. "But the fight must go on until young women can attend a seminary not just for three years, but for four years just as men do, until women can be seated side by side with men in colleges and until all the professions and careers now restricted to men are also open to women!"

Mary Lyon died in 1849, long before women were to be granted these additional opportunities in work and education. But she died in the knowledge that the establishment of Mt. Holyoke Seminary was an important step toward the realization of her faith and vision.

299

NEW TIMES, NEW TRAINING

(PETER COOPER)

How do you make a shoe?

Peter Cooper answered that question by ripping an old shoe apart and studying it. Then, at his workbench, set up in his New York home, he went ahead and made one.

"Peter," his mother asked, "what are you doing now?"

"Making a pair of slippers for Sister," Peter said. "And after that, I will make a pair for you."

What a saving that would be, his mother exclaimed. A good boy, Peter, always busy with his hands. But one day she wondered if those hands had not been *too* busy, and in the wrong way. Astonished, she stared at the barrel in which she did the family wash. What were all those strange gadgets, those wheels and handles rigged onto it?

"It's always a hard day for you, Mother," Peter explained, "when you do the wash. Bending over, churning, pounding the clothes. But now watch. I turn this handle. See?"

Under his hands, the mechanism pounded away.

"How wonderful!" she said. "It will do the hardest part of the work for me!"

In later years, Peter Cooper went on to invent more important things than a primitive washing machine. He became a distinguished man, a builder of industries, a force in our national growth. He had nimble hands and a nimble brain, but it is unlikely that his mother, despite her pride in his ability, could have foreseen for him so eminent a future.

The son of a hard-working father who, by turns, worked as a hatter, a brewer, a storekeeper and a brickmaker, Peter Cooper reached manhood with little formal education. All through his life, he was to be conscious of this lack. Later, this feeling gave rise to an ambition he never forsook: to set up a school that would provide needy youngsters with what he had missed, an education in the arts, the crafts, the sciences.

In 1826, people laughed at Peter Cooper for having such dreams. He had bought three strips of land on which, he said, he would someday erect schools! At thirty-six, Peter Cooper was the owner-operator of a general store. A good man, true, and industrious, but he couldn't even spell "carrot" though he sold bunches of them.

Build schools? "Mr. Cooper, at your age, it would be wiser if you were content with your business." "And another thing, Mr. Cooper, you have a wife and a family. What's this we hear about your wanting to buy a glue factory?" Another laugh on Mr. Cooper; schools and a glue factory! "How do these two dreams fit together—we might even say how do they *stick* together—Mr. Cooper?"

Peter Cooper smiled. Let them laugh. For him, the connection between glue and dreams was quite clear. In England and Germany they made fine glue. Why? Because they had trained chemists who had worked for many years to evolve the proper formulas. But here, in America, where chemists were scarce, a really good glue was unknown. So, using his small capital, Cooper acquired a factory in New York and began to experiment.

Without scientific training, he worked many months before he mastered the techniques of research. Yet within two years he found what he wanted: a glue that was even better than any made in Europe. During that time he solved many difficult problems in chemistry. And, in the meantime, he had been working on a project more ambitious than making glue: building a steam locomotive.

In the 1820's the story of American invention had scarcely begun. With few trained scientists, Americans had to look abroad for many manufactured products. They had begun to build railroads, for instance, but the locomotives had to be imported from England. Built for a less rugged country, these British engines could not negotiate our sharper curves, our steeper mountains. The problem thus presented interested Cooper. He built a model of a locomotive, and then purchased an ironworks near Baltimore. Here, by 1829, through "tinkering" a bit, he succeeded in building a locomotive adapted to American needs. In October of that year, the executives of the Baltimore & Ohio Railroad agreed to give it a test.

On the newly laid rails near Mount Clare, Maryland, there was considerable excitement—and a good deal of laughter, already a familiar sound to Cooper.

"Mr. Cooper," a railroad executive inquired, "what do you call this monstrous engine of yours?"

"Tom Thumb."

"These vertical tubes to the boiler—" another director asked, "what are they, Mr. Cooper? They look oddly familiar."

"Those are musket barrels, Mr. Croft."

"And that wash-boiler set in endwise?"

"Well, it's the same *idea* as a wash-boiler, Mr. Croft."

From those assembled beside the tracks came more laughter. Tom Thumb—why, the whole thing seemed to be put together out of odds and ends, like a child's toy. And, among the thirty-six gentlemen who climbed into the coach behind the engine, and the six who clambered aboard the engine itself, there were many who doubted they would ride a single foot. And some may have wondered, are we safe with this gluemaker from New York? Will the whole fantastic contraption blow up?

The Tom Thumb, however, had no intention of blowing up. And it traveled far more than a foot; it carried its passengers forward and Peter Cooper into fame.

In his middle forties, Peter Cooper became a man of great importance. He continued inventing, and his achievements seemed endless: improvements in steam-boilers, in grinding marble and metal substances, in salt-making, in methods for hauling boats on the Erie Canal, in dozens of other mechanical processes that were building the new America. He was a leading spirit in the first attempts to lay an Atlantic cable.

But in the back of Peter Cooper's mind his early dream remained: to found a great school, a free school, with lectures and courses for young mechanics and engineers, a school where American youth could obtain the scientific and technical training he had been denied.

With industry expanding and becoming more mechanized, trained engineers were needed more than ever. Work was begun on a building in New York City which was to be named "The Union of Science and Art." However, those who know of his generous efforts to give the city's youth free educational opportunities called it "The Cooper Union."

Then, threatening to blast his most cherished hopes, came the panic of 1857. The country encountered grave economic distress. One business after another failed. And in Cooper's office there was great excitement. Looking down from his office window, Cooper could see a line of people three blocks long in front of the Union Bank. He knew what they were doing: fearing the banks themselves would fail, they were demanding their money back. "The most frightful panic the country has ever known," one of Cooper's younger associates called it. "The United States is done for."

"Mr. Cooper!" cried another, rushing in. "We've just had bad news from the ironworks. Blackwell and Company have failed. It looks as if we'll never collect from them. And Gridley and Weston can only pay us a little of what they owe."

"Some firms," said a volunteer adviser, "are shutting down while they're still solvent. A wise idea, if we were to do the same, Mr. Cooper. That way, we'd be able to save something out of the wreckage. And as for the Institute of Arts and Sciences—you're not going on with that, Mr. Cooper? You must hold on to every cent of capital you have. Take my word for it, Mr. Cooper, we'd better—"

No, Cooper said, this was no time to panic. "This plant and the ironworks will remain open, at the service of the country." And as for the Institute, "The building's nearly finished. It may be the last building ever erected in New York, but it's going to go up as I planned."

Cooper Union was completed in the midst of a general panic, by a man who had faith in his country's future. It became one of the first great technical schools in the country. It showed American industry, already aware that the old apprentice system was too leisurely for modern life, how to train men scientifically for skilled posts.

Cooper Union.

UP FROM SLAVERY

(BOOKER T. WASHINGTON)

I was born a slave. And I believe my childhood was like that of most slaves. I do not remember being cruelly treated, nor do I ever remember having time for play. I worked—cleaning the yard, taking water to the men in the field, carrying corn to the mill to be ground. The nearest I came to school was when I was given the task of carrying my young missy's books. But I was allowed no nearer to the schoolhouse than the yard.

The "I" of this story is Booker T. Washington, and this, in essence, is what he wrote in the beginning of his autobiography, *Up from Slavery*.

By way of education, I was taught to "hush my mouth." But that did not prevent me from hearing a great deal of talk about a war, which the grown-up slaves whispered was being fought over us. The war took on a puzzling reality when a soldier came to our plantation and told the slaves that they were free. Free to go. But where?

When I asked my mother why we were leaving, she could not tell me. She had no more understanding of her freedom than she had had of her slavery. Not that she, like all my people, did not want freedom. I never knew a slave who would not have given his life for it. But I had also never met a slave who could read or write. Kept in ignorance all their lives, they were now called upon to assume responsibilities for which they had no training or experience.

My mother did the best she could. She took her children to a little town in West Virginia called Malden. There, for several years, I worked in the mines. But I could see in my new life only an extension of the old—with the same dirt, poverty and overwork. Determined not to spend the rest of my life digging coal and tending salt furnaces, I applied for work in the home of a Yankee lady, a Mrs. Ruffner. After I had finished the day's chores, she agreed to help me get an education.

I had to start from the very beginning. When I came to her I did not even have a proper name. Booker. Booker what? Should I explain to her that in the South my people were known simply as "Tom" or "Betsy"? Sometimes a colored man would take the name of his white owner, becoming "Tom Hatcher" or simply "Hatcher's Tom." But that hardly seemed appropriate now. I stood before her, searching for a name which would express not my oppression but my hopes. "Booker—Washington," I said at last. "Booker T. Washington."

From Mrs. Ruffner I learned to work with my hands, to dress neatly, to use a toothbrush. But of book learning, acquired during infrequent hours at school and study at night in my attic room, I received not much. So in the fall of 1872 I managed to work my way the five hundred miles from Malden to Hampton, Virginia, where I presented myself to the Hampton Institute, a newly founded school for Negroes.

When General Samuel C. Armstrong, the white director of Hampton Institute, asked me what I wanted to do in life, I answered that I wanted to learn. But learn what? I had heard that Latin and Greek were the fundamentals of a good education. Uncertainly, I replied that I would like to learn Latin and Greek.

"Yes," sighed General Armstrong, "and algebra and calculus and astronomy and medicine and jurisprudence. Isn't that so?" I could see his eye doubtfully upon me.

The thought of being turned down by a school for my own people filled me with despair. I tried to explain to General Armstrong how hard I had worked to save

enough money and how my mother and brother were helping me, too. The day before I left home, my friends had gathered round me, giving what they could—a nickel or a quarter or even a handkerchief—because they wanted to be proud of me. I would have begun sooner on my formal education, but it was not easy. I had had nothing to go on but my dreams.

The interview was interrupted by a secretary, who complained that classes were scheduled to begin that afternoon and that the recitation rooms were filthy. Without thinking, I offered to sweep them out. That, after all, was a job I knew.

"You didn't come all this way to Hampton just to take a broom in your hands again, did you?" asked General Armstrong severely.

Quietly, I answered, "No."

"Did you think that by offering it you'd curry favor with me?"

How could he talk that way, I asked. If I were to study in those classrooms, I felt it as my responsibility to help keep them clean. I had come because I wanted to help my people. I wanted to help them more than anything in the world. But I could not begin until I had learned to help myself.

General Armstrong looked at me as though he were seeing me for the first time. "That's right, Booker," he said. "I guess you'll do to enter this institution."

For the next nine years Hampton Institute was very much a part of my life. I graduated, and after I had spent an interval of teaching at Malden, General Armstrong took me on his staff. Then, one morning in 1881, the general called me into his office. "I've received a letter from some gentlemen in Alabama who want to start a normal school for Negroes in Tuskegee," he explained. "They've asked me to recommend someone to take charge. Do you think you could fill the position?"

"I, sir?"

"That's right."

"Won't they want a white man?" I pressed.

"I think they'll accept my recommendation," he said.

Arriving at Tuskegee, I discovered what a difficult task I had undertaken. To build a whole school we had only a few hundred dollars, raised by the Citizens' Committee of Tuskegee. The state legislature had granted a small appropriation for teachers' salaries, but it had provided no money whatsoever for land, buildings or books. I saw that our only hope for starting any school would be for the students to build it themselves.

We bought an abandoned plantation house outside of town and there, in the parlor inhabited previously, as our new neighbors told us, by haunts and ghosts, I called my first assembly. The students had heard the saying, "You've made your bed; now you can lie in it." Well, here at the Tuskegee Institute we'd have to *build* our beds before we could lie in them. Besides the house, we had only a little food on credit, a little money given by friends here and in the North, and our own will to succeed. I had to ask my students to do more than derive learning from books. I had to ask them to plant crops and cut timber and dig clay for bricks.

As the plan went into operation, there were complaints. Just as with myself ten years before, these young Negro men and women could attend school not only because of their own efforts but because of the efforts of their families and friends. Were they to spend their time like field hands and day laborers? As one student put it to me, his daddy came out from town to see his books and when he arrived, found his son on his knees digging sweet potatoes.

His daddy, as I learned, could neither read nor sign his name. Being able to read books meant education to him.

I intended to demonstrate to my students that an education is more than books. The day would be arranged so that there would be time for everything. When the students graduated, I wanted them to be able to better the life of their own communities. What the Negro people needed was not Latin or Greek. They needed bricks and wagons and houses and the knowledge of how to make them. Once they had those things, then perhaps a need would arise for the Latin and Greek. In the meantime, I told them, he who could do what the world wants done—at the right time—would make his way, whether he were Negro or white.

But regardless of our collective labor, the school could not earn enough money to support itself. Seventeen dollars this month from vegetables. Fifty-five from bricks sold. We were still two hundred dollars in debt. The school would have failed if word had not got around of what we were trying to do.

Our deliverance first came in the form of an old Negro woman who slipped unannounced into my office and stood looking at me. When I asked her her name, she answered, "I ain't got no real name, Mistah Washin'ton. Jus' Hattie. Jus' ole Hattie. Onliest name I evah had." She had heard that the boys and girls in our school didn't have enough to eat. "I knows you's tryin' to make bettah men and women foh de colored race," she said. "I ain't got no money to give, but I got dese eggs heah I bin savin' up f'm my hens. They bin layin' real good and I got dese eggs heah an' I want you to take 'em." She paused. "You'll take 'em, won' you, Mistah Washin'ton?"

As we sat in my office, I told Hattie the story of Moses and the burning bush—how, in a time of sorrow and pain, the Lord God appeared to Moses in a burning bush and

Booker T. Washington in his later years.

said to him, "I have seen the affliction of my people and I will deliver them into a good land." Those eggs were to us our burning bush, and it was people like her who made it worth all the sweat and toil and struggle. When I took them, I told Hattie that they were the finest eggs I'd ever seen.

Hattie was followed by many others. It was with their help that we were enabled to transform the Tuskegee Institute into a fine college which gave service to my race and, thereby, to all of America.

THE HUMANITARIANS

"I believe . . . that every human mind feels pleasure in doing good to another."

THOMAS JEFFERSON, Letter to John Adams, 1816.

MEDICINE'S GREAT FRIEND

(JOHNS HOPKINS)

It was the year 1807. In the quiet and modestly furnished plantation home of the Quaker Samuel Hopkins, the family sat before the large fireplace, listening to young Johns Hopkins reading. He was interrupted by the unexpected return of his father, who had been away on some business.

"What is it, Samuel?" asked his wife.

"Hannah," he replied, "we must have a talk and the children may as well listen, too." Then Samuel Hopkins announced that he had decided to free his slaves.

His decision, dictated by his conscience, was to change all their lives, especially young Johns'. Then only twelve, he left school because the boys of the family were needed to work on the plantation. For him and the other boys began five years of the hardest toil, from early morning to dark, day after day.

When Johns was seventeen his father sent him to Baltimore to live with his uncle Gerard Hopkins, a prosperous wholesale grocery and commission merchant. The boy showed a surprising aptitude for business. Through his alertness his uncle's business expanded, especially during one period when his uncle was away several months on a trip to Ohio and Johns had to carry on in Baltimore alone.

While he was gone something important happened to the young man; he fell in love with his employer's daughter, his pretty first cousin Elizabeth. On his uncle's return, Johns asked for her hand in marriage.

"Impossible," Uncle Gerard angrily declared.

"But why, sir?" asked Johns.

"You're cousins and it's wrong for cousins to marry. There will be no such wedding in this family!"

Gerard Hopkins not only forbade the marriage; he forbade his nephew the house. Young Johns Hopkins had to board out, but he continued in business with his uncle. The parting was bitter to the young lovers. Both Elizabeth and Johns vowed never to wed anyone else, a vow they kept, though both lived to be eighty-odd.

More than ever now, business absorbed Johns' energies. In 1819, a depression year, many of the Hopkins' customers from outlying regions asked to be allowed to pay for their goods in whiskey, which they distilled from their own grain. Johns approved of this method of payment, but his uncle objected; to him Johns' actions were nothing short of "selling souls into perdition." The matter was brought to the attention of members of the Quaker Society of Baltimore, which read young Johns out of meeting.

This violent disagreement with his uncle forced Johns to go into business for himself. His associates in his new firm were his three brothers. Curiously enough, during the early years the records show that their uncle financed the new company's operations. One year they bartered two hundred thousand dollars' worth of goods for whiskey, which the brothers resold under the brand name of "Hopkins' Best."

Johns Hopkins prospered and his business expanded, through Virgina, North Carolina and over the Alleghenies to Ohio.

308

He became a banker, bought up warehouses and sent wagon-trains over the mountains. When the council of the city of Baltimore refused to accept a proposal to build a railroad over the wagon-route to Ohio, Hopkins stepped in.

"Gentlemen," he said, "since the representatives of this town have neither the vision nor the courage, I propose to finance this railroad myself. It shall be called the Baltimore & Ohio Railroad."

Stock in the new venture was sold to the public, including members of the city council, and the railroad was built. From then on, Johns Hopkins' rise in the business world became still more rapid and he became a multimillionaire. He helped the city of Baltimore financially during the Civil War and again during the depression of 1873, when his contributions averted financial disaster.

It was during an epidemic of cholera that Hopkins, who had been infected, realized the urgent need of a good hospital for his city. The poor were dying by the thousands, and the city was deserted by those who could afford to leave it. Hopkins was nursed back to health by an old Negro servant. Of all his family and friends, only his cousin Elizabeth, who had not been permitted to become his wife, stayed at his side during the crisis.

As a result of his experience he had his lawyer draw up a will leaving seven million dollars to be divided equally between Johns Hopkins University, soon to be erected, and the Johns Hopkins Hospital, created by funds he had made available. The will also provided for a hospital and orphanage for Negroes and left funds for the education of the youth of Baltimore and the care of the dependent.

Johns Hopkins thus became one of the greatest of American philanthropists. American medicine and American education owe much to his benefactions. The two institutions which preserve his name rank among the world's finest.

The Four Great Doctors of Johns Hopkins: W. H. Welch, W. S. Halsted, William Osler, H. A. Kelly. From the painting by Sargent.

ANGEL OF MERCY

(CLARA BARTON)

On December 15, 1862, the newspapers of Washington, D.C., carried headlines about the battle at Fredericksburg. Their reports, however, showed that no one knew exactly what had happened. They were full of such phrases as "Troops take up new positions," "It is believed that the enemy suffered severe losses," "Indecisive conclusion to a seesaw battle," and so forth.

There was one person in Washington who knew exactly what had happened, a little travel-weary woman entering Lincoln Hospital with the Senator from her home state of Massachusetts. Clara Barton was about to take the first step of her plan. She was sure that if she could conduct Senator Wilson through the endless wards of this soldiers' hospital, he would begin to see the reasonableness of her demands.

Clara, forty-one at this time, was one of the many volunteer nurses who were trying to help out in the overcrowded hospitals. Clara was a special kind of volunteer: she had chosen to risk her life on the battlefield itself. She knew exactly what had happened at Antietam and at Fredericksburg. She had hastened to Washington directly from that bloody defeat of the Union forces.

"I'm sorry that this visit to the hospital will delay your lunch," said Clara to Senator Wilson, "but I am determined to accomplish my mission *today*, not tomorrow."

"So many wounded soldiers!" exclaimed Senator Wilson as he looked down the crowded rows of cots.

"There are others at the front not so fortunate as these," said Clara. "Nothing to rest on but pallets of straw and no roof over them. They just lie there—dying—in the sun and the rain."

Clara stopped before one of the cots. "I know this man," she whispered. "He's a Confederate soldier. I helped put him on the train at Fairfax Station. He can't possibly live more than a day or two."

Going over to the man, she touched his hand gently and when he opened his eyes, she said, "Hello, Jimmy."

"Oh, hello," said the man at last. "You're not the real nurse; you're that other nurse who said she would write a letter for me."

"That was just when the train was leaving," said Clara. "But now, up here, there will be time to write the letter."

"I wish you would write it, ma'am," said Jimmy, "for if I died here in Yankee territory, my kinfolk might never know. The orderly got my address in my papers. Will you ask him for it, ma'am, and write to my ma? But wait a minute! You're just trying to fool me! There's no mail through the lines! I know that."

"Somehow, Jimmy, I'll get a letter to your kinfolk," said Clara. "Will you believe me?"

"Yes, yes, I'll believe you—I'll believe you," said Jimmy as he settled back again and closed his eyes.

"I'm beginning to see why you insisted that I come here," said Senator Wilson as they moved on down the aisle. "Jimmy could be one of *our* boys, lying in a hospital somewhere down South. I'll draw up a bill to arrange for a mail exchange across the lines—and other points in your plan for solving these human problems. I begin to see its merits, Clara. Now I'll write a note for you to the Secretary of War and arrange for you to see him this afternoon."

Through the bare branches of the trees lining Pennsylvania Avenue, the lawn surrounding the White House seemed drab and neglected under the winter sky. A hulking figure of a man was crossing the lawn in great strides while curious citizens peered through the scrollwork of the gate.

"That's Stanton on his way to the War Department," somebody said.

Someone else added, "They say even *he* doesn't know what really happened at Fredericksburg."

Standing before Edwin McMasters Stanton, the busy, bristling Secretary of War, was the little travel-weary woman from the battlefield.

"It's a small thing I ask, Mr. Secretary," she said. "Ten wagons, one equipped for ambulance duty. The supplies I can raise myself, privately. But transport has to be arranged through this office."

"Miss Barton," said Stanton impatiently, "there might be wagons in Washington. But horses—the Quartermaster-General can't buy horses at any price!"

"Then commandeer them," said Clara.

"In the Army we must follow a certain procedure," replied Stanton. "Otherwise we'd be lost in confusion."

"But I tell you the procedure is wrong," said Clara. "Many of these supplies never reach the front in time. The best that can be done for most of the men is simply to bed them down on a bit of straw in an open field. There were no medical supplies of any kind at Fredericksburg or at Antietam, no bandages. Those men are lying there now, dying of their wounds, and you sit here and quibble about the proper procedure of caring for them. There's only one way to do that and that is to take the supplies there in wagons. Give me the wagons and I will do it myself."

"But there is simply no agency to authorize such an action," said Stanton.

"Then create such an agency. Or authorize me to do it," Clara replied. "There should be a separate organization for this, anyway."

"I'm sorry, ma'am," said Stanton in a voice that made it clear he would prefer to terminate the conversation. "Only the Commander-in-Chief himself can authorize such an agency. And a matter of ten wagons and some bandages can hardly be referred to the President as a detail of our grand strategy, now, can it?"

"I suppose not," said Clara, "but nevertheless I shall make an attempt to do so."

The President was in the midst of a meeting, but he asked his young secretary, John Hay, to take careful note of Clara Barton's request. "He wishes to send you his belated compliments on your splendid work at Antietam," said Hay.

"He—he heard about that?" asked Clara incredulously.

"On these matters, you will find that the President is as well informed as anyone in Washington," said Hay.

"Then he knows about Fredericksburg?" asked Clara.

"Fredericksburg?" repeated Hay. "Why, no, there's been no particular news from there. In fact, the President is becoming anxious about that front."

"There isn't any front," said Clara. "Our forces were destroyed. I came from there today. There's nothing but starvation, untended wounds and utter disorganization."

"I'm afraid I shall have to cut our conversation short," said Hay. "I must give the President your information and I shall have to contact the Quartermaster-General at once. What was it you wanted to request, Miss Barton?"

"Oh, some wagons—ten at least," said Clara. "And some muslin—and, oh, little things—I'll give you a list. I know they seem trivial, but nobody knows how much these little things mean at the front."

"I think, Miss Barton," said Hay, "that the President knows very well what they mean."

"Then tell him for me," said Clara, "that there is one person in this country who will not rest until she has found a way to get these little things—these important little things—*where* they are needed and *when* they are needed. Tell him that I know how

Clara Barton.

it can be done."

Late that night, Clara Barton left Washington with a train of ten wagons loaded with the supplies that were to save a thousand lives at Fredericksburg. This one little woman was the first of millions of untiring, selfless men and women turning their faces toward the battle when others would prefer to turn away. Those ten wagons were to be followed, in time, by shining ambulances, braving bombs and shrapnel to carry aid to the wounded and comfort to the battle-weary. For the miracle of that great organization of mercy, the American Red Cross, was born of Clara Barton's indomitable and merciful spirit. In 1877 she succeeded in founding a permanent organization for emergency aid—the American National Committee. This became the American Red Cross in 1881, and Clara Barton served as its president for almost twenty-five years.

313

SOCIAL SERVANT

(JANE ADDAMS)

When she was only seventeen, Jane Addams began dedicating herself to helping the poor. She was shocked by the poverty and the miserable slum conditions she saw across the tracks in her home town of Cedarville, Illinois. Nobody seemed to be doing anything about it.

"We can't turn our backs on those people. We've got to find some way to help them," she told her father. That gentleman thought marriage and not social conditions the proper concern of a young lady, and did everything he could to persuade her to give up her ideas of "reforming the world." He sent Jane and her sister Ellen to Europe, hoping that in her travels abroad Jane would find a new interest.

For the Addams sisters, however, their trip abroad was spoiled by the sight of European slums. Other tourists might ignore them, but not Jane. What had happened in the Old World, she thought, should not have been allowed to happen in the new cities of the New World. Yet she had heard that already the brand-new city of Chicago had slums as squalid as those in Europe. "When I get home, Ellen," she told her sister, "I intend to walk up and down Chicago and find out for myself."

In 1883, after their father's death, Jane and Ellen Addams moved into a building known as Hull House on Halsted Street in Chicago. All around them, for blocks and blocks, were incredibly rundown tenements crowded with immigrant families—Poles, Slovaks, Italians and Irishmen. Yes, here were disgraceful slums— and the new Americans had to live in them. There was no place else for them to go.

A few months after Jane had set up her

headquarters in Hull House, a manufacturer named Siller called upon Regan, the local political ward boss.

"You've got to do something about this woman at Hull House," said Siller. "She's stirring up trouble with the girls in my factory. Got them coming to me asking to work less hours. And it's not just me; it's the landlords, too. She's supporting all those foreign tenants who are always complaining about the rents and the broken stairs. She has meetings in Hull House all the time. And when there isn't a meeting on, she's got people just sitting around there all day, taking it easy."

The following day, the *Free Press* printed an editorial and cartoon on its front page. The cartoon attempted to

314

make a laughing-stock out of Jane, while the editorial gave a shrewdly distorted picture of her work with the less fortunate people in her neighborhood. It said that, due to her meddling in the affairs of these people, the employers had no choice but to fire them all and hire more trustworthy workers.

Regan's plan succeeded. The *Free Press* editorial was put into the hands of his political henchmen, who whipped up a crowd of Jane's neighbors and led them against Hull House. Jane's attempt to unmask Regan to the mob was useless. Instead, they stoned the windows and stormed into Hull House and broke up the furnishings. Jane narrowly escaped physical injury at their hands. There were people in the crowd who had been her former friends. But she did not blame them, for she knew how they had been incited. She was determined to raise funds and reopen Hull House. She went directly to the Manufacturers' Association, which gave her a few minutes at their meeting.

"Gentlemen," she said, "I represent Hull House, and Hull House represents every man, woman and child in the ninth ward. It should, in turn, represent every man here, but apparently it doesn't. I used to believe in the innate reasonableness of the members of the employing class. I thought that if actual abuses were pointed out to them, they would do what was in their power to correct them. But one of the men in this very room is working a ten-year-old child from fifteen to eighteen hours a day. What is he going to do about it? One of the men in this room is paying a child five cents a day to do fine sewing in a dark room—and that child is going blind. What is he going to do about it? One of the men in this room is heating a textile factory with oil stoves, and the whole floor is covered with inflammable material. And there are forty girls working in that factory and—"

Mr. Siller broke in, "That's none of your business, Miss Addams!"

"Thank you for speaking up, sir," said Jane. "I ask you—what are you going to do about it? There are hundreds of factories like yours where girls are working under those dangers. What if a fire breaks out?"

Several other manufacturers took up Siller's tone against Jane, and the chairman was forced to stop the discussion.

"I'm sorry, Miss Addams," he said, "but we have no more time for this matter. I suggest, gentlemen, that the Association advance Miss Addams one hundred dollars as an indication of our interest in her program at Hull House."

That evening a member of the Manufacturers' Association called on Jane. She remembered him as a man with a friendly face who had stood quietly in the rear of the meeting-hall.

"I was ashamed of the Association today," he said, "and I have spent all my time since the meeting talking to some of the other manufacturers. Here is my check, and here are theirs. Every decent businessman in Chicago is going to be rooting for you by the time I get through. And then we'll start on the politicians."

The checks were for very large sums and Jane Addams knew that at last Hull House could be re-established, this time on a permanent basis.

Not long afterward there was just the kind of fire Jane Addams had warned against, and it occurred in a factory owned by Mr. Siller. All of the forty girls working there were burned to death. A few hours later, Regan was informed that Jane Addams was calling for a public investigation of the tragedy. He hurried over to speak with her.

"But I was there, Mr. Regan," remonstrated Jane. "I have the facts. Why did that fire hose break? Because it was rotten and useless. Who pocketed the money

315

that would buy a good one? You did. I saw firemen struggling with a ladder that wouldn't work either. You had taxpayers' money to buy proper equipment. You didn't. *You*, too, are responsible for the deaths of those girls—you, along with Mr. Siller. And I am determined that this shall end with your resignation and with Mr. Siller's imprisonment for criminal negligence. It won't be long, Mr. Regan, before there will be a law to protect the working people of Illinois from greed and selfishness."

From this point on, Jane Addams' life was a record of achievement in securing a better life for the poor. Her Hull House gained international fame for its pioneer work in social service. She sponsored labor laws for the improvement of working conditions and they were enacted by the Illinois legislature. Partly as a result of her support of women's suffrage, women were

finally permitted to vote throughout the nation. Several years before her death in 1935, Jane Addams organized the Women's International League for Peace and Freedom. For this and her other contributions to the cause of world peace she was awarded the Nobel Prize.

In her speech of acceptance, Jane Addams declared, "I receive this award for all men and women who find in service to their fellow man the highest expression of God. No one stands alone in the battle for human rights. Progress is not automatic; the world grows better because people wish that it should and take the right steps to make it better. It is only in sharing the sorrows of humanity that we know the full joy of possessing our whole humanity. For all stand equal in the shadow of the grave, wherein no man calls his brother lord or master. So are we lifted up together above our petty differences into an encompassing sense of unity."

Jane Addams campaigns for Votes for Women.

THE ARTISTS

NOVELIST OF OUR NATIVE SCENE

(JAMES FENIMORE COOPER)

One evening in 1820 James Fenimore Cooper, a Westchester country gentleman, was at home reading a novel aloud to his wife. It was the latest novel by Mrs. Opie, one of the most popular English writers of the time. With increasing impatience Cooper plowed on through Mrs. Opie's sentimental tale of the British upper classes. Finally, in complete disgust, he flung the volume to the floor.

"James!" cried Susan Cooper. "In the eight years we've been married, I've never seen you display such temper!"

"I could write a better book than that myself!" said Cooper.

"You who admit to being the worst penman in America!" scoffed Susan. "Why, you told me that the principal reason you agreed to live here in Westchester was so you'd be spared the need of writing to me when I went home to visit my parents!"

"There's some truth in that," Cooper admitted, "but I still maintain that I could write a better book than this trash from England!"

"I dare you to try it," said Susan.

"That settles it," said Cooper. "I will!"

It could not be said that Cooper's qualifications for writing a book were notable. During his youth in upstate New York, then a wilderness, he showed no outstanding literary aptitude. In 1808, at the age of nineteen and after two years at Yale, he secured a commission as a midshipman in the United States Navy. In 1811 he resigned, married Susan de Lancey and settled in the countryside north of New York City. He seemed to be a typical American gentleman, with a touch of frontier experience in his youth, but with a leaning toward England for the cultural amenities, now that he was a man of leisure.

Boldly accepting his wife's challenge, Cooper began his first novel, which he called *Precaution*. There was little in it to suggest the qualities that were to make him America's first great novelist—except a marked strength and vitality. Solely to please his wife, he published it without signing his name to it, printing a few hundred copies at his own expense. In the tradition of English fiction of that time, *Precaution* was a story of English high society. It was well enough received to make Cooper feel that he had succeeded. Yet he was actually unhappy over the outcome. Here he was, a democratic American, writing about high society and London, a city he had never seen. And the book sounded to him like an imitation of Mrs. Opie.

Cooper might not have written another book if it had not been for a casual conversation at the home of his friend, Judge John Jay. In the drawing-room after dinner, Cooper and his wife were startled to hear another of the guests, a Miss McDonald, ask Judge Jay if he had read the new novel *Precaution*.

James Fenimore Cooper.

"Yes, Miss McDonald," said Judge Jay, "I have. And I found it very interesting."

"Interesting enough," said Miss McDonald, "but I am indignant when the booksellers say an American gentleman wrote it! That book was undoubtedly written by the English novelist Mrs. Opie."

On their way home that night, Cooper told his wife how ashamed he was of his slavish imitation of the fashionable English writer. "The only country I really know," he said, "is America! Westchester—Cooperstown—Lake Otsego—"

"But no one ever writes about America,"

said his wife. "It's too crude, too violent, too new. There's nothing in *America* to interest readers."

"I wonder about that," said Cooper dreamily. "I'm afraid, Sue, that I shall have to write another book."

Cooper called his second book *The Spy,* and when he delivered the manuscript into the hands of his bookseller and publisher friend, Charles Wiley, he had high hopes for its success. A few days later he drove back into the city and called on Wiley.

"Well, Wiley, what do you think of it?"

"Can't you see the faults of the book?" asked Wiley. "You're an intelligent man, Cooper. Surely you must know no book like this has ever been written! A novel with a setting in the American wilderness!"

"Is it your honest judgment that no American would read a book about his own country?" asked Cooper.

"It's the judgment of any sane man, Cooper!" declared Wiley. "Americans want to read of life and manners in polished European circles. They know too much about Indians and rough frontiersmen already!"

Only Susan Cooper's enthusiasm for the book prevented her husband from destroying it. Once again Cooper had to foot the expense of publishing his book. But this time the book carried the name of the author—James Fenimore Cooper.

And despite the fact that books were distributed slowly in those days of stagecoaches and packet boats, scarcely a year had passed before *The Spy* had been declared a remarkable work of fiction. Cooper was applauded even by the London critics.

He followed up the success of *The Spy* with another novel, *The Pioneer,* and still another, *The Pilot.* But his most famous book was yet to be written. He was to begin this book on an afternoon in 1825 while recovering from a serious illness.

From his bedroom he called out to his wife, "Sue, dear, please bring me some paper and a pen!"

When he found that he was not yet strong enough to write for any length of time, he asked Susan to sit beside him and take his dictation.

"Most of the action takes place in Glens Falls, New York," he said. "That cave on the rocky island—a perfect hiding place for Indians—the ideal setting. . . ."

"Yes," said his wife, trying to calm him, "you told me about your trip to Glens Falls last summer. It must have been a beautiful sight!"

"Uncas—the last of his tribe—the Mohicans!" Cooper exclaimed. "Yes, that's it —*The Last of the Mohicans!* Susan, are you ready to write?"

Swiftly, Cooper shaped the vivid sentences, and his wife's fingers raced on after his voice: "The breech of Hawkeye's rifle fell on the naked head of his adversary, whose muscles appeared to wither under the shock. When Uncas had brained his first antagonist, he turned like a hungry lion to seek another. Suddenly darting at each other, the two combatants closed and came to the earth, twisted together like twining serpents in pliant and subtle folds. Covered as they were with dust and blood, the swift evolution of the two men seemed to incorporate their bodies into one. The fiery eyes of Magua were seen glittering. . . ."

At first Susan thought that Cooper had become feverish and that she was being engulfed in a nightmare. She soon realized, however, as the narrative reeled out on the page before her, that she was sharing with her husband the excitement of creation.

The Last of the Mohicans was to establish James Fenimore Cooper as a great American novelist. And it would become clear that he had achieved his reputation through his conviction that American artists should turn for inspiration to the vivid past of their native land.

THE GOOD GRAY POET

(WALT WHITMAN)

A man who never had more than five years of formal schooling became one of the greatest figures in American literature and probably the foremost influence on modern poetry in the entire world. He is Walt Whitman, the Good Gray Poet (he dressed, usually, all in gray).

Curiously, he himself, who affected so many others, provides an extraordinary demonstration of how the mind of one man as expressed in his writings can influence the life of another. It was Ralph Waldo Emerson who influenced Whitman, and whom Whitman considered, at least in his early days, his "Master."

Walter Whitman's career was not extraordinary or especially distinguished until he was thirty-five years old. He was a country schoolteacher when he was seventeen, and worked on newspapers in the summertime. When he was twenty years old he started the *Long Islander*, a weekly newspaper published in Huntington, L.I., near the place where, in 1819, he was born. (The Whitman family had moved to Brooklyn when he was four,

Whitman's Birthplace at West Hills, near Huntington, Long Island.

Walt Whitman. Painting by Thomas Eakins.

A late photograph of Whitman.

then back to Huntington when he was fourteen.) But Walter, loving city life, sold his paper and went back to Brooklyn to write for New York newspapers. In 1848 he became editor of the Brooklyn *Daily Eagle*.

He was still a typical young newspaperman, who occasionally made stump speeches during election campaigns, did some hack writing, and wrote mediocre stories and poems. His accounts of the games of the early Brooklyn teams were probably the first baseball reporting ever published. The reports themselves showed no remarkable talent. What is notable is that he went to the games, recognized them as news, mingled with the spectators and players, sat around in the beer-gardens, eating, drinking and talking with them. His companions were clerks, factory workers, day-laborers, stevedores and other unexceptional people and he liked them. He got close to them, knew and understood them. Perhaps that is why later he could become their voice.

As he approached his middle thirties Whitman began to be dissatisfied with his life and achievements. He was reading Emerson, he was stimulated, and aspirations started within him. "I was simmering, simmering," he said. "It was Emerson who brought me to a boil."

He changed his way of life, gave up time-consuming sidelines such as politics, shortened his name to Walt, and started on his lifetime project—writing and publishing the composite and growing work of poetry, *Leaves of Grass*. It was in 1855 that he set the type for and manufactured the first edition, containing his first twelve poems. There were 800 or 900 copies of it and, except in literary circles, it made barely a ripple. Emerson wrote an enthusiastic letter to Whitman about it, but most of the critics condemned the work as crude and vulgar.

Whitman was not discouraged by this criticism. On the contrary, he was spurred by Emerson's praise, and in the forthcoming years he issued edition after edition of *Leaves of Grass*, each time adding new poems to the old.

Clearly, Whitman's poetry was different, in form and in subject matter. The poems were generally in uneven, unrhymed lines, and their purpose, he said, was to be "commensurate with a people," to "incarnate" its life and to reveal the American soul and body.

Only when you read Whitman's poetry and compare it to that of the New England poets of the time can you realize the extent of Whitman's pioneering and the importance of the new trails he blazed in literature. For soon, cued and inspired by Whitman, and seeing the advantages and values of the "new" poetry, many poets and writers all over the world had the courage to break away from tradition.

This self-educated man expanded enormously the scope of poetry and gave new expression and enjoyment to the world. Perhaps that was because he refused to be restricted and disciplined within established and conventional bounds. He was an outstanding example of the truth that continues to amaze the world: true genius, regardless of disadvantages and handicaps, will find its way.

Golden Eagle. Painting by Audubon.

THE BIRDS OF AMERICA

(JOHN JAMES AUDUBON)

In the early years of the nineteenth century, like many another ambitious young European, John James Audubon came to America to make his fortune. Born in Haiti, of French parents, he had spent some time in France, where he studied painting with the famous artist Gerard David. When he landed on our shores, at the age of nineteen, he had little in the way of worldly goods or cash. And it might be said right here that he never did succeed in amassing the fortune he had come to make. Yet he left us a heritage for which we remain forever in his debt.

Perhaps we owe something to Lucy Bakewell, too. If Audubon hadn't found and married her, our story would have been different. And, for a time, it certainly looked as if their marriage was an unlikely thing. Wasn't he French? Wasn't she English by birth? Hadn't his father, a naval captain, been confined for years in a British naval prison?

John James Audubon had little love for

Ruby-throated Hummingbird. Painting by Audubon.

Baltimore Oriole. Painting by Audubon.

the British, and the day he galloped up to the door of the Bakewell estate—Fatlands —outside of Philadelphia, he had little reason to suspect that the girl who would become his wife would answer his knock. This was merely a polite return of a social call Mr. Bakewell had paid him. As he dismounted from his horse and looked up at the great house, he had occasion to wonder what he was doing here. Well, the visit would be a brief one and afterward he would return down the road to the small estate which he managed for his father.

Lucy received him coldly. Her father was out, but she would certainly inform him of Audubon's call. Then, as Audubon turned to leave, she cried out, "What is that sound?"

Going to his horse, Audubon opened a saddlebag and drew forth a small, chirping bird, a nuthatch.

"But it's injured!" Lucy cried.

"Yes," said Audubon. "I found it on the road, as I was coming here. One of its legs is hurt, but I will fix it."

"And then—?"

"I will draw, perhaps paint, a picture of it." Gently, but firmly, he spread the bird's wings. "Is it not beautiful—a work of art? The birds of America," he went on, "are they not wonderful?" Oh, yes, he had loved the birds of France, but the birds of *America!* Such profusion! So varied! Was it not high time that someone captured them on paper, on canvas?

"You like it here in America?" Lucy asked.

Indeed he did. The colorful pageant of the turning leaves in autumn—the scarlet and gold brilliance of the woods—there was nothing to compare with it in all of France, he declared.

"Nor in England." Lucy watched him. And she blushed, for already her coolness had melted.

Oh, granted the young Frenchman was handsome, said Lucy's father. He had charm, he had wit—but what were his prospects? Why, he seemed to have nothing to do but spend his days riding in the fields and the woods, trapping the birds that had not already flown south and tying small bands of silken thread around their legs. Now they may go south, Audubon told her, and in the spring I shall watch to see if the same birds return to this neighborhood. By these threads, I will know them.

Hardly a fit occupation for a young man! As the friendship between Lucy and this bird-painter threatened to ripen into love, Mr. Bakewell became disturbed. A most unsuitable son-in-law, he said.

And Audubon himself agreed with him and resolved to reform his life. He would go into business. In this exciting America of 1804, the frontier beckoned. By daring, by hard work, and with a little luck a man could grow rich with the country. So, asking Lucy to wait for him, he traveled to Kentucky to make his fortune. There with what little capital he had, he set up a store, selling tea and sugar, petticoats and eggs, anything and everything needed by the people building a new territory.

In the spring he returned to Pennsylvania, to his Lucy. Along the way, traveling across the mountains, fording the rivers, he paused to capture quickly, on paper, the outlines of the mourning dove, the scarlet tanager and a host of lesser-known birds. In the forests, under the tall trees lit by shafts of sunlight, the green leaves alive with the whirring of wings, he felt a joy surge through him. And what was that call? Another unknown bird, or at least a bird unknown to the East. The mountain people here knew it, had a name for it; and Audubon would write the name down, with a brief description of the rare

bird's habits. Lucy would marvel at his drawing.

But, of course, he told Mr. Bakewell as he was summoned to discuss his prospects by Lucy's father, this bird-work of mine is only a hobby. My business in Kentucky prospers; one day I will be rich, like you.

But was it only a hobby? Wasn't it, after all, the thing he was born to do, his life's work? Lucy, after their marriage, had many years to ponder this question. On the Kentucky frontier they were happy together for a while. Children came to them; they began to raise a small family. Then the business failed. One venture after another came a cropper, and disaster followed disaster. Finally, despite all Audubon's efforts, they were bankrupt and they lost even their furniture. No, he was not really suited to running any kind of business. They might as well face it, Lucy said. But he did have one great gift. Over the years he had continued to paint his beloved birds. It was clear what he must do. Clear, but not simple, not easy.

So, while Lucy took the children to Cincinnati where she taught school, Audubon roamed the face of America. North, south, east and west, in all seasons, through all kinds of weather, he pursued the feathered ones. Penniless, dressed in frontier clothing, he sketched the owl, the eagle, the heron, in their natural habitat, painting these birds in all their astonishing colors.

His skill increased. "Looka there!" a farmer might say. "A wild turkey cock! Why, the way you've drawn it, Mister, I might be right out there in the woods, lookin' at it!" Or in Maine, where the waves clashed against the rocky coast, the natives might exclaim over the manner in which he'd painted the birds of sea and marsh, so true, so lifelike.

He took odd jobs, to keep himself going, and sometimes he painted the portrait of a farmer, a merchant, a banker, to pay his way. But there wasn't much to be gained

John J. Audubon

Bluejay. Painting by Audubon.

along that line. After all, who was impressed by an unknown artist in ragged clothes?

There was little demand for his birds. Rejoining his Lucy, as he did at intervals, he would ask, "Why do I go on? No one wants my work." No one would pay solid cash for paintings of birds, many of them so familiar they could be seen by anyone in woods and fields. And at times, lonely in the forests, along the dim trails, suffering hardship and hunger, Audubon would despair.

So the years went by and Audubon remained virtually unrecognized. He tried to get his bird pictures published, but his project was turned down by every American printer or engraver whom he approached. His only remaining hope was to go to Europe. Over there, he might be appreciated. Over there, the people had begun to take an interest in all things American. To them, this was a strange land, an exotic land, where incredible things were happening. They might be fascinated by his birds, his animals, the wild life he had suffered so much to capture.

But how could he go? It would cost a great deal, not merely for the voyage there and back, but for the long months of trying to make his name and work known. He could not expect an instant success. From whom would the money come for such a venture?

It came from Lucy. Once more she showed her faith in Audubon. For two years, out of her earnings as a teacher, she had saved. And now in 1826, with her savings paying his way, John James Audubon sailed for England in a last desperate effort to have his paintings brought before the public.

A long silence followed. And then, over the months, his letters began arriving. At first, he spoke of difficulties, discouragements, trials. Would he suffer defeat again? Were all his years, and hers, of hardship, hard work and deprivation to come to nothing? And then the letters began to change, to become more hopeful, even optimistic. He had met Sir Walter Scott, the writer, who was most enthusiastic. He had met Lord Elgin, the art collector, who drank a toast to him. And then, most encouraging of all, his paintings were to be exhibited in the gallery of the Royal Society.

The exhibition, he finally wrote excitedly, had been a success, a marvelous success. "Remember my painting of the wild turkey cock? You will not believe it, Lucy, but the appraiser for the Royal Society says it is worth at least a hundred guineas. And in Liverpool—again you will not believe it! There we had another exhibition, and so many came to see my work, we turned the crowds from the door. I have cleared a hundred pounds from exhibiting alone. And listen to what a former countryman of mine writes, for we are American now, are we not, Lucy, no longer English or French? 'Looking at these pictures,' this French critic says, 'a magic power transported us into the forests. Imagine a landscape wholly American—trees, flowers, grass, even the tints of the sky and the waters quicken with a life that is real, peculiar, trans-Atlantic. It is a palpable vision of the New World, and this realization of an entire hemisphere, this picture of a nature so lusty and strong, is due to the brush of a single man.' "

Today, we have but to open Audubon's *Birds of America* to see why Lucy kept her faith. For these are more than beautiful and accurate records of America's wild life. As we turn the leaves, the birds, in all their splendor and vitality, stand magnificently before us. And we see, as well, the history of our land; we step into earlier woodland scenes, we walk deep into the forests and over the grassy plains where our forefathers plodded their pioneer way.

MUSEUM PIECE

(CHARLES WILLSON PEALE)

Charles Willson Peale in his Museum in Philadelphia.

Inventor, scientist, portrait painter and patriot, Charles Willson Peale was a citizen of some considerable importance to the new Republic, but a man of unusual habits and fancies.

"Eccentric?" Charles Peale protested. "A trifle out of the ordinary, yes. But eccentric? Never! I have been called headstrong, reckless, unpredictable—all arrant nonsense, sir! I am a prosaic, humdrum *normal* individual."

Would Miss Elizabeth de Peyster of Philadelphia have agreed with Peale, now a widower? She knew of his children, each one named after a painter—Raphael, Rembrandt, Titian, Rubens—well, just how

many children were there in all?

"Six, I believe," Peale answered thoughtfully. "Or is it seven? Now, let me see—"

"I have heard you are something of an inventor," Elizabeth hastened to say. "And a watchmaker. Is it true you are a dentist also?"

Peale studied her mouth closely.

"No, no, Mr. Peale," Elizabeth laughed. "My teeth are in excellent condition, thank you."

"I would say," Peale agreed, "that you are in excellent condition altogether, Miss de Peyster. And by the bye, are you fond of children?"

It was not an idle question, as Elizabeth well knew. But if his proposal of marriage did take her by surprise, she soon recovered. A spinster, getting on in years, she couldn't afford to be haughty toward Opportunity, even if it came *hammering* on the door like this.

"By the help of which of your many professions do you mean to support me, Mr. Peale?" she asked.

"Which?" Peale echoed in astonishment. "Why, all, of course."

"Then I am afraid I must decline your proposal. A man of so many professions can be master of none. But if you concentrated on your painting, you could do most handsomely. I understand you have already made a reputation in that field."

"A reputation, yes, but not much money, my dear Elizabeth."

"But you have painted General Washington and Benjamin Franklin. Why, you have a host of famous friends—Mr. Jefferson, Robert Morris, Dr. John Morgan. Wouldn't they like their portraits painted?"

"Perhaps," Peale said. "But I cannot run to them and ask, madam. It would be too much like beggary. I refuse to consider it. I refuse, do you hear! Now, madam, I will give you twenty minutes in which to answer my proposal. And I warn you: if it is not the answer I wish, I shall leave this house and propose marriage to the first, the very first, female I encounter on the street."

It was not necessary for Peale to make good his threat. And, after his marriage to Elizabeth, both of them being intelligent people, they struck a compromise. Peale dedicated himself to painting portraits.

In his studio, some months later, he said to his friend Dr. Morgan, "She is an excellent mother to my children. But then, am I not at heart a gentle soul, Doctor?"

Dr. Morgan found this amusing but made no answer. Tiring of posing, he went over to Peale's easel.

"Very good, Peale," he said. "I think you have caught me there. Elizabeth indeed gave you excellent—ah—shall I say, 'advice'?"

"Of course my painting is superb," said Peale. "But I cannot make a living at it."

"But what about your Art Gallery? I should think that would yield you something."

"Not enough, I'm afraid."

"Have you ever thought of turning it into a museum?"

"But my Gallery is a museum."

"I mean a museum of natural history, Peale. A museum containing the great natural wonders with which our country abounds. The flora and fauna of America. Geological specimens, animal life—"

"Stuffed animals?" Peale said. "But who would stuff them, Dr. Morgan? I'm no taxidermist."

"You could learn," Dr. Morgan said.

A few days later, Elizabeth entered her husband's workshop in search of her paring knife. She found Peale dissecting an owl with it.

"Charles Willson Peale," Elizabeth said firmly, "I will not have this house cluttered up with dirty old owls—stuffed or otherwise!"

"You need not worry, madam," Charles Peale said. "When I have finished stuffing, I shall take the bird to my new Museum of Natural History."

"And that's another thing," Elizabeth said. "When we were married, you gave me your word: you agreed to give up all such nonsense. Museum of Natural History, indeed! Scatterbrained nonsense!"

"The great natural wonders of America, nonsense?" he cried. "Have you no thirst for knowledge, no curiosity? And furthermore, madam, where is your patriotism? Would you have the European nations continue to regard us as a country devoid of culture—the only nation on the globe with no repository for the flora and fauna that enrich its landscape?"

And, for a while, it appeared that Elizabeth's fears were justified. Though the new museum displayed in 1786, for the first time in the Western Hemisphere, America's natural wonders, few showed any interest.

It was Mr. Abernathy Bain who suggested, "What you need, Mr. Peale, are exhibits of a more—shall I say, *sensational* nature? Now, you take the Columbia Museum in Boston, of which I happen to be the proprietor. I have a thousand paying visitors in a single week."

"What do you do?" growled Peale. "Re-enact the battle of Bunker Hill and shoot live redcoats?"

"No, sir," Mr. Bain protested, "though that's not a bad idea. Hmm. I must consider it. But, no, no. I show them clocks. Not ordinary clocks, of course. On one of my clocks, for instance, when the hour strikes, a tableau appears from the mechanism, portraying Mary Queen of Scots bidding an affectionate farewell on her way to the executioner's block. Very moving, Mr. Peale, don't you think? Persons of the female sex have been known to faint at the very sight of it."

Charles Willson Peale's portrait of his friend John Lewis.

"Most instructive," Peale said. "But I shall run *my* museum as intended—as a repository for the natural wonders of our nation."

Public lack of enthusiasm for natural history continued until, finally and surprisingly, fortune smiled. In New York, near Newburgh, the bones of a prehistoric animal had been dug from the ground. The thigh-bone itself measured eighteen inches in circumference. The ground had yielded other bones as well, and if all the rest could be found, this would be the first complete mammoth ever unearthed. What a find! What a treasure for Peale's Museum!

Mr. Peale hastened to Newburgh, studied the bones, and was convinced that here, most certainly, were the fossil remains of

a gigantic prehistoric beast. Unfortunately, the skeleton was not complete. Further digging would be necessary. Equally unfortunate was the fact that the farmer who had accidentally unearthed the bones demanded $300 for them and permission from him to continue the digging.

Fortune's mouth had opened in a mammoth smile, but a rather sardonic one, for Peale didn't have $300 to his name. When he returned home Elizabeth said, "Charles, is it your intention to borrow $300 for these—these rotten old bones?"

"I have written to my friend President Jefferson," Charles Peale replied with dignity. "Let me read you what he says. 'My dear Mr. Peale: No person on earth can entertain a higher idea than I do of the value of your museum collection nor give you more credit for the unwearied perserverance and skill with which you have prosecuted—'"

"Never mind all that," Elizabeth cut in. "Will he give you the money?"

"No," Peale said.

"Well, it was nice of him to answer you anyway," Elizabeth said. "Now where will you get the money?"

"I have already got it, Elizabeth, from the American Philosophical Society of Philadelphia."

So Peale went back to Newburgh, and dug up the bones. And the bones seemed to multiply as he dug. In fact, there seemed to be *more* bones than had ever belonged to one mammoth. For the price of one, he was digging up the bones of *two* prehistoric beasts. And when he had assembled them, and their towering skeletons were displayed at Peale's Museum, business picked up marvelously.

From all over the world came letters bearing the signatures of presidents, kings, and men of science, all praising Peale for his and America's contribution to science.

"I must admit," Elizabeth said smilingly, "it is difficult for me to remain disappointed in you, Charles."

PIONEER IN PAINTING

(JAMES ABBOTT McNEILL WHISTLER)

In the year 1872 the Council of the British Royal Academy called a session to judge the paintings which had been submitted for its forthcoming exhibition. Among them was a canvas by an American, James Abbott McNeill Whistler. It was a profile portrait of a woman in a black dress with a white fichu—Whistler's "Mother"—now one of the world's best-loved paintings.

It is hard to believe that anyone who saw it would fail to respond to its beauty. Yet the Council termed it too "revolutionary." Only the portrait painter Sir William Boxall had the discernment to recognize the artistic values within its surprising new form, and the courage to speak up for it. He called it a work of genius.

One of the objections to the painting was Whistler's title for it, "An Arrangement in Gray and Black." Imagine calling the portrait of one's mother "an arrangement in gray and black!" But Boxall, who knew of the affectionate relationship between mother and son, defended Whistler. "That's just what the painting is—an arrangement in gray and black. Whistler's particular interest is color. And I, too, think it's time to return to seeing paintings as arrangements of color instead of as illustrations."

When the discussion was ended and a vote was taken on Whistler's entry, Boxall's was the sole voice raised in its favor. Boxall was so incensed by the Council's rejection of the painting that he rose and announced his resignation. Rather than lose a member of his standing, the Council decided to accept Whistler's entry.

Perhaps if Whistler's painting were hung in an inconspicuous place, it would go unnoticed. There would then be no risk of protest over the inclusion of something so

"The White Girl." Painting by Whistler.

"revolutionary." But to their great astonishment, Whistler's canvas was one of the

great successes of the exhibition. It now hangs in the Louvre, the first painting by an American to be placed in the national gallery of France.

Much of Whistler's career followed this unexpected pattern. A man of strong individuality, he hated the conventional and never shrank from a fight. In fact, he liked to start one and expounded his philosophy of belligerence in his book, *The Gentle Art of Making Enemies*.

These forceful traits had first shown themselves in Whistler's youth. He could not endure routine. In his first job as a draftsman on a coastal survey, he lasted only a few weeks. His habit of embellish-ing the maps he drew with chance portraits, and reporting to work late, or not at all, soon cost him his government job. This Whistler considered a stroke of luck: it gave him more time in which to paint.

Five years after the exhibition in which the painting of his mother was shown, a new controversy rose over Whistler. Invited to show eight canvases at an exhibition at the Grosvenor Gallery in London, he submitted one of his "Nocturnes." His original title for these pictures, which were usually scenes of moonlight above water, had been "Moonlights," but his friend Leyland had called them "Nocturnes" and Whistler adopted the name.

"Whistler's Mother." ("Arrangement in Grey and Black.") Painting by Whistler.

Whistler's self-portrait.

Many found these "Nocturnes" strange. People at that time were accustomed to paintings which told a definite story, and Whistler's did not. People were also confused by the lack of outline in his pictures. Whistler felt that he was emphasizing, rather than evading, the reality of mist along water in his shadowy forms. Most of the critics were loud in their condemnation of his unusual compositions.

Foremost among these was John Rus-

kin, then an Oxford professor and universally accepted as one of the final authorities on art in England. Ruskin's prejudice against Whistler was so intense that he refused to meet him socially. He wrote scathingly of Whistler's first "Nocturne," which the artist had priced at two hundred guineas: "Sir Coutts Lindsay ought not to have admitted works into the gallery in which the ill-educated conceit of the artist so nearly approaches the aspect of willful

335

imposture. I have seen and heard much of Cockney impudence before now, but never expected a coxcomb to ask two hundred guineas for flinging a pot of paint in the public's face."

Whistler responded with a libel suit that made history. He was in deadly earnest, because he was convinced that a critic should not be permitted to publish such lengths of public abuse as would destroy an artist's means of livelihood. He felt that by ridiculing the price, Ruskin was doing just that, and he demanded damages.

Most of the leading English artists, although they expressed sympathy with Whistler, privately refused to speak up in court in his favor. They were fearful that Ruskin would retaliate in his comments on their work. Only one or two risked the powerful critic's displeasure and testified publicly for Whistler.

Ruskin's lawyer subjected Whistler to a grueling cross-examination. He pointed to a portrait that Whistler had done of a certain Mr. Irving. "Why do you call Mr. Irving 'An Arrangement in Black?'" Whistler retorted, "I don't. That's what I call the *picture*."

After forcing Whistler to admit that he had spent no more than two days on the "Nocturne," he thundered, "How dare you ask two hundred guineas for two days' work!" And Whistler replied calmly, "I ask it for the knowledge of a lifetime."

At first, the spectators at the trial, and the jury as well, were noticeably hostile to Whistler. But as the trial proceeded, his courage made an impression on them. By the time the jury retired to deliberate, the smart guessers were no longer so sure that the case would go against him.

The jury brought in a verdict for Whistler, though they imposed only nominal damages on Ruskin—one farthing. At the time it was thought that Ruskin had not come off badly. Some were even of the opinion that the one-farthing award was a vindication of Ruskin. But as time passed,

it became clear who was the real winner and who the loser. Whistler's reputation soared; Ruskin's declined. More and more of Whistler's pictures were bought, and at ever-rising prices. Ruskin's authority as a critic ebbed. The British public turned elsewhere for guidance in art matters.

Only a few years after the trial, one of Whistler's Nocturnes, "Battersea Bridge in Moonlight," one of the very paintings that had been ridiculed in the courtroom, was purchased by the British National Fund—not for two hundred guineas, but for two thousand!

Whistler has been regarded by some as a "chip-on-the-shoulder" man who became embroiled in unnecessary quarrels. He not only might have avoided some of the controversies he became involved in, but it is possible that he might have deliberately provoked them. Perhaps not all of Whistler's battles were necessary. But some of these violent encounters were inescapable if Whistler was to win public consideration of new and daring art forms. And it is fortunate that he had the agile mind and the battling spirit that made him such an effective fighter.

The suit against Ruskin was Whistler's last great battle for recognition. It meant recognition not only for himself as a painter, but for American painting as well. It meant also a spotlight focused on the importance of experimentation and individuality. The progress of modern art might have been much more difficult had Whistler not fought—and won—those early battles.

Whistler now holds an established rank among the world's masters. The foremost art galleries of the nation take pride in their Whistlers. In Washington there is an entire building dedicated to Whistler's memory. In it is the famous Peacock Room he designed for Leyland. On its walls are a number of Whistler's beautiful "Arrangements" and "Nocturnes," now valued among the nation's art treasures.

"The Cavalry Charge." Painting by Frederic Remington.

RECORDER OF THE LAST FRONTIER

(FREDERIC REMINGTON)

The Apache Indian sat on his horse, silhouetted against the sun. A wild figure in a wild landscape, he looked as if at any moment he might shout a war cry, then lift his rifle and send a bullet right between your eyes.

"I am most certainly glad," said the art critic, "that it's only a painting."

He stepped back to get a better look at the framed canvas hung on the gallery wall. "Between you and me," he went on, "if this were the *real* thing, I'd be under the bed, hiding. I understand the Apaches are on the warpath again. How *does* this fellow Remington do it? The details are superb, but how does he get close enough to study a warrior like that?"

"Bosh," another New York critic said. "If you want my opinion, Remington's not a bad painter, but he's a faker."

"Oh, come now," the first art critic protested. "He's constantly making trips West, to Arizona and the Indian Territory. Why, look at the details in this picture; you can't fake a thing like that."

"I'll lay you a wager," the other critic scoffed, "Remington hired that Indian to pose for him in a nice peaceful attic. Here—I'll prove it. Look at those moccasins. Just look at them! This Indian—*no* Indian— ever wore such fancy moccasins. You'll find such things only in a theater!"

In a way, the skeptical critic was right. That particular Indian wasn't wearing

Frederic Remington.

those fancy moccasins when Frederic
Remington first saw him. And, even if he
had been wearing a pair *like* them, the
Apache was too far away for even Remington's sharp eyes to take in such a detail.
Off at a distance, the Apache, followed by
several of his tribesmen, was racing his
horse around a waterhole, yipping a war
cry and taking a few potshots. And in the
dried-up waterhole, three men crouched,
listening to the whine of the bullets overhead.

Two of the men in that waterhole were
white. The third was a friendly Indian
guide, who lay on his back, his feet almost
in Frederic Remington's face. But Remington didn't seem to mind. In fact, he was
studying the moccasins the Indian wore.

"Never seen that type of beadwork before," Remington said. "How about it, One
Horse? Will you sell them to me?"

A bullet whined overhead.

"What for?" the Indian guide asked
calmly.

"Do you see that Apache on his horse,

up there? See, he's stopped to reload his
rifle. See how he's silhouetted against the
sun? I've made a sketch of him. Look."
Remington displayed his pad.

"Good," One Horse grunted admiringly.

"Well," Remington explained, "when I
get back East, I'd like to do a painting of
him. And I'd like the model to be wearing
your moccasins."

One Horse grunted. "One dollar."

"Remington!" the other white man
shouted. "Are you crazy? Two dozen
Apaches shootin' at us, and all you can do—
Don't you realize we may be *dead* any
minute?"

But as Remington told his wife later, in
New York, "None of us got hurt. When the
U.S. Cavalry came riding up, those Apaches
scooted for the hills. One dollar," he said,
holding up the moccasins. "Aren't they
beautiful?"

Eva sighed. "Yes, dear, they're lovely.
But must you take such risks?"

"Well, it wasn't my idea to get caught in
that waterhole," Frederic protested. "And

338

"A Miss Deal." Painting by Frederic Remington.

I can't say it was much fun. But—risks? Well, I'm afraid I do have to take them, once in a while, Eva. It can't be helped. That is, if I'm to accomplish what I'm after."

What *was* he after?

At Yale University, where Remington had played football, he had taken a fine-arts course. Having graduated, he had become an illustrator for magazines. He found the work dull. "I'm sick of 'em!" he said to his wife one day. "Men with whiskers in frock-coats, kissing women in bustles. I'm sick of drawing them. I'd like to paint—paint anything that comes into my head."

"Why don't you, dear?" Eva said. "We can get along for a while on what we've saved. You could start tomorrow—go into the woods, paint some mountain laurel, perhaps, or—or ferns. Or you could paint . . ."

But mountain laurel or ferns, houses or church steeples—these subjects were too tame for Remington in 1884. Alone, he took a train West for Arizona and the Indian country. Here the skies were a pure cobalt, contrasting with the powder blue of the immense hills. At first, Remington didn't like the great emptiness, the silence. One day, that silence ended abruptly. An Indian put a bullet-hole through the crown of his hat.

This was a dangerous region for a man armed only with a sketch-pad and a pencil. Remington took to carrying a gun. And he took to something else, as well—the country.

Still, the West *was* changing; even he could see that. The old wild days were going. The herds of buffalo were thinning out. Civilization was reaching more deeply into these parts. The Indians still caused trouble—Comanches, Sioux, Apaches; one never knew when they might ride out of their reservations and wage war. But soon this excitement, too, would be gone. In future generations, school children would marvel over these things, but only from

339

"The Fight For the Water Hole." Painting by Frederic Remington.

reading about them in their history books.

When Remington came East again, loaded down with drawings and sketches, he said, "We were born too late, Eva. We're only just in time to see the end of three American centuries of smoke, dust and sweat. In a little while, it'll be gone. Gone without a sign, without a trace. Out there, I talked to some of the old-timers. 'Paint what you see here,' they told me. 'Paint this dying West, and you'll be doing a darn sight more than all the history books ever printed. You'll be preserving the memory of this country, saving it for future generations to *see*.'"

"Well," Eva said resignedly, "when do you leave again?"

"What?" Remington said. "And leave you alone again? I love you, Eva. I can't—"

But Eva knew what he wanted, what he now hoped to accomplish. And she would not stand in his way.

"I'll only stay three months, this time," he promised.

He kept that promise. Later, however, he made other trips. He lived with cowhands, with cavalry troops, with half a dozen Indian tribes. Everywhere he went, he carried his sketch-pad. And when he came home, he would say, "Got some great ones, this time. Comanches and Kiowas. And horses, all kinds of horses. Pintos, mustangs—and here—a herd of wild ones, stampeding over a cliff. See those Indian scouts chasing them? Those horses would rather die than be caught."

Today, in the great museums of our country, you will find them: the sketches, the paintings, the statues in bronze. These are Frederic Remington's gift to us, a record of that vanished time and place—the Old West.

"The Cowboy." Painting by Frederic Remington.

WE'LL ALWAYS SING HIS SONGS

(STEPHEN FOSTER)

"Thirty-eight cents," the attendant at New York's Bellevue Hospital called out, to complete the record sheet on the man who had just died.

"Thirty-eight cents. I've got it down. Find anything else in his pockets?"

"Not a thing, except some note here."

"What's it say?"

"Ah, nothin'. Just 'Dear friends and gentle hearts.'"

"Yup, a dreamer. Like so many of those poor fellows they bring in here from the Bowery."

"He's better off dead. Well—got the name right? Stephen Foster, with the 'ph,' not 'v.' And make sure you make it 1864. It's past New Year's, you know."

This was the paradoxical end of a man whose incomparable success still continues. He gave, and still gives, great pleasure to many Americans. Since 1848, just about every American has heard, whistled or sung his beloved songs. No, despite his miserable death, Stephen Foster did not fail.

Stephen Collins Foster was born near Pittsburgh in 1826—on July 4, appropriately enough. He grew to be a shy and gentle child, staying much to himself. He was happiest when he could sit beside his mother while she played and sang her favorite hymns.

Throughout his childhood, little attention was paid to Stephen's fondness for music. But when, as an adolescent, he began to occupy himself with making up tunes and setting them down on paper, his parents were seriously concerned. In the 1840's, while American pioneers were still moving westward, music was regarded as the province of women. A man had greater jobs to do.

It was decided, therefore, that Stephen would go out to Cincinnati, where his older brother Dunning Foster had already set himself up in business.

"You will be his bookkeeper," said Mr. Foster to Stephen. "And I've written him not to show you any favors. Perhaps this job in Cincinnati will give you a start toward a business of your own. Think of the West, Stephen. Young fellows like you are going out there every day and becoming men of wealth and power."

Stephen Foster turned out to be a good bookkeeper and his brother wrote encouraging reports about him to their parents. Dunning did not know, however, that in his brother's mind figures kept turning into the notes of melodies and that it was only with the greatest effort that he was able to make his account-books balance.

And then, one evening Stephen called secretly on William Roark. Roark, a minstrel, was performing that week at Melodeon Hall—and Stephen knew that minstrels were always on the lookout for new songs. Modestly, Stephen placed before him the last song he had written.

"It's a comic song," said Stephen, "and if you like it, I'd be grateful if you tried it out on the audience."

Roark *did* like the song and he and his company of blackface minstrels introduced it the following Saturday afternoon. It was "Oh, Susanna," now one of our song classics. It caught on, and in a few months the whole country was singing it. Only a few people knew that it had been written by Stephen Collins Foster.

That didn't bother Stephen very much. He had proved to himself that he could write a song that people throughout the country would sing with pleasure. That meant, too, that he might even make money someday as a song writer, a particularly important consideration, for he was about to marry lovely Jane MacDowell.

To make it possible to marry Jane, Stephen stuck to his bookkeeping and saved enough money for the wedding and the honeymoon. At last he and his Jeanie were off together, newlyweds, sailing down the Mississippi for New Orleans. As they sailed, the beauty of the wide river, its green banks, its brilliant birds, the sounds of the shrill boat whistles and the churning paddle wheels, the chants of the stevedores rolling the great bales of cotton all fused in his mind into haunting melodies.

"What would you think, Jeanie, if I didn't go back to work for my brother?" asked Stephen. "If instead, I settled down seriously to composing songs? 'Susanna' would have made a lot of money for me if I'd handled it right. And I know I can write other songs just as good. And I know that at least I could make a living."

"I want you to do exactly what you want most to do," said Jane, "and I'm sure that you will succeed."

And so Stephen did not go back to book-keeping upon his return from New Orleans. Instead, he made the rounds of the music publishers, trying to sell them a song he had composed on his honeymoon. When no publisher would buy it, Stephen took it to E. P. Christy, a well-known minstrel singer.

"Why, this is a great song!" exclaimed Christy. "I see you have crossed out the title. Doesn't it have a name yet?"

"When I showed it to the publishers," said Stephen, "it was called 'Way Down Upon the Suwannee River.' But they said nobody had ever heard of that river, so I think I'll call the song 'Old Folks at Home.'"

"And what do you want from me?" asked Christy.

"You're a famous man," said Stephen. "And I think if you put your name on the song as if you had written it and then took it back to the publishers Firth and Pond—well, I think they'd publish it. And you could make some arrangement with me."

It was agreed that Christy would pay Foster fifteen dollars as an advance and two cents a copy thereafter for every copy sold—that is, if the firm of Firth and Pond published the song.

Stephen was right. With Christy's name on it, the music publishers were eager to issue the song which they had previously rejected. They hurried it through the press and it caught on instantly. Soon it was as popular as "Oh, Susanna." But the use of Christy's name turned out to be the begin-

"Old Kentucky Home." Painting by Eastman Johnson.

Stephen Foster.

ning of disaster for Stephen Foster.

He continued to compose beautiful songs —"My Old Kentucky Home," "Massa's in the Cold, Cold Ground," "Old Dog Tray," "Nelly Was a Lady"—and many others. But because the authorship of "Old Folks at Home" was credited to Christy, the publishers regarded Foster as an unestablished composer. They paid him mere pittances for his work. When he ventured to claim authorship of "Old Folks at Home" and "Oh, Susanna," the song that had become the marching song of the Forty-niners on their way to California, the publishers looked at him as if he were mad.

Jane tried to remain cheerful and en-couraging, but there was a child now, a girl. It was decided that Jane should go back to her family for a while so that the child could be properly cared for. With the last of his money, Stephen took the train for New York. Surely, in that great city, his talent would be recognized.

This was not to be. A few new songs appeared, but they brought little money. Foster was finally reduced to the pitiful condition of the nameless poor on the Bowery. After three years of this privation, Foster died in Bellevue Hospital, reminding us of his warmth and sweetness with his last words, "Dear friends and gentle hearts."

THE TRADITION OF GREAT ACTING

(EDWIN BOOTH)

'I cannot stand being tutored in arithmetic here in my father's dressing room while he is out there on the stage. Please, Mr. Dugas, let me go stand in the wings and listen to the play for a few minutes."

And Louis Dugas, his tutor, gave young Edwin Booth permission to do as he wished. Dugas had recognized months ago that no matter how much Junius Brutus Booth, the famous father of this talented youngster, might rail against his son's desire to become an actor, the boy was determined to have his way.

On September 10, 1849, the elder Booth and his company were playing in Shakespeare's *Richard III* at the Boston Museum. Edwin, now fifteen, had still not managed to persuade his father to give him a chance on the stage. He was, therefore, very envious of his friend William, a young actor

345

in the company, who was playing the role of Tressel.

As they talked together a half-hour before curtain time, it developed that William wanted very much to go to a party that night at the house of some friends. Demonstrating that he knew the few lines of William's role perfectly, Edwin persuaded his friend to slip off to the party but to pretend that he had been taken ill. As Edwin was putting on William's costume, the elder Booth appeared. At first he refused to let the boy go on; but, consenting to hear him speak the lines, he was so impressed by his son's delivery that he permitted him to take the part.

Within three years, Edwin Booth was a full-fledged member of his father's company and had even played the difficult role of *Richard III*.

It was his dream to act the role of Hamlet. Everybody said that his father was the greatest Hamlet in the United States, but young Edwin did not entirely approve of his father's performance. He found it too vigorous in gesture and too loud in voice. He had decided that, inasmuch as the play might best be described as the tragedy of a man who couldn't make up his mind but who had a lot of mind to make up, the role should be played thoughtfully, quietly. He also insisted on using Shakespeare's own text instead of the adaptation used at that time.

At the age of nineteen, Edwin Booth portrayed Hamlet for the first time under the most extraordinary circumstances. A few months earlier, he had arrived in San Francisco with his father's company, but the elder Booth had been so discouraged by the obstacles of stage production for the rough frontier audiences that he decided to return to New York. Edwin then reorganized the company and decided to present *Hamlet* at the San Francisco Hall.

There was a momentary silence in the audience as the curtain went up. Then, as the first lines of the classic tragedy fell upon their ears, the audience laughed and jeered. But Edwin Booth continued calmly, playing his part with such cool courage that cries of "Give him a chance!" were soon heard. The audience began to respond to the beauty of the Shakespearean lines and were impressed by young Booth's admirable self-possession and poise.

Thus, before the tense, gaunt faces of the rough frontier folk, one of the wonders of the age was taking place: Edwin Booth was portraying Hamlet for the first time. As though in contrast to the din which had greeted the young actor's entrance on the stage, the hall was hushed as the drama drew to a close. Then cheers burst from the throats of the audience—full, lusty shouts of approval. Edwin Booth had completely won over the hostile audience.

On Edwin's return to the East, his company's *Hamlet* was enthusiastically received. He was called "the hope of the living drama, the idol of the American stage and the greatest tragedian in the history of our theater." It was at about this time that he told his friend, Dr. A. O. Kellogg, of three ambitions he hoped to attain.

"First," he said, "I want to build my own theater in New York. It must be the best in the world and a credit, I hope, to my profession. Second, I want to make the world realize that our people know the power of the great Shakespearean dramas. I should like to play *Hamlet* longer than anyone has ever played it, sixty nights in succession, or seventy. Third, I want to see in New York an actors' club of such dignity that it will improve the standing of the profession throughout the nation. I think its name should be simply 'The Players.'"

Edwin Booth was to achieve all of these. The theater would be built and The Players' Club established. The first task he had set for himself he accomplished by presenting *Hamlet* for a hundred nights, from November 26, 1864, to March 25, 1865, at the old Winter Garden in New York. At that time this was a record run.

Edwin Booth as Hamlet.

The year 1865, however, instead of marking for Booth his undisputed triumph, was to mark for him, with shocking impact, the beginning of his lonely and haunted later years. This was the year John Wilkes Booth, Edwin's younger brother, assassinated President Abraham Lincoln and plunged the nation into mourning.

Later, Edwin was to recall every painful detail of his last meeting with his brother. John Wilkes, himself an actor, had been appearing with Edwin in *Julius Caesar*. Edwin was playing the part of Brutus and John Wilkes, the part of Mark Antony.

How could Edwin ever forget that moment when his brother deviated from the words of the text to shout at the audience: "Listen to me! Southern blood is the rich, red blood of the pioneers. It is drenching this soil now. This blood is being spilled by that abolitionist ape, Abraham Lincoln. Drive him from the White House, I say! Abraham Lincoln is a traitor! The day of judgment is at hand!"

When the curtain was rung down, Edwin had leaped at his brother, shouting, "I'll tear your lying tongue from your mouth! You're not a fool. You're a madman!"

The brothers had been pulled apart. Edwin remembered John Wilkes Booth's parting words to him: "I have other things to do—not with words, but by deeds! We shall hear the name Booth—and very soon!"

Why had not Edwin realized the portent of his brother's words? Possibly because to him they had seemed merely the wild threats of a madman. But that such an unspeakable deed as cold-blooded murder could be committed by *his own brother* . . .

The tragic news of Lincoln's assassination by John Wilkes Booth did not reach Edwin immediately, and he appeared at the New York theater for his matinee performance of *Hamlet* as usual. There were often many people at the stage door waiting to get a look at the famous Hamlet as he entered the theater. Booth observed that on this day there seemed to be an extraordinary number of bystanders; then, quickly, he understood that their aspect was far from friendly.

"Down with the Booth family!" someone shouted, and the cry was taken up. "Assassin!" "Give him the rope." "Don't let him get away!"

But Booth managed to fight his way into the theater, where he was informed of the tragedy in Washington. Shaken, he declared, "I shall go out and explain to those people that I am *Edwin* Booth, not John Wilkes Booth. Don't they understand?"

When Edwin Booth reappeared before them, the crowd permitted him to speak, then stared at him silently as he re-entered the theater. For Edwin it was the bitter turning point of his life. Thereafter, though he continued to dazzle the world with his brilliance as an actor, he was to become more and more inaccessible and melancholy until his death in 1893.

On November 13, 1918, on the eighty-fifth anniversary of Edwin Booth's birth, Edmond Quinn's statue of Booth as Hamlet was unveiled in Gramercy Park in New York City. The windows of The Players' Club, founded by Booth, look out on Gramercy Park, and its members are each day reminded of the undimmed splendor of the great American tragedian.

CHAMPION OF HUMOR

(MARK TWAIN)

Once, when the newspapers mistakenly carried headlines about his having died, Mark Twain, his eyes twinkling, appeared suddenly before a lecture audience and said, in his Mississippi drawl, "Ladies and gentlemen, I'd like to say now that the reports of my death are highly exaggerated."

"Half man, half catfish, that's me," he would say. Born Samuel Clemens in 1835, he grew up in Hannibal, Missouri, beside the banks of the Mississippi. The waters of that great river were his playground. Fishing it, swimming it with his companions, he'd shout to the boats going by, the barges loaded with lumber from the North, cotton from the South. And sometimes he'd climb aboard, dripping, and visit with the bargemen, listening to the tales of adventure that reflected their rough, brawling lives.

Like every other boy in Hannibal, Sam dreamed of living on the river, even as a Nantucket or Gloucester boy dreams of going to sea. Steamboats rode through his dreams. "Sam," his mother would say, "get on with those chores. No, you're *not* going down to the landing!"

"But, Ma, if I don't watch 'em dock, how can I learn how to be a pilot? Hear that whistle? That's the *Blue Wing* coming in! She's got a lightning pilot—brings that steamboat in against the current, her stern low, eggs-*act*-ly right—"

Loaded with cargo, decks swarming with passengers sailing for New Orleans or Natchez or Baton Rouge, the steamboats were the queens of the Mississippi. Their pilots and captains were the kings, men of standing and honor, the full length of the great water highway. One by one, Sam's friends went off to become rivermen— Willy and Bart Brown, for instance, who became pilots on the St. Louis-New Or-

leans run. "I'll be a pilot, too," Sam Clemens vowed.

For a while, though, it seemed that Sam might not reach that goal. Growing up and practicing the trade of journeyman printer, he had reached his middle twenties before he walked into the pilothouse of the steamboat *Paul Jones*. "Any chance you'd be needing a hand on this ship, Captain Bixby? I'd like to be taken on as an apprentice pilot."

"You!" Captain Bixby snorted. "A cub pilot? What do you know about this river?"

"It's been my life," Sam Clemens answered. "And—"

"You're lazy and shiftless," Captain Bixby stated. "I can tell by the way you drawl your words."

"Well, I'm lazy, right enough," Sam grinned. "But I'm not shiftless, Cap'n. And aside from steamboats, why, I guess I've steered everything else there is, on this river. Rowboats, rafts, a barge, logs—"

Humph—that might be—but could he learn 1,200 miles of river? Could he learn the depths every inch of the way? Could he memorize every foot of the banks, going north or heading south? Why, he'd have to know the look of every landmark, every bluff, every tree and grove, by day and by night, and in different kinds of moonlight, and in the rain. . . .

And, Bixby warned, once he learned the banks and the depths, he'd have to learn 'em all over again—and again. For the banks of the Mississippi were always shifting. An unruly, crazy river at times, the Mississippi. One day, sailing down, you'd see a house on the right bank. Next week, sailing up, returning, you'd naturally expect to find that house on your left, but there it was, still sitting on your right! The raging spring waters had broken the banks

Mark Twain in his younger days.

and had altered the river's course so that it was flowing east now instead of west. Or maybe that poor little house wouldn't be there at all, but just a weathervane sticking up, a lone rooster perched atop it, crowing his alarm above the flood.

For two years Sam Clemens studied this wonderful, disconcerting river from the pilothouse.

"Labboard, leadsman there . . . Stab-board . . . Take your soundings!" Bixby would call.

And the leadsman, larboard, dropping his weighted line in the water to test the depth: "Ma-a-a-rk three!"

And the starboard leadsman, following suit: "Quarter less three . . . Half twain . . . Quarter twain. . . ."

"Mark twain," the larboard leadsman would cry.

Mark Twain in his later years.

Mark twain: two fathoms—twelve feet deep. Safe waters.

"You've been a good apprentice, Sam," said Captain Bixby finally. "Today, this morning—right now, in fact—I'm goin' to let you take her across alone, from this shore to t'other. Think you can do it, Sam?"

"Thank you, Cap'n," said Sam. "And, sir, will you recommend me for my pilot's license afterward?"

"We'll see," Bixby said, ducking out of the cabin.

Alone, hands on the wheel, Sam gave the signal and guided the steamboat out into the river. From here, across to the other bank, he knew the water's depth. In the past two years he had memorized it, along with what seemed a million other details, but, like a true pilot, he was leaving nothing to chance. "Leadsman," he called. "Give me a sounding."

"Mark twain!" the leadsman cried.

Mark twain—twelve feet? But that couldn't be—it should be at least forty feet right here. Or had the sandy bottom shifted? "Give me that reading again!"

"Four feet!" the leadsman called.

Four feet? Impossible! The ship would run aground! "Captain Bixby!" Sam shouted in alarm.

"Trouble, Sam?" Bixby inquired, entering the cabin.

"We—we were just heading for a sandbank," Sam said. "I don't understand it, Cap'n—four feet—but now we're—well, look, we're moving right on."

"How deep should it be right here?"

"Forty feet. But the leadsman said *four* feet!"

Captain Bixby scowled at him. "I told the leadsman to call the wrong depths, Sam. You lost your head. Till you learn how to keep it, you can't be a river pilot."

Sam Clemens was not discouraged. Didn't he know every inch of this river? And he *would* learn to keep his head. For what could compare with the feel of the tiller in your hand . . . the feel of the boat sulking a little . . . jerking . . . warning him in the dark that the water was getting shallower. On the green shore, the pines and oaks blending into swamp country, the cornfields into cotton. And on the steamboat, the decks alive with farmers, planters, plain folk, rich folk, ladies in silks, traders, gamblers and thousands of immigrants on their way to the opening West. In later years he would boast, "Never lost a passenger or harmed a cargo."

Courage was an everyday quality in a pilot and so was humor. From Cairo to New Orleans, Sam Clemens became famous as a storyteller, as a humorist. And, if he was learning the river until it was as familiar as the palm of his hand, he was also learning about people.

Had it not been for the Civil War, Sam Clemens might have spent the rest of his days on the Mississippi. The War made the river a kind of No Man's Land between North and South, ending the steamboat's reign. Sam's job was done there and he wandered out West, becoming in turn a prospector, a silver-miner, a newspaperman, a storyteller, signing his stories not Samuel Clemens but Mark Twain.

How often, leaning against a steamboat rail, had he drawled his stories, keeping the passengers laughing? Now he began to make the whole country laugh. And then, as his fame spread across the ocean, Mark Twain and the Mississippi became familiar names on foreign lips. *Huckleberry Finn, Tom Sawyer, Roughing It, Innocents Abroad*—his books were being read by people of many nations, by Englishmen, Frenchmen, Germans.

Wherever he went, whatever laurels he acquired, Sam Clemens never forgot his beloved Mississippi. In his seventies, he returned to it, riding its waters this time as a passenger, not as a pilot. In some ways, this voyage was a sad one. Most of his friends were long since gone, and the glory of steamboating had been dimmed by the railroads. He wrote about this in his *Life on the Mississippi*. "The basin of the Mississippi," he said, "is the body of the nation." And he told how it rose and flowed and rolled on, from the fir-clad mountains of the North some three thousand miles to the Gulf.

But Sam was never one to be solemn long. "So live," he once wrote in a little boy's autograph book, "that when you die, even the undertaker will be sorry."

The Mississippi gave Mark Twain to the world. With equal truth we may say that Twain gave the world the Mississippi. His love brought the great river alive for millions on other continents, millions who might not otherwise have heard of this pulsing heart of America. And Sam himself —well, they say he died in 1910, but when we pick up *Huckleberry Finn*, might we not echo the former river-pilot and say that the "reports of his death are, indeed, highly exaggerated?"

APPENDIX

The Declaration of Independence

☆ ☆ ☆ ☆ ☆ ☆ ☆ ☆ ☆ ☆ ☆ ☆ ☆ ☆

WHEN, IN THE COURSE OF HUMAN EVENTS, IT BECOMES NECESSARY FOR ONE PEOPLE TO DISSOLVE THE POLITICAL BANDS WHICH HAVE CONNECTED THEM WITH ANOTHER, AND TO ASSUME, AMONG THE POWERS OF the earth, the separate and equal station to which the laws of nature and nature's God entitle them, a decent respect to the opinions of mankind requires that they should declare the causes which impel them to the separation.

☆

We hold these truths to be self-evident, that all men are created equal; that they are endowed by their Creator with certain unalienable rights; that among these are life, liberty, and the pursuit of happiness. That to secure these rights, governments are instituted among men, deriving their just powers from the consent of the governed; that, whenever any form of government becomes destructive of these ends, it is the right of the people to alter or to abolish it, and to institute a new government, laying its foundation on such principles, and organizing its powers in such form, as to them shall seem most likely to effect their safety and happiness. Prudence, indeed, will dictate that governments long established should not be changed for light and transient causes; and, accordingly, all experience hath shown, that mankind are more disposed to suffer, while evils are sufferable, than

to right themselves by abolishing the forms to which they are accustomed. But, when a long train of abuses and usurpations, pursuing invariably the same object, evinces a design to reduce them under absolute despotism, it is their right, it is their duty, to throw off such government, and to provide new guards for their future security. Such has been the patient sufferance of these colonies, and such is now the necessity which constrains them to alter their former systems of government. The history of the present King of Great Britain is a history of repeated injuries and usurpation, all having, in direct object, the establishment of an absolute tyranny over these States. To prove this, let facts be submitted to a candid world:

He has refused to assent to laws the most wholesome and necessary for the public good.

He has forbidden his governors to pass laws of immediate and pressing importance, unless suspended in their operation till his assent should be obtained; and, when so suspended, he has utterly neglected to attend to them.

He has refused to pass other laws for the accommodation of large districts of people, unless those people would relinquish the right of representation in the legislature; a right inestimable to them, and formidable to tyrants only.

He has called together legislative bodies at places unusual, uncomfortable, and distant from the depository of their public records, for the sole purpose of fatiguing them into compliance with his measures.

He has dissolved representative houses repeatedly, for opposing, with manly firmness, his invasions on the rights of the people.

He has refused, for a long time after such dissolutions, to cause others to be elected; whereby the legislative powers, incapable of annihilation, have returned to the people at large for their exercise; the State remaining, in the meantime, exposed to all the dangers of invasion from without, and convulsions within.

He has endeavored to prevent the population of these States; for that purpose, obstructing the laws for naturalization of foreigners; refusing to pass others to encourage their migration hither, and raising the conditions of new appropriations of lands.

He has obstructed the administration of justice, by refusing his assent to laws for establishing judiciary powers.

He has made judges dependent on his will alone, for the tenure of their offices, and the amount and payment of their salaries.

He has erected a multitude of new offices, and sent hither swarms of officers to harass our people, and eat out their substance.

He has kept among us, in times of peace, standing armies without the consent of our legislatures.

He has affected to render the military independent of, and superior to, the civil power.

He has combined, with others, to subject us to a jurisdiction foreign to our constitution, and unacknowledged by our laws; giving his assent to their acts of pretended legislation:

For quartering large bodies of armed troops among us:

For protecting them by a mock trial from punishment, for any murders which they should commit on the inhabitants of these States:

For cutting off our trade with all parts of the world:

For imposing taxes on us without our consent:

For depriving us, in many cases, of the benefit of trial by jury:

For transporting us beyond seas to be tried for pretended offenses:

For abolishing the free system of English laws in a neighboring province, establishing therein an arbitrary government, and enlarging its boundaries, so as to render it at once an example and fit instrument for introducing the same absolute rule into these colonies:

For taking away our charters, abolishing our most valuable laws and altering fundamentally, the powers of our governments:

For suspending our own legislatures, and declaring themselves invested with power to legislate for us in all cases whatsoever.

He has abdicated government here, by declaring us out of his protection, and waging war against us.

He has plundered our seas, ravaged our coasts, burnt our towns, and destroyed the lives of our people.

He is, at this time, transporting large armies of foreign mercenaries to complete the work of death, desolation, and tyranny, already begun, with circumstances of cruelty and perfidy scarcely paralleled in the most barbarous ages, and totally unworthy the head of a civilized nation.

He has constrained our fellow-citizens, taken captive on the high seas to bear arms against their country, to become the executioners of their friends and brethren, or to fall themselves by their hands.

He has excited domestic insurrections amongst us, and has endeavored to bring on the inhabitants of our frontiers, the merciless Indian savages, whose known rule of warfare is an undistinguished destruction of all ages, sexes, and conditions.

In every stage of these oppressions we have petitioned for redress in the most humble terms; our repeated petitions have been answered only by repeated injury. A prince whose character is thus marked by every act which may define a tyrant, is unfit to be the ruler of a free people.

Nor have we been wanting in attention to our British brethren. We have warned them, from time to time, of attempts made by their legislature to extend an unwarrantable jurisdiction over us. We have reminded them of the circumstances of our emigration and settlement here. We have appealed to their native justice and magnanimity, and we have conjured them, by the ties of our common kindred, to disavow these usurpations, which would inevitably interrupt our connections and correspondence. They, too, have been deaf to the voice of justice and consanguinity. We must, therefore, acquiesce in the necessity which denounces our separation, and hold them, as we hold the rest of mankind, enemies in war— in peace, friends.

We, therefore, the representatives of the United States of America, in General Congress assembled, appealing to the Supreme Judge of the World for the rectitude of our intentions, do, in the name and by the authority of the good people of these colonies solemnly publish and declare, That these United Colonies are, and of right ought to be, Free and Independent States; that they are absolved from all allegiance to the British crown, and that all political connection between them and the State of Great Britain is, and ought to be, totally dissolved; and that as free and independent States, they have full power to levy war, conclude peace, contract alliances, establish commerce and to do all other acts and things which independent States may of right do. And for the support of this declaration, with a firm reliance on the protection of Divine Providence, we mutually pledge to each other our lives, our fortunes, and our sacred honor.

Josiah Bartlett
William Whipple
Matthew Thornton
John Hancock
Samuel Adams
John Adams
Robert Treat Paine
Elbridge Gerry
Stephen Hopkins
William Ellery
Roger Sherman
Samuel Huntington
William Williams
Oliver Wolcott
William Floyd
Philip Livingston
Francis Lewis
Lewis Morris
Richard Stockton

John Witherspoon
Francis Hopkinson
John Hart
Abraham Clark
Robert Morris
Benjamin Rush
Benjamin Franklin
John Morton
George Clymer
James Smith
George Taylor
James Wilson
George Ross
Cæsar Rodney
George Reed
Thomas McKean
Samuel Chase
William Paca
Thomas Stone

Charles Carroll of Carrollton
George Wythe
Richard Henry Lee
Thomas Jefferson
Benjamin Harrison
Thomas Nelson, Jun.
Francis Lightfoot Lee
Carter Braxton
William Hooper
Joseph Hewes
John Penn
Edward Rutledge
Thomas Heyward, Jun.
Thomas Lynch, Jun.
Arthur Middleton
Button Gwinnett
Lyman Hall
George Walton

The Constitution

WE THE PEOPLE OF THE UNITED STATES, IN ORDER TO FORM A MORE PERFECT UNION, ESTABLISH JUSTICE, INSURE DOMESTIC TRANQUILLITY, PROVIDE FOR THE COMMON DEFENSE, PROMOTE THE GENERAL welfare, and secure the blessings of liberty to ourselves and our posterity. do ordain and establish this Constitution for the United States of America.

Article One

SECTION I. All legislative powers herein granted shall be vested in a Congress of the United States, which shall consist of a Senate and House of Representatives.

SECTION II. 1 The House of Representatives shall be composed of members chosen every second year by the people of the several States, and the electors in each State shall have the qualifications requisite for electors of the most numerous branch of the State legislature.

2 No person shall be a representative who shall not have attained to the age of twenty-five years, and been seven years a citizen of the United States, and who shall not, when elected, be an inhabitant of that State in which he shall be chosen.

3 Representatives and direct taxes shall be apportioned among the several States which may be included within this Union, according to their respective numbers, which shall be determined by adding to the whole number of free persons, including those bound to service for a term of years, and excluding Indians not taxed, three fifths of all other persons. The actual enumeration shall be made within three years after the first meeting of the Congress of the United States, and within every subsequent term of ten years, in such manner as they shall by law direct. The number of representatives shall not exceed one for every thirty thousand, but each State shall have at least one representative; and until such enumeration shall be made, the State of New Hampshire shall be entitled to choose three, Massachusetts eight, Rhode Island and Providence Plantations one, Connecticut five, New York six, New Jersey four, Pennsylvania eight, Delaware one, Maryland six, Virginia ten, North Carolina five, South Carolina five, and Georgia three.

4 When vacancies happen in the representation from any State, the executive authority thereof shall issue writs of election to fill such vacancies.

5 The House of Representatives shall choose their speaker and other officers, and shall have the sole power of impeachment.

SECTION III. 1 The Senate of the United States shall be composed of two senators from each State, chosen by the legislature thereof for six years; and each senator shall have one vote.

2 Immediately after they shall be assembled in consequence of the first election, they shall be divided as equally as may be into three classes. The seats of the senators of the first class shall be vacated at the expiration of the second year, of the second class at the expiration of the fourth year, and of the third class at the expiration of the sixth year, so that one third may be chosen every second year; and if vacancies happen by resignation, or otherwise, during the recess of the legislature of

any State, the executive thereof may make temporary appointments until the next meeting of the legislature, which shall then fill such vacancies.

3 No person shall be a senator who shall not have attained to the age of thirty years, and been nine years a citizen of the United States, and who shall not, when elected, be an inhabitant of that State for which he shall be chosen.

4 The Vice President of the United States shall be President of the Senate, but shall have no vote, unless they be equally divided.

5 The Senate shall choose their other officers, and also a president *pro tempore*, in the absence of the Vice President, or when he shall exercise the office of President of the United States.

6 The Senate shall have the sole power to try all impeachments. When sitting for that purpose, they shall be on oath or affirmation. When the President of the United States is tried, the chief justice shall preside: and no person shall be convicted without the concurrence of two thirds of the members present.

7 Judgment in cases of impeachment shall not extend further than to removal from office, and disqualification to hold and enjoy any office of honor, trust or profit under the United States: but the party convicted shall nevertheless be liable and subject to indictment, trial, judgment and punishment, according to law.

SECTION IV. 1 The times, places, and manner of holding elections for senators and representatives, shall be prescribed in each State by the legislature thereof; but the Congress may at any time by law make or alter such regulations, except as to the places of choosing senators.

2 The Congress shall assemble at least once in every year, and such meeting shall be on the first Monday in December, unless they shall by law appoint a different day.

SECTION V. 1 Each House shall be the judge of the elections, returns and qualifications of its own members, and a majority of each shall constitute a quorum to do business; but a smaller number may adjourn from day to day, and may be authorized to compel the attendance of absent members, in such manner, and under such penalties as each House may provide.

2 Each House may determine the rules of its proceedings, punish its members for disorderly behavior, and, with the concurrence of two thirds, expel a member.

3 Each House shall keep a journal of its proceedings and from time to time publish the same, excepting such parts as may in their judgment require secrecy; and the yeas and nays of the members of either House on any question shall, at the desire of one fifth of those present, be entered on the journal.

4 Neither House, during the session of Congress, shall, without the consent of the other, adjourn for more than three days, nor to any other place than that in which the two Houses shall be sitting.

SECTION VI. 1 The senators and representatives shall receive a compensation for their services, to be ascertained by law, and paid out of the Treasury of the United States. They shall in all cases, except treason, felony and breach of the peace, be privileged from arrest during their attendance at the session of their respective Houses, and in going to and returning from the same; and for any speech or debate in either House, they shall not be questioned in any other place.

2 No senator or representative shall, during the time for which he was elected, be appointed to any civil office under the authority of the United States, which shall have been created, or the emoluments whereof shall have been increased during such time; and no person holding any office under the United States shall be a member of either House during his continuance in office.

SECTION VII. 1 All bills for raising revenue shall originate in the House of Representatives; but the Senate may propose or concur with amendments as on other bills.

2 Every bill which shall have passed the House of Representatives, and the Senate, shall, before it become a law, be presented to the President of the United States; if he approve he shall sign it, but if not he shall return it, with his objections to that House in which it shall have originated, who shall enter the objections at large on their journal, and proceed to reconsider it. If after such reconsideration two thirds of that House shall agree to pass the bill, it shall be sent, together with the objections, to the other House, by which it shall likewise be reconsidered, and if approved by two thirds of that House, it shall become a law. But in all such cases the votes of both Houses shall be determined by yeas and nays, and the names of the persons voting for and against the bill shall be entered on the journal of each House respectively. If any bill shall not be returned by the President within ten days (Sundays excepted) after it shall have been presented to him, the same shall be a law, in like manner as if he had signed it, unless the Congress by their adjournment prevent its return, in which case it shall not be a law.

3 Every order, resolution, or vote to which the concurrence of the Senate and House of Representatives may be necessary (except on a question of adjournment) shall be presented to the President of the United States; and before the same shall take effect, shall be approved by him, or being disapproved by him, shall be repassed by two thirds of the Senate and House of Representatives, according to the rules and limitations prescribed in the case of a bill.

SECTION VIII. 1 The Congress shall have power to lay and collect taxes, duties, imposts and excises, to pay the debts and provide for the common defense and general welfare of the United States; but all duties, imposts and excises shall be uniform throughout the United States.

2 To borrow money on the credit of the United States;

3 To regulate commerce with foreign nations, and among the several States, and with the Indian tribes;

4 To establish an uniform rule of naturalization, and uniform laws on the subject of bankruptcies throughout the United States;

5 To coin money, regulate the value thereof, and of foreign coin, and fix the standard of weights and measures;

6 To provide for the punishment of counterfeiting the securities and current coin of the United States;

7 To establish post offices and post roads;

8 To promote the progress of science and useful arts by securing for limited times to authors and inventors the exclusive right to their respective writings and discoveries;

9 To constitute tribunals inferior to the Supreme Court;

10 To define and punish piracies and felonies committed on the high seas, and offenses against the law of nations;

11 To declare war, grant letters of marque and reprisal, and make rules concerning captures on land and water;

12 To raise and support armies, but no appropriation of money to that use shall be for a longer term than two years;

13 To provide and maintain a navy;

14 To make rules for the government and regulation of the land and naval forces;

15 To provide for calling forth the militia to execute the laws of the Union, suppress insurrections and repel invasions;

16 To provide for organizing, arming, and disciplining the militia, and for governing such part of them as may be employed in the service of the United States, reserving to the States respectively the appointment of the officers, and the authority of training the militia according to the discipline prescribed by Congress;

17 To exercise exclusive legislation in all cases whatsoever over such district (not exceeding ten miles square) as may, by cession of particular States and the acceptance of Congress, become the seat of the government of the United States, and to exercise like authority over all places purchased by the consent of the legislature of the State in which the same shall be, for the erection of forts, magazines, arsenals, dockyards, and other needful buildings; and

18 To make all laws which shall be necessary and proper for carrying into execution the foregoing powers, and all other powers vested by this Constitution in the government of the United States, or in any department or officer thereof.

SECTION IX. 1 The migration or importation of such persons as any of the States now existing shall think proper to admit, shall not be prohibited by the Congress prior to the year one thousand eight hundred and eight, but a tax or duty may be imposed on such importation, not exceeding ten dollars for each person.

2 The privilege of the writ of *habeas corpus* shall not be suspended, unless when in cases of rebellion or invasion the public safety may require it.

3 No bill of attainder or *ex post facto* law shall be passed.

4 No capitation, or other direct, tax shall be laid, unless in proportion to the census or enumeration hereinbefore directed to be taken.

5 No tax or duty shall be laid on articles exported from any State.

6 No preference shall be given by any regulation of commerce or revenue to the ports of one State over those of another; nor shall vessels bound to, or from, one State be obliged to enter, clear, or pay duties in another.

7 No money shall be drawn from the treasury, but in consequence of appropriations made by law; and a regular statement and account of the receipts and expenditures of all public money shall be published from time to time.

8 No title of nobility shall be granted by the United States; and no person holding any office of profit or trust under them, shall, without the consent of the Congress, accept of any present, emolument, office, or title, of any kind whatever, from any king, prince, or foreign State.

SECTION X. 1 No State shall enter into any treaty, alliance, or confederation; grant letters of marque and reprisal; coin money; emit bills of credit; make anything but gold and silver coin a tender in payment of debts; pass any bill of attainder, *ex post facto* law, or law impairing the obligation of contracts, or grant any title of nobility.

2 No State shall, without the consent of the Congress, lay any imposts or duties on imports or exports, except what may be absolutely necessary for executing its inspection laws; and the net produce of all duties and imposts laid by any State on imports or exports, shall be for the use of the treasury of the United States; and all such laws shall be subject to the revision and control of the Congress.

3 No State shall, without the consent of Congress,

lay any duty of tonnage, keep troops, or ships of war in time of peace, enter into any agreement or compact with another State, or with a foreign power, or engage in war, unless actually invaded, or in such imminent danger as will not admit of delay.

Article Two

SECTION I. 1 The executive power shall be vested in a President of the United States of America. He shall hold his office during the term of four years, and, together with the Vice President, chosen for the same term, be elected, as follows:

2 Each State shall appoint, in such manner as the legislature thereof may direct, a number of electors, equal to the whole number of senators and representatives to which the State may be entitled in the Congress: but no senator or representative, or person holding an office of trust or profit under the United States, shall be appointed an elector.

3 The electors shall meet in their respective States, and vote by ballot for two persons, of whom one at least shall not be an inhabitant of the same State with themselves. And they shall make a list of all the persons voted for, and of the number of votes for each; which list they shall sign and certify, and transmit sealed to the seat of the government of the United States, directed to the president of the Senate. The president of the Senate shall, in the presence of the Senate and House of Representatives, open all the certificates and the votes shall then be counted. The person having the greatest number of votes shall be the President, if such number be a majority of the whole number of electors appointed; and if there be more than one who have such majority, and have an equal number of votes, then the House of Representatives shall immediately choose by ballot one of them for President; and if no person have a majority, then from the five highest on the list the said House shall in like manner choose the President. But in choosing the President, the votes shall be taken by States, the representation from each State having one vote; a quorum for this purpose shall consist of a member or members from two thirds of the States, and a majority of all the States shall be necessary to a choice. In every case, after the choice of the President, the person having the greatest number of votes of the electors shall be the Vice President. But if there should remain two or more who have equal votes, the Senate shall choose from them by ballot the Vice President. (*This clause was changed by the Twelfth Amendment.*)

4 The Congress may determine the times of choosing the electors, and the day on which they shall give their votes; which day shall be the same throughout the United States.

5 No person except a natural born citizen, or a citizen of the United States, at the time of the adoption of this Constitution, shall be eligible to the office of President; neither shall any person be eligible to that office who shall not have attained to the age of thirty-five years, and been fourteen years a resident within the United States.

6 In case of the removal of the President from office, or of his death, resignation, or inability to discharge the powers and duties of the said office, the same shall devolve on the Vice President, and the Congress may by law provide for the case of removal, death, resignation, or inability, both of the President and Vice President, declaring what officer shall then act as President, and such officer shall act accordingly, until the disability be removed, or a President shall be elected.

7 The President shall, at stated times, receive for his services a compensation, which shall neither be increased nor diminished during the period for which he shall have been elected, and he shall not receive within that period any other emolument from the United States, or any of them.

8 Before he enter on the execution of his office, he shall take the following oath or affirmation:—"I do solemnly swear (or affirm) that I will faithfully execute the office of President of the United States, and will to the best of my ability, preserve, protect and defend the Constitution of the United States."

SECTION II. 1 The President shall be commander in chief of the army and navy of the United States, and of the militia of the several States, when called into the actual service of the United States; he may require the opinion, in writing, of the principal officer in each of the executive departments, upon any subject relating to the duties of their respective offices, and he shall have power to grant reprieves and pardons for offenses against the United States, except in cases of impeachment.

2 He shall have power, by and with the advice and consent of the Senate, to make treaties, provided two thirds of the senators present concur; and he shall nominate, and by and with the advice and consent of the Senate, shall appoint ambassadors, other public ministers and consuls, judges of the Supreme Court, and all other officers of the United States, whose appointments are not herein otherwise provided for, and which shall be established by law: but the Congress may by law vest the appointment of such inferior officers, as they think proper, in the President alone, in the courts of law, or in the heads of departments.

3 The President shall have power to fill up all vacancies that may happen during the recess of the Senate, by granting commissions which shall expire at the end of their next session.

SECTION III. He shall from time to time give to the Congress information of the state of the Union, and recommend to their consideration such measures as he shall judge necessary and expedient; he may, on extraordinary occasions, convene both Houses, or either of them, and in case of disagreement between them with respect to the time of adjournment, he may adjourn them to such time as he shall think proper; he shall receive ambassadors and other public ministers; he shall take care that the laws be faithfully executed, and shall commission all the officers of the United States.

Section IV. The President, Vice President, and all civil officers of the United States, shall be removed from office on impeachment for, and conviction of, treason, bribery, or other high crimes and misdemeanors.

Article Three

Section I. The judicial power of the United States shall be vested in one Supreme Court, and in such inferior courts as the Congress may from time to time ordain and establish. The judges, both of the Supreme and inferior courts, shall hold their offices during good behavior, and shall, at stated times, receive for their services, a compensation which shall not be diminished during their continuance in office.

Section II. 1 The judicial power shall extend to all cases, in law and equity, arising under this Constitution, the laws of the United States, and treaties made, or which shall be made, under their authority;—to all cases affecting ambassadors, other public ministers and consuls;—to all cases of admiralty and maritime jurisdiction;—to controversies to which the United States shall be a party;—to controversies between two or more States;—between a State and citizens of another State;—between citizens of different States,—between citizens of the same State claiming lands under grants of different States, and between a State, or the citizens thereof, and foreign States, citizens or subjects.

2 In all cases affecting ambassadors, other public ministers and consuls, and those in which a State shall be party, the Supreme Court shall have original jurisdiction. In all the other cases before mentioned, the Supreme Court shall have appellate jurisdiction, both as to law and fact, with such exceptions, and under such regulations as the Congress shall make.

3 The trial of all crimes, except in cases of impeachment, shall be by jury; and such trial shall be held in the State where the said crimes shall have been committed; but when not committed within any State, the trial shall be at such place or places as the Congress may by law have directed.

Section III. 1 Treason against the United States, shall consist only in levying war against them, or in adhering to their enemies, giving them aid and comfort. No person shall be convicted of treason unless on the testimony of two witnesses to the same overt act, or on confession in open court.

2 The Congress shall have power to declare the punishment of treason, but no attainder of treason shall work corruption of blood or forfeiture except during the life of the person attained.

Article Four

Section I. Full faith and credit shall be given in each State to the public acts, records, and judicial proceedings of every other State. And the Congress may by general laws prescribe the manner in which such acts, records and proceedings shall be proved, and the effect thereof.

Section II. 1 The citizens of each State shall be entitled to all privileges and immunities of citizens in the several States.

2 A person charged in any State with treason, felony, or other crime, who shall flee from justice, and be found in another State, shall on demand of the executive authority of the State from which he fled, be delivered up to be removed to the State having jurisdiction of the crime.

3 No person held to service or labor in one State, under the laws thereof, escaping into another, shall, in consequence of any law or regulation therein, be discharged from such service or labor, but shall be delivered up on claim of the party to whom such service or labor may be due.

Section III. 1 New States may be admitted by the Congress into this Union; but no new States shall be formed or erected within the jurisdiction of any other State; nor any State be formed by the junction of two or more States, or parts of States, without the consent of the legislatures of the States concerned as well as of the Congress.

2 The Congress shall have power to dispose of and make all needful rules and regulations respecting the territory or other property belonging to the United States; and nothing in this Constitution shall be so construed as to prejudice any claims of the United States, or of any particular State.

Section IV. The United States shall guarantee to every State in this Union a republican form of government, and shall protect each of them against invasion; and on application of the legislature, or of the executive (when the legislature cannot be convened) against domestic violence.

Article Five

The Congress, whenever two thirds of both Houses shall deem it necessary, shall propose amendments to this Constitution, or, on the application of the legislature of two thirds of the several States, shall call a convention for proposing amendments, which, in either case, shall be valid to all intents and purposes, as part of this Constitution, when ratified by the legislatures of three fourths of the several States, or by conventions in three fourths thereof, as the one or the other mode of ratification may be proposed by the Congress: Provided that no amendment which may be made prior to the year one thousand eight hundred and eight shall in any manner affect the first and fourth clauses in the ninth section of the first article; and that no State, without its consent, shall be deprived of its equal suffrage in the Senate.

Article Six

1 All debts contracted and engagements entered into, before the adoption of this Constitution, shall be as valid against the United States under this Constitution, as under the Confederation.

2 This Constitution, and the laws of the United States which shall be made in pursuance thereof; and all treaties made, or which shall be made, under the authority of the United States, shall be the supreme law of the land; and the judges in every State shall be bound thereby, any-thing in the Constitution or laws of any State to the contrary notwith-standing.

3 The senators and representatives before mentioned, and the members of the several State legislatures, and all executive and judicial officers, both of the United States, and of the several States, shall be bound by oath or affirmation to support this Constitution; but no religious test shall ever be required as a qualification to any office or public trust under the United States.

Article Seven

The ratification of the conventions of nine States shall be sufficient for the establishment of this Constitution between the States so ratifying the same.

☆　　☆　　☆

*A*mendments added to the Constitution.

THE BILL OF RIGHTS
(The First Ten Amendments, 1791)

Article One

Congress shall make no law respecting an establishment of religion, or prohibiting the free exercise thereof; or abridging the freedom of speech, or of the press; or the right of the people peaceably to assemble, and to petition the government for a redress of grievances.

Article Two

A well regulated militia, being necessary to the security of a free State, the right of the people to keep and bear arms, shall not be infringed.

Article Three

No soldier shall, in time of peace be quartered in any house, without the consent of the owner, nor in time of war, but in a manner to be prescribed by law.

Article Four

The right of the people to be secure in their persons, houses, papers, and effects, against unreasonable searches and seizures, shall not be violated, and no warrants shall issue, but upon probable cause, supported by oath or affirmation, and particularly describing the place to be searched, and the persons or things to be seized.

Article Five

No person shall be held to answer for a capital, or otherwise infamous crime, unless on a presentment or indictment of a grand jury, except in cases arising in the land or naval forces, or in the militia, when in actual service in time of war or public danger; nor shall any person be subject for the same offense to be twice put in jeopardy of life or limb; nor shall be compelled in any criminal case to be a witness against himself, nor be deprived of life, liberty, or property, without due process of law; nor shall private property be taken for public use without just compensation.

Article Six

In all criminal prosecutions, the accused shall enjoy the right to a speedy and public trial, by an impartial jury of the State and district wherein the crime shall have been committed, which district shall have been previously ascertained by law, and to be informed of the nature and cause of the accusation; to be confronted with the witnesses against him; to have compulsory process for obtaining witnesses in his favor, and to have the assistance of counsel for his defense.

Article Seven

In suits at common law, where the value in controversy shall exceed twenty dollars, the right of trial by jury shall be preserved, and no fact tried by a jury shall be otherwise re-examined in any court of the United States, than according to the rules of the common law.

Article Eight

Excessive bail shall not be required, nor excessive fines imposed, nor cruel and unusual punishments inflicted.

Article Nine

The enumeration in the Constitution of certain rights shall not be construed to deny or disparage others retained by the people.

Article Ten

The powers not delegated to the United States by the Constitution, nor prohibited by it to the States, are reserved to the States respectively, or to the people.

Article Eleven
(1798)

The judicial power of the United States shall not be construed to extend to any suit in law or equity, commenced or prosecuted against one of the United States by citizens of another State, or by citizens or subjects of any foreign State.

Article Twelve
(1804)

The electors shall meet in their respective States, and vote by ballot for President and Vice President, one of whom, at least, shall not be an inhabitant of the same State with themselves; they shall name in their ballots the person voted for as President, and in distinct ballots the person voted for as Vice President, and they shall make distinct lists of all persons voted for as President and for all persons voted for as Vice President, and of the number of votes for each, which lists they shall sign and certify, and transmit sealed to the seat of government of the United States, directed to the president of the Senate.—The president of the Senate shall, in presence of the Senate and House of Representatives, open all the certificates and the votes shall then be counted;—The person having the greatest number of votes for President shall be the President, if such number be a majority of the whole number of electors appointed; and if no person have such majority, then from the persons having the highest numbers not exceeding three on the list of those voted for as President, the House of Representatives shall choose immediately by ballot, the President. But in choosing the President, the votes shall be taken by States, the representation from each State having one vote; a quorum for this purpose shall consist of a member or members from two thirds of the States, and a majority of all States shall be necessary to a choice. And if the House of Representatives shall not choose a President whenever the right of choice shall devolve upon them, before the fourth day of March next following, then the Vice President shall act as President, as in the case of the death or other constitutional disability of the President. The person having the greatest number of votes as Vice President shall be the Vice President, if such number be a majority of the whole number of electors appointed and if no person have a majority, then from the two highest numbers on the list, the Senate shall choose the Vice President; a quorum for the purpose shall consist of two thirds of the whole number of senators, and a majority of the whole number shall be necessary to a choice. But no person constitutionally ineligible to the office of President shall be eligible to that of Vice President of the United States.

Article Thirteen
(1865)

Section I. Neither slavery nor involuntary servitude, except as a punishment for crime whereof the party shall have been duly convicted, shall exist within the United States, or any place subject to their jurisdiction.

Section II. Congress shall have the power to enforce this article by appropriate legislation.

Article Fourteen
(1868)

Section I. All persons born or naturalized in the United States, and subject to the jurisdiction thereof, are citizens of the United States and the State wherein they reside. No State shall make or enforce any law which shall abridge the privileges or immunities of citizens of the United States; nor shall any State deprive any person of life, liberty, or property, without due process of law; nor deny to any person within its jurisdiction the equal protection of the laws.

Section II. Representatives shall be apportioned among the several States according to their respective numbers, counting the whole number of persons in each State, excluding Indians not taxed. But when the right to vote at any election for the choice of electors for President and Vice President of the United States, representatives in Congress, the executive and judicial officers of a State, or the members of the legislature thereof, is denied to any of the male inhabitants of such State, being twenty-one years of age, and citizens of the United States, or in any way abridged, except for participation in rebellion, or other crime, the basis of representation therein shall be reduced in the proportion which the number of such male citizens shall bear to the whole number of male citizens twenty-one years of age in such State.

Section III. No person shall be a senator or representative in Congress or elector of President and Vice President, or hold any office, civil or military, under the United States, or under any State, who, having previously taken an oath, as a member of Congress, or as an officer of the United States, or as a member of any State legislature, or as an executive or judicial officer of any State, to support the Constitution of the United States, shall have engaged in insurrection or rebellion against the same, or given aid or comfort to the enemies thereof. But Congress may by a vote of two-thirds of each House, remove such disability.

Section IV. The validity of the public debt of the United States, authorized by law, including debts incurred for payment of pensions and bounties for services in suppressing insurrection or rebellion, shall not be questioned. But neither the United States nor any State shall assume or pay any debt or obligation incurred in aid of insurrection or rebellion against the United States, or any claim for the loss or emancipation of any slave; but all such debts, obligations and claim shall be held illegal and void.

Section V. The Congress shall have the power to enforce, by appropriate legislation, the provisions of this article.

Article Fifteen
(1870)

Section I. The right of citizens of the United States to vote shall not be denied or abridged by the United States or by any State on account of race, color, or previous condition of servitude.

Section II. The Congress shall have power to enforce this article by appropriate legislation.

Article Sixteen
(1913)

The Congress shall have power to lay and collect taxes on incomes, from whatever source derived, without apportionment among the several States, and without regard to any census or enumerations.

Article Seventeen
(1913)

SECTION I. The Senate of the United States shall be composed of two Senators from each State, elected by the people thereof, for six years, and each Senator shall have one vote. The Electors in each State shall have the qualifications requisite for Electors of the most numerous branch of the State Legislatures.

SECTION II. When vacancies happen in the representation of any State in the Senate, the Executive authority of such State shall issue writs of election to fill such vacancies, provided that the Legislature of any State may empower the Executive thereof to make temporary appointments until the people fill the vacancies by election as the Legislature may direct.

SECTION III. This amendment shall not be so construed as to affect the election or term of any Senator chosen before it becomes valid as part of the Constitution.

Article Eighteen
(1919)

SECTION I. After one year from the ratification of this article the manufacture, sale, or transportation of intoxicating liquors within, the importation thereof into, or the exportation thereof from the United States and all territory subject to the jurisdiction thereof for beverage purposes is hereby prohibited.

SECTION II. The Congress and the several States shall have concurrent power to enforce this article by appropriate legislation.

SECTION III. This article shall be inoperative unless it shall have been ratified as an amendment to the Constitution by the legislatures of the several States, as provided in the Constitution, within seven years from the date of the submission hereof to the States by the Congress.

Article Nineteen
(1920)

The right of citizens of the United States to vote shall not be denied or abridged by the United States or by any State on account of sex.

Congress shall have power to enforce this article by appropriate legislation.

Article Twenty
(1933)

SECTION I. The terms of the President and Vice-President shall end at noon on the twentieth day of January, and the terms of Senators and Representatives at noon on the third day of January, of the years in which such terms would have ended if this article had not been ratified; and the terms of their successors shall then begin.

SECTION II. The Congress shall assemble at least once in every year, and such meeting shall begin at noon on the third day of January, unless they shall by law appoint a different day.

SECTION III. If, at the time fixed for the beginning of the term of the President, the President-elect shall have died, the Vice-President-elect shall become President. If a President shall not have been chosen before the time fixed for the beginning of his term, or, if the President-elect shall have failed to qualify, then the Vice-President-elect shall act as President until a President shall have qualified; and the Congress may by law provide for the case wherein neither a President-elect nor a Vice-President-elect shall have qualified, declaring who shall then act as President, or the manner in which one who is to act shall be selected, and such person shall act accordingly until a President or Vice-President shall have qualified.

SECTION IV. The Congress may by law provide for the case of the death of any of the persons from whom the House of Representatives may choose a President whenever the right of choice shall have devolved upon them, and for the case of the death of any of the persons from whom the Senate may choose a Vice-President whenever the right of choice shall have devolved upon them.

SECTION V. Sections I and II shall take effect upon the fifteenth day of October following the ratification of this article.

SECTION VI. This article shall be inoperative unless it shall have been ratified as an amendment to the Constitution by the Legislatures of three-fourths of the several States within seven years from the date of its submission.

Article Twenty-one
(1933)

SECTION I. The Eighteenth Amendment to the Constitution of the United States is hereby repealed.

SECTION II. The transportation or importation into any State, Territory, or possession of the United States for delivery or use therein of intoxicating liquors, in violation of the laws thereof, is hereby prohibited.

SECTION III. This article shall be inoperative unless it shall have been ratified as an amendment to the Constitution by conventions in the several States, as provided in the Constitution, within seven years from the date of the submission hereof to the States by the Congress.

Article Twenty-two
(1951)

SECTION I. No person shall be elected to the office of the President more than twice, and no person who has held the office of President, or acted as President, for more than two years of a term to which some other person was elected President shall be elected to the office of President more than once. But this Article shall not apply to any person holding the office of President when this Article was proposed by the Congress, and shall not prevent any person who may be holding the office of President, or acting as President, during the term within which this Article becomes operative from holding the office of President, or acting as President during the remainder of such term.

SECTION II. This Article shall be inoperative unless it shall have been ratified as an amendment to the Constitution by the legislatures of three-fourths of the several States within seven years from the date of its submission to the States by Congress.

Delaware

Pennsylvania

New Jersey

Georgia

Maryland

Massachusetts

Connecticut

South Carolina

North Carolina

New York

Virginia

New Hampshire

Rhode Island

THE SEALS OF THE ORIGINAL THIRTEEN UNITED STATES

DETAILED LIST OF ILLUSTRATIONS

PICTURE SOURCES

Bettmann Archive, 197, 228, 229, 262, 286, 310, 330, 338

F. Bourges Collection (American Museum of Photography), Fr., 18, 19, 23, 39, 42, 43, 63, 67, 74, 75, 232, 233, 321, 324, 328, 332, 333, 337, 340, 341

Brady-Handy Collection, 77, 81, 89, 105, 107, 108, 110, 130, 153, 159, 235, 253

Cities Service Company, 188, 288

Culver Service, 13, 17, 25, 27, 29, 31, 32, 48, 53, 57, 58, 59, 60, 61, 65, 69, 73, 77, 80, 97, 98, 101, 103, 109, 113, 115, 117, 118, 121, 123, 124, 127, 134, 135, 139, 142, 143, 147, 148, 165, 167, 169, 171, 173, 174, 175, 179, 182, 184, 189, 190, 199, 205, 207, 210, 214, 238, 239, 244, 246, 249, 251, 255, 257, 258, 266, 269, 283, 292, 293, 299, 301, 305, 307, 309, 313, 314, 316, 327, 335, 345, 347, 350, 351

Dexter Press, Inc., 95

E. I. du Pont de Nemours Company, Inc., 273, 274, 275

John Hancock Mutual Life Insurance Company, 47, 87, 161, 212, 221, 237

Index of American Design, 11, 79, 91

New York Life Insurance Company, 51, 177

Steelways, 226

Travelers Insurance Company, 55, 83

U. S. Naval Institute, 14

Wide World, 218

Yale University Art Gallery, 35

INDEX

INDEX

(A number in boldface indicates a main article.)